THE BRIDGE WITH BROKEN ARCHES

David S. [signature]

First published in 2003
by Maclean Dubois
Hillend House, Hillend, Edinburgh
in an edition limited to xxx copies

Typeset by Linda Morris, aset@blueyonder.co.uk
Cover designed by Cate Stewart

Printed by
Antony Rowe Ltd.,
Chippenham,
Wilts SN14 6LH

THE BRIDGE WITH BROKEN ARCHES

(The Journals of a Scottish Family Doctor)

1943–1986

by
David Illingworth

For those who made me what I am
– so few of whom have grown old.

"The bridge, said he, is Human Life. I found it consisted of three score and ten entire arches with several broken arches. Innumerable trapdoors lay concealed in the bridge through which the passengers fell."

The Spectator, No. 159

"The Vision of Mirza" - Joseph Addison (1672–1719)

FOREWORD

Doctors are fortunate people for more than one reason. They are, of course, members of a profession that everyone, or just about everyone, likes. They bring us into the world and see us out again. They heal; they make life more bearable. And to do all this well they should ideally be equipped with a strong sense of professional obligation and, very importantly, a good sense of humour.

David Illingworth belongs to a generation of doctors brought up in the finest tradition of Scottish medicine. In his professional career, in which he looked after the most humble of patients and the very grandest, he has always been guided by that particularly rigorous sense of duty and vocation which Scottish medical training has sought to inculcate. But at the same time, he has been able to appreciate the humorous possibilities which the practice of medicine inevitably presents, and many of these richly comic situations are presented in these memoirs.

Of course doctors cannot spill all the beans, and this book is written with all the discretion and tact which one would expect of one of Edinburgh's most urbane, charming and beloved physicians. But such beans as are spilled are delightful in the savouring, and along with the thanks which many devoted patients owe David Illingworth for a lifetime of care, appreciation will also be voiced by many for this fine contribution to the medical chronicles of our city and our time.

Alexander McCall Smith

INTRODUCTION

The attainment of excellence is the privilege of few. Yet these are the people who are familiar with appreciation and admiration, the crowded hour, the ecstasy of success and fame whose autobiographies are avidly read. Mediocrity is the fate of the vast majority. Nobody ever writes about this group. Society is pre-occupied with the unusual—and the abnormal.

This narrative of forty years of medical experience is an attempt to re-dress the balance. Being based on diaries, the incidents described, and the conversations are—sometimes regrettably—true and accurate accounts. Outside hospital walls, clinical medical practice is a disturbing art form which has driven many excellent doctors back into the sequestered serenity of the scientific life of the laboratory. Therefore, no apology is offered if a printed embarrassment is provoked into a revulsion.

Occasional telescoping of events and chronological interchange is a permissible liberty—as is the avoidance of embarrassment if a few characters don masks. Those who remember will understand and forgive.

To mitigate the unpleasant aspects of medical care practised under stress or adversity would be a misrepresentation and a rejection of one of the finest aphorisms of the physician who has most influenced my life and thinking.

"When in doubt, tell the truth!"

Moira Fotheringhame's decyphering and presentation of material have made this story possible.

PART I

CASUALTY OFFICER

CHAPTER ONE

That June evening in 1943, after her younger son's telephone call, I knew that my mother felt happy but uneasy. She was familiar with insecurity, having contracted in haste and impressionable youth—there was another war on at the time—one of those marriages which soon ebbed and flowed until ultimately, the rocks remained permanently uncovered. The social disciplines of the period had denied both partners even the contemplation of divorce. The two children carried the emotional stigmata of a mediocre marriage and were driven to weave a fabric of parental fiction. Such imaginary creations probably deceived nobody, but these fantasies preserved my childish dignity as I blithely explained my sea-going father's ever-increasing absences in terms of secret service work, continental exploration and the attempted ascent of inaccessible mountain peaks—once for diplomatic reasons and under an assumed name! Lying came easily with practice and this cultured ability to prevaricate and dissemble created a personality well-adapted for a career in crime—or possibly in medicine. I recall only three meetings with my father, though, rarely, we corresponded—once in mid-Atlantic.

In 1938 one circumstance anticipated any crisis of professional choice for the boy about to leave George Watson's College for Boys. War became inevitable.

This development not only conveniently explained my father's prolonged absences from home but rapidly changed me from a potential recidivist to a reasonably responsible adolescent. I was embarrassed to realise that the trouble with my falsehoods was not only a vague moral guilt, but, as I had never appreciated, any fabrication has to be remembered—once I had even located my father simultaneously working undercover in Germany, testing new destroyers and freeing himself of leeches in the Amazon jungle. The emergent threat of war compelled me to face reality and made me accept the control of my own destiny. This was not easy after the years of confusion and uncertainty.

No framework had ever developed to assist my upbringing and maturation. Life progressed on an ad hoc basis—with rules as haphazard and changeable as Scottish spring weather.

My elder brother and I grew up to regard the world as a bewildering unpredictable contest against obscure adversaries. There was always something to prove. There was always an elusive person who might be let down by us. Excellence was expected; failure was intolerable and would shame the family—a family which consisted entirely of women-folk—whose male relatives had emigrated, died or disappeared. The absurdity was that each of the departed had left behind him an oft-told legend of stunning exploits. This ancestry of apparent supermen forced both of us into compulsive aspirations to unattainable achievements. The fabulous standards of our male forebears were quite beyond us and we matured unwholesomely stained by frequent failures. The parrot-cry, "Don't let us down!" was only partly successful. The guilt was awful.

Vulnerable and shy, my elder, more intelligent brother found stability and respectable anonymity as an archivist. I, the younger brother, decided to emulate my many relations who had entered medical school because, in truth, they couldn't think of any other course compatible with their inherited combination of reasonable intelligence, general uncertainty and total lack of motivation. I was, at sixteen years of age, a medical student—a painfully raw creature who avoided associating with females under thirty and felt uncomfortable in public—being convinced that my head was visibly shaking. Plagued by a stammer and episodes of total neuronal failure amounting to fugue, somewhere I found in my odd genetic inheritance an appreciation of the ridiculous and an indomitable resolution to make something of value out of the modest pieces of protoplasm with which I had been endowed. So I drove myself to join in all social activities, employing a type of "gallows humour" to make tolerable my gauche over-sensitivity and consistent fallibility. No experience was wasted. Although ultimately rejected by the local dramatic club I observed at rehearsal that when I had to play a role requiring a foreign accent I lost my stammer. In altering my voice I became something other than my own uncertain complex personality. Thereafter I could string words together unerringly—although friends claimed I sounded like some weird American/Polish hybrid. The outbreak of War in 1939 attracted me prematurely to the local hospital which I served faithfully if timidly—due to clinical ignorance. Native aggression was partially expressed on the rugby field but increasing short-sightedness made me unsure of the location of the ball and in dull weather I sometimes wondered which side I was playing for. When the Home Guard was formed I felt much more fulfilled and, when Britain stood alone, the bespectacled infant medico discovered a remarkable facility in handling weapons. Formidably patriotic, I secretly longed for the German invasion and the chance to prove myself. When denied this opportunity I converted my energy into paroxysmal bursts of intense study. With my country staggering, one HAD to graduate as soon as possible. In 1941, for the first time, there had developed a dedication to Medicine. Here was a chance to display some merit—no more "letting them down". Inevitably there were "lapses and incidents" —but that is another story. Now in June 1943, I was twenty-one years old. Six hours had passed since the telephone call to my mother about the results of "Finals".

CHAPTER TWO

I vaguely wondered why my friends were carrying me face downward, as in the stark daylight of a summer evening in Edinburgh's suburbia, a strange procession moved up the centre of the road.

"Good thing he's face down—he won't inhale it!"

Tom Matheson, the senior bearer because he had my head end, was proved correct as even more beer, whisky, liqueur and tonic wine splashed the road surface.

No passing motorist viewed the regurgitation of this fiendish infusion. There were no cars about in the middle of the War; but eyes in plenty glowered or gleamed from behind lace curtains.

The pallbearers began their umpteenth chorus of "The Ball at Kirriemuir", as the cortège advanced again. Unwilling listeners blushed for those fledglings of the healing arts; but some understood—"Finals" results had been posted that afternoon in the University quadrangle and Newington had a "village" approach to life.

At 2 pm ten anxious and astonished eyes had focussed on five names on a typed list from the Dean's office. Before the Students' Union engulfed me I had remembered to telephone my mother from a call box. She seemed unsurprised at her son's success though perhaps a trifle disturbed to learn that the celebrations were about to start. However, after five years of fierce activity, maybe her boy deserved one last blowout before medical respectability overcame him. That was MY personal view of things.

From a University family in a University town she was sitting with her widowed—and wealthy—sister in the bay window, basking with the redoubtable "Granny" in the evening sunshine of Newington. But even my well-indoctrinated mother fought to summon all her experience of the student life when she realised that the three choristers had relinquished me, her son, on the pavement—face down—and noisily exited up the street.

Lying there like a stranded whale, it seemed logical to deceive any on-lookers by executing a lithe manly leap over the front gate. In this attempt I failed lamentably and, unable to mislead the audience as completely as I had my examiners, I compromised and crawled the rest of the way to the front door praying that I hadn't been spotted.

"Auntie", the financial hope of the side, was a reincarnation of Miss Havisham. In spite of forty pairs of unworn shoes her feet were always encased in soft slippers (with red pom-poms on them). Creeping, tortoise fashion, to the top of the first flight of stairs my eyes dimly saw the familiar footwear. Nemesis and nausea struck together as she reviled me.

"A more degrading exhibition was never presented to the south side of Edinburgh. And now you're a doctor!"

The response was a prompt vomit on the "pom-poms" as I was being informed that I was to be disinherited. I never discovered who put me to bed after those awful slippers went into orbit, but twelve hours later, cleaner and fresher, I boarded a tramcar and re-inspected the pass list, still hungry for reassurance. Two close friends had failed—students of such ability that I began to wonder if my own name had appeared through some appalling clerical error.

Slipping away to the Union Bar to restore fluid balance I was promptly congratulated by the imperturbable earthy Gibson and by Tom Whiston—mature and dapper as ever.

"David", Gibbo said, looking more anthropoid than usual, "I've just heard that I've got "The Gilks" house job. What about you?"

Depressed by this reminder that the medical world was apparently a perpetual series of horizons, congratulations were muttered, the proffered beer accepted, as I replied that the next target was probably a visit to "the gents". Gibson was always eager to help vacillators.

"Heavens man, you'll have to get a job—and soon. What's your strong point?"

"Bridge" groaned a nauseated neophyte. As his moody friend peered into his tankard, Gibson's lateral thinking operated. He never could control his enquiring, penetrative mind.

"Bridge! You made me think of ships. Isn't your father at sea?" There was a sudden "jigsaw" feeling of harmony and assurance—rarely experienced in my random world of casual bewilderment. I responded at once.

"You've got it, Jimmy! I can see it! A small ship doctor—that's for me!

Whiston ventured more specific advice to his bleary rather inadequate friend.

"Casualty it must be then, chum, —but all the blood and guts jobs at the Royal are spoken for. What about Leith?" My mind switched from the prospect of two weeks of incessant tennis to making an approach to Mr Band, the chief surgeon at Leith Hospital.

Tommy Whiston changed my life in that chance encounter. A series of happy accidents was initiated by him. I don't think I ever told him what he did for me. Now it's too late!

An hour later I was looking at the beautifully groomed surgeon and telling him of my next aspiration—a Naval Medical Officer in a destroyer.

He listened. "Six months in our Casualty Department will prepare a young doctor of your ambitions as nothing else can", declared Band. Disregarding the fact that there might be other applicants, I shook hands and was told to report after fourteen days holiday—arranged at Lundin Links.

The ease with which I got the appointment escaped me until I was three days into my tennis marathon with the Balmer sisters and a schoolboy, Tony Gunn, destined for surgical eminence. Suddenly I realised that responsibility for others was to replace years of study and play which had carried no accountability—except to myself. Peoples' lives in my uncertain hands! Why me? —perhaps I was the only applicant.

The new medico promptly double-faulted.

CHAPTER THREE

The tramcar stopped at Leith Hospital. The sunburnt new boy carted an old suitcase up to the Residency. Because of its peripheral situation in Edinburgh, there was a remarkable bond between the local population and THEIR hospital. My quarters looked like Van Gogh's bedroom. Next door was a large, comfortable lounge shared with the four other housemen who ran this remarkable establishment. Along the corridor at the top of the hospital existed another world—that of the Resident Surgical Officer. Lean, ascetic and imperturbable, he limped into the Mess that first evening. The five novices were cynically inspected—overawed to meet the legendary "Ben" Murray. This brilliant young Australian surgeon made it clear to the apprehensive quintet that he would be their confessor, supporter and friend—provided they behaved and didn't bother him with trivialities. They were never to be let down.

Ben explained that the hospital was, in every sense, a general one. All things in medical life were abnormal—but as having babies was a natural function, there would be no obstetrics. They were responsible to two hundred in-patients, him, each other and the teeming thousands who would attend the all-embracing out-patient departments. "Chiefs" would visit but the real work was for simple mortals.

"Such as you, David, you are the Casualty Officer but you also do Ear, Nose and Throat and stand in for the House Surgeon and the Out-patient Physician (who also does eyes and anaesthetics)."

It was all as clear as mud and the job description sounded quite impracticable.

"Any questions, pommies?" But there was no response from Ben's unnerved sheep. I felt sick and was sure my duodenum would soon ulcerate as the young Aussie surgeon concluded.

"At 7.30 breakfast I'll fill in the gaps." "Bye."

Sleep did not come and in the morning, Ben grinned heartlessly at his infant doctors.

"Cheer up, pommies, you get free bed, board and laundry—AND 27/6 a week. Of course, you won't have time to eat anyway. And incidentally, there's no off-duty unless you arrange it yourselves. But before you weep with self-pity, in my day there wasn't even a salary!"

8.30 am with a sinking stomach and spotless white jacket, I walked, with affected jauntiness, into the Casualty Department. The out-going incumbent, who looked incredibly old and wise, showed me round my kingdom, presented the novice to Sister and departed—forever. An apparent seven feet of starched serenity peered down at me.

"You'll soon pick it up, doctor. Please remember the chocolate biscuits are for the consultants and there's a list of ten 'minor ops' at nine", Sister said.

"Fine," I quavered, returning a Staff Nurse's appraising glances.

"Who's the surgeon?

"You are!" replied Sister Cowan.

The new boy at once forgot his ambitions about the blonde Staff Nurse and sought sanctuary in the nearest toilet.

"If only I'd become a market gardener", I thought as I pled for divine support.

Casualty theatre, 9 am, greeted me, white-robed and whiter faced. Peering in the mirror through steamed-up spectacles, imminent death looked back at me. I shifted my misted vision to the theatre team—one blonde Staff Nurse, two other nurses and a confident male medical student.

"Payne's the name, sir, will you let me assist?"

I at once warmed to Payne—until he confessed he was only in first year medicine!

Jack Wilson, my counterpart in the Medical Department, breezed in.

"Cheer up lad, and if you need any general anaesthetics I'm just along the corridor. I'll send in the first victim!"

Jack proved to be the ideal colleague, as a man, wearing three golf balls on his shaven head, walked in. With a murmured prayer of thanks I recognised the rounded objects as sebaceous cysts. I had even seen one removed! Staff Nurse put a large syringe into my trembling fingers.

"Why can't I get the needle into the top of the bottle of local anaesthetic?"

"Staff" winked and smiled.

"Sorry doctor, my fault—unsteady hands."

Ninety minutes later the list was finished. We had even drained two breast abscesses in an atmosphere strong with Wilson's anaesthetics and encouragement. Peeling off the gloves to meet new referrals, I hadn't only met God, we also understood each other. At two thirty, my bravura and I strutted into the Mess dining room. There stood the imperturbable Margaret, the housekeeper.

"I've kept you something, doctor."

I gulped some food and, sighing with relief, dragged at a cigarette—when the phone rang.

"Sister here. Afternoon clinic is very full already."

I remembered to thank Margaret who was to be a great digestive comforter and ally for the next six months, before I returned to Casualty.

By 6 pm the arena was clear but, as I was reflecting on my first day, a distraught young mother ran in clutching her baby. It was my first "cot death" and, as I probed mind and heart for something to say, Sister was at my elbow.

"I'll look after her, doctor." Another muffled word of appreciation, particularly for nurses, went upwards through the evening sky that August.

Four other strained faces were sitting at dinner. Ben Murray took charge. From the head of the table he inspected the fearful five, one by one—Wilson, Macqueen, Smith, Young and me.

"Well" said the Australian twang, "If you're going to tell me how many lives you've saved today I don't want to know. You may feel like God Almighty now—but it won't last. Any sensible questions?"

None of the five cerebral cortices could function at all.

As one who never found silence bearable, I felt compelled to speak. Apprehensively, in an obviously artificial attempt to break the tension with a little levity, I forced out—

"Is it true, sir, that you have a wooden leg?" Ben stuck his face up against my pallor.

"Obviously you're the joker in this pack of mental defectives. Yes, I do have, as you crudely call it, a wooden leg. Now I expect you to enquire why and how."

The four other mental defectives took over from their stammering colleague—face now suffused. They learned the limb had been shot off when Ben was ten years old.

"Bloody silly thing to do—mishandled a twelve-bore."

Contrite and guilty I muttered, "Of course, an accident."

Ben rose from the table. Softly drifted back from the door.

"Of course not, you silly bastard. I just didn't like the look of it."

Macqueen, the Children's House Officer, was visibly upset for Ben.

"Hell's bells, man, now you'll get some sauce—by return! Clumsy oaf" No tact!"

He opened the tomato sauce bottle, shook it over my head and departed, leaving me to survey my shattered world through a red mist. Margaret, the ever-patient, also vanished—with the giggles and a word of comfort.

"All my boys are the same; I'm used to it."

Weary beyond caring, I struggled up the Residency stairs to my Spartan room. How could I possibly be expected to translate the patois of a young mother?

"The wee bugger's got a bealin' atween his dirt hole and his wee thruster" into—"The baby has a perineal boil!"

Sleep came at once. Willie, the asthmatic night porter, had trouble in shaking the Casualty officer awake.

"1 a.m., sir, and a bad stab wound in Casualty."

Willie possessed that professional intensity and pride common in hospital porters and autopsy attendants, when something dramatic occurs.

I struggled into my trousers.

Willie said "It's hanging right out, sir."

The embarrassed Casualty officer, after a quick downward glance, queried, "What is?"

"His stomach, sir!"

Our descent into the department was precipitate—where we found a very drunk man, about forty years old, lying on a trolley. His middle was covered with a sterile green towel which, with studied casualness, I removed.

"Not too bad, Doc?" slurred the injured man, smiling vacuously. A horrified young medico was beginning to learn the art and value of facial control—particularly when looking at a human stomach lying pouting, entire, on the abdominal skin. The knife wound was large.

"We'll just have to pop it back—but we'll give you a whiff of something to put you to sleep."

"She didn't mean it doctor", muttered the patient, "Are these my tripes?" As shock set in, he shivered.

The damage was much greater than seemed apparent at first, and, in spite of hours of endeavour, the victim lost the battle as dawn came. The police, almost always humane and understanding, arrived and inevitably had to write it all down. They knew the deceased through their local constable on the beat and subtly conveyed that he wouldn't be a great loss. I was to learn that the common factor in such episodes was alcohol misuse; in philosophical mood, I kept returning to the multiple toxins with which mankind was obsessed; addictions, potentially lethal, which had been skilfully developed and refined. Cynically, I used to like my theory that one way to succeed in life was by exploitation of other peoples' misfortunes and weaknesses. But why my enjoyment of cigarettes and beer? The relevant quotation kept eluding me until I recalled my

English master, Edward Albert, declaiming in 1936—before I left school

"There is no base intention o'er which does not ride the shadow of an angel; no good intention which does not have a dwarfish footman at its stirrup." I decided to cling to this aphorism, which was so in harmony with my uncertain disposition.

Free by 8 am and breakfasted I was called to see a young girl scalped by a machine in the local rope works. Her mates had thoughtfully brought along the scalp, and the surgical houseman, Douglas Young, said he'd try—of course. Due to the excellent supply of scalp tissue, the cosmetic result was superb and rewarded hours of careful suturing. So the first two days and sleepless nights ended—I was still standing!

There were other frenetic days like "tonsil day" which came inexorably once a week. Twenty trembling children were wheeled into the Casualty ante-room. One by one, they were tenderly carried into the care of Jack Wilson, the anaesthetist, and myself, the operator. A nameless consultant initially guided my fumbling fingers, then said that I would do the rest—while he was "available"—and sat chain-smoking in the corner of the theatre.

Ethyl chloride, gag, guillotine and curette!

Wilson was superb and steadied the children—and the staff. I was terrified to fail by leaving the tonsil "roots" and kept thinking of meat processing in Chicago. Such was the standard practice of the time. And no-one questioned it. Indeed the parents and children gladly acquiesced and were grateful! At least none died and the few "tonsil" patients encountered years later had no recollection of this slaughter of innocents. And all this with seven days experience!

The staff at Leith Hospital were considered a breed apart. Seldom did we pay for cigarettes, newspapers or cinema seats. I was appointed Honorary Surgeon to the Eldorado Sports Stadium, and attended the all-in-wrestling each week. Thousands crowded in to see the gladiators inflicting mayhem on each other. There was but one patient in six months. Good luck or good games management?

But it wasn't all success. Penicillin and cortisone were still years away. Infections and accidents were repetitive problems. Sometimes human failure worsened the problem—as when the theatre staff equipped us with a spent cylinder of oxygen, and one scalded infant was asphyxiated. It was an appalling incident lightened only by the fact that we'd have lost the child anyway through the extent of the injury.

That was the day when Payne volunteered to take over the weekly Bougie clinic. I did not enjoy stretching male urethras with metal rods to relieve the end result of gonorrhoea. Jimmy Payne's excellence foretold his wonderful professional career in London as a consultant anaesthetist.

One month into my appointment I had not known a whole night's sleep and, when a ship blew up in the docks, I had snoozed off in my office. Within five minutes of the explosion I was looking at four dead people. The entire medical and nursing staff were at work on the twenty injured and even the consultants were appearing to stifle my criticisms of indifference. Mr Carlow, the senior surgeon, put his hand on my shoulder as the intravenous therapy started.

"Good work with the drips, son, but look at this skull—the top's pushed in. Come and do a lumbar puncture on this youngster over here."

Carlow held the lad as the needle went into the spinal space.

"Oh God!" said the surgeon, "let's move on to where we'll be useful—that's pure blood. He's got gross brain damage."

Midnight saw those who were likely to survive being intensively treated. Carlow's two "rejects" as he predicted, had died.

Although realising I had passed some sort of test, I had enough humility to remember the rescue men, the police, the ambulance men and the nurses. Those at the scene of the disaster were the bravest of all I decided, as I fell into a virginal bed. That night, although undisturbed thereafter, Wilson insisted on doing alternate nights for Casualty. As I had just shot a needle in the depths of my left hand I was relieved beyond expression. Fatigue was destroying efficiency and physical resistance. Worse, I KNEW it to be true!

Ben Murray, the hand expert—looked grimly at my swollen hand.

"Splints and sulpha, sonny; we might just get by without you."

Murray's hand clinic was famous in Scotland. His pioneer work is still remembered with gratitude—not least by me. I recovered in two days. Murray was the best surgeon, teacher and man—he was a unique gift to his profession and was cruelly unappreciated.

On my return I opened three septic hands—there were no antibiotics available as yet. That same morning we incised the scarlet eardrum of three year old Catriona whose earache was intense. While the sight of instant pus cheered us, she was not well next day and the mastoid bone was tender. On the following morning, the consultant surgeon performed an emergency mastoid operation. Two days later, Catriona was mortally ill and my spinal puncture confirmed meningitis and impending death.

Catriona was not the last to die in this way and the post-mortem on the tiny child was unforgettable and deeply disturbing. One year later, the advent of penicillin was to re-write the care of "mastoid patients". Therapeutics continually mocks prognosis.

This little waif, in dying, somehow released the suppressed emotions of the Mess. A barrel of beer appeared that evening. When "the big white chief", Mr Band, phoned about the next day's work, a guitar and piano accompanied my debagging. The trousers vanished out the window.

Band was always less than tolerant. Worse, he thrived on destroying his juniors' self confidence. Perhaps he got better service and more attention that way, but, by the time he hung up the telephone, I had lost my shoes, socks and underpants and Band had lost his temper because of noises off. However, there was an escape clause offered me.

If I stole Ben Murray's artificial leg my trousers would be returned. Ben, perhaps in self-preservation, had retreated into his bathroom—leaving the limb outside the door. The deed was done. I captured Ben's leg and my trousers were retrieved—but not the underpants.

Half an hour later there was a stream of Australian expletives of great novelty and power as a real-life Long John Silver erupted hopping into our sitting-room. The five Scotsmen simply wilted under the barrage and then found Ben wouldn't leave until a quart of beer was inside him. So much for hollow legs! That artificial limb became an inviolate, even a holy object, thereafter and still retains its own legendary tales.

Two days later, Matron informed the doctors that a pair of underpants was flying from the hospital flagpole. On retrieval by Willie, the porter, they had been beautifully embroidered with pink and blue flowers and bore the inscription "Gone but not forgotten!" At my Naval Medical some weeks later, a startled Surgeon-Commander viewed the doctor and the decorated briefs with grave suspicion.

"They're my mother's, sir."

"My God, I hope so" was the reply.

The evening pink gin session must have been a little brighter at Naval Headquarters.

CHAPTER FOUR

Not all legs were as hallowed as Ben Murray's. Kathy, a War-time railway shunter, sheltered from the heavy rain under a goods wagon. She was sitting with her legs over the line when the truck suddenly moved.

Although she was still conscious when she reached Casualty, her lower limbs were attached by only a few pathetic pieces. Four hours later she entered the general surgical ward from the operating theatre. Band and I had, with endless patience, rejoined all severed pieces of any tissue whatsoever, concentrating particularly on the blood vessels. I was weary but quite determined to talk to her weeping family. Band called me over.

"Don't waste your energies, Illingworth. Emotions are a luxury. It's technique that counts!" Careless of Band's rank and reputation for petty behaviour, the older man suddenly found that even his mild houseman had a limit of tolerance. Band never forgave me for the crisp, swift rebuke—and I extended my revenge by eating the chief's chocolate biscuits. My God! There was a row over that.

Two nights later, Kathy's left leg was dead from mid-thigh.

"So much for technique, care and gallons of blood", grunted Ben Murray through his mask as he amputated.

Midnight and the other limb was suspect. Ben, now love-smitten, was out "courting". The five housemen were struggling. David Smith, the house physician, wise beyond his years, was called in for a fresh opinion.

"More blood; I'll inform old Carlow", he quietly said. Young, the house surgeon, nodded his thanks. We were desperate for help—but united.

"There's still one more vein."

One hour and two pints of blood later, Kathy was losing ground. The drip had blocked. I phoned the priest. Spiritual help arrived as the drip was cleared with normal saline passed by an exhausted nurse to a tired doctor. Only it wasn't saline she proffered in the ward's dim light, it was absolute alcohol for skin disinfection.

Kathy died fifteen minutes later fortified by the last rites and a high blood alcohol. Her dying had been prolonged, but perhaps bettered. There's a time to let go!

In the doctor's room, comforting the distraught Irish nurse who had made the irrelevant error in the ward was the priority.

"Kathy's death was inevitable anyway. You must accept birth and death as natural events" was the best cliché my inchoate medical brain could contrive.

Nurse Reilly wiped her tears and murmured, "My birth wasn't in the least natural. I appeared in the W.C.!"

The unlucky Magnus Ogg broke his elbow in a work accident. The chief was unhappy, however, about the position of the fragments and opted for open operation and suturing with catgut. Ten days later, Magnus complained that he couldn't control his face properly.

"My mouth keeps twisting."

A timely demonstration during ward rounds left no doubt in his audience's minds. They were witnessing the "risus sardonicus" of tetanus—the uncontrollable bitter smile of "lockjaw".

But what was the source of this awful infection? As Magnus had no external wounds, could it have been the catgut? He was immediately isolated in a darkened, sound proof room—in the knowledge that the slightest stimulus might provoke convulsions. I bent over the heavily sedated man to test the depth of consciousness. That minor movement was sufficient to trigger a tetanic spasm. Ogg's good right arm trapped my neck in an irresistible stranglehold. The contraction relaxed just in time to avert a ridiculous homicide.

Magnus died a terrible death twelve hours later. He had nearly taken the doctor with him. Ironically the appalling mortality of this refractory disease soon became entirely avoidable by prior immunisation.

Hospital Christmas is magic. In the sands of hospital memory, Father Christmas's footprints remain forever. Those not on duty became other people. The irascible young consultant was transformed into a red-nosed clown, smoking a large cigar and kissing nursing staff indiscriminately. Theatre Sister was bound to a trolley and wheeled round the wards. Ben Murray arrived in the nick of time before the "patient" was peeled off and prepared for operation.

What remained of the night was peaceful for the doctors—who could not be wakened anyway. Willie, the porter, was so upset that he developed asthma. Night Sister cured him with an injection of sterile water.

Hogmanay's approach put all staff at battle stations. It began with two large men carrying a third, smaller man into Casualty.

"How'd it happen?!" I said gently. First mistake! Out came a knife.

"Fix him up, Doc, or you'll join him. No police—see?" I "saw" and began to repair a split in the lower lip which ran down to the chin. Staff Nurse disappeared, unnoticed, and, even before the red lip junction was apposed, four policemen were in the doorway. Twenty minutes later, with the only anaesthetic that which was self-administered by the oral route, the wee man and his two pals disappeared—with the police. Six hours later, the Casualty Officer looked round the wreckage.

"Happy New Year, Staff", I mumbled to my blonde colleague. She looked as stunning as ever, apart from a puffy left eye where a fist had landed. My hands were painful, from strain (or restraint). I reached out my hand to her and was amazed that I could still feel the tick of a hormone or two.

Fortunately, Jack Wilson was standing in the doorway.

"Gosh! You chaps are up early. The hospital dance starts in the Stadium in twelve hours. See you then—I'm off for a walk." His walk only got him as far as the front door of Leith Hospital—where he met the local "bobby" supporting a bloodstained youngster.

"Found him hanging by his chin from a spike on the iron railing round the park."

The lad had tried to climb over the eight foot metal barrier—and had slipped. The point had penetrated through the floor of his mouth and up into his hard palate.

After excising, under-cutting and suturing for an hour, Ben Murray had restored the would-be athlete. I marvelled at his dexterity and imperturbability. Ben, a surgeon's surgeon, and a gifted being, was to return to his native Australia to become, within a year, an eminent surgical consultant. What a loss to Edinburgh surgery!

And yet, so soon, he and other Australian colleagues were to be shot dead when a patient, enraged by Ben's directness, ran amok in a clinic in Brisbane. For Ben's five "mental defectives" that sad and dismal feeling of waste and futility continues—forty years on. My grief remains.

New Year's Day in Wartime Scotland; there were few tramcars, taxis, buses or cars. Only Ben had a vehicle and he was using it to take a young lady to lunch—but he offered a lift "up town". Time as a civilian was running out and I wanted to take leave of "Granny". However, as soon as I reached her house, the years were rolled back. I was sent to bed with a cup of tea! Six hours later, I awoke, had more tea and found a taxi to take me to Leith Hospital.

At 8 pm, in a dinner jacket which had rather outgrown me, I entered the Stadium. There was a slim, blonde girl in a green dress who looked familiar and smiled shyly at me. She made the arena seem quite empty. I hesitantly asked her to dance.

"Aren't you from the hospital?" I stammered—because of a strange feeling of urgency. Her eyes matched her dress.

"Look nurse, forget about this hospital dance, please—will you see me again?" I sounded so banal and clumsy.

"I could arrange a day off on Sunday—because I'm on nights in "Kids"."

"But how can you do without sleep?"

She could. She did. And Lesley, of tough Buchan stock, became my universe. Disciplined, yet flexible, strong yet sensitive, when her emerald eyes sparkled, my heart tumbled about inside me. Her presence evoked a weird feeling of taut nausea—while the soft Buchan dialect made the enchantment complete. The Casualty Officer became instantly, hopelessly besotted.

I visited my goddess at strange times, though persecuted by the Night Superintendent—who suspected something. During the small hours, I'd be hidden in empty laundry baskets—on which the Night Super occasionally sat! Or in a broom cupboard in which I once met another doctor. But ultimately I met guile with guile when the Night Super started removing her shoes and creeping noiselessly up the staircase. This problem was solved by positioning a few drawing pins. The path of true love was smoothed.

Even when the side gate—twelve feet high (with spikes) was locked early, we defeated this also. Getting over it was simple. I lifted Lesley onto my shoulders; she then scrambled along a fifteen foot high wall and over a roof into the conveniently open window of her best friend's room.

Now I had to get back over the private gate. Men wore belted coats in those days and on the last agonising occasion, as I dropped down on the street side, the spike passed beneath my belt. And there I hung—unable to move—until I remembered my habit of always carrying scissors in my breast pocket.

The coat looked better without a belt anyway.

By January 1944 I knew we would marry. We couldn't bear the thought of separation without something concrete. Not in a physical sense; you don't touch goddesses. But I yearned for an understanding. After all, I had just become twenty two and my non-medical contemporaries had joined up and were dying. Yet the times still discouraged emotional release and marriage was never imagined as a franchise for the ineffectual.

There was yet another problem. There always would be! Accepted for the Royal Navy, destroyers were my ambition, and, although the tide was turning against the enemy, each weekend seemed to bring bad news. Even my father had been twice "in the drink"! I tried to balance married bliss with the risks of service in a small ship. I failed! But in any case, an outcry of two mothers desolated the pair of us. Towards the end of February, a very cold (and single) David headed for Plymouth on an icy train. Reflecting the needs and losses of the services at that time, three of the five housemen at Leith had entered the Royal Navy. Alec Macqueen claimed that his fine appearance would be best enhanced by RAF uniform, while another of the five, David Smith, re-affirmed the pacifist convictions of his school days, and said he would serve anywhere, in any capacity, but NOT in uniform. This courageous stand was rewarded by a reference from his chief which stated that "He has conducted himself to his own entire satisfaction."

Wilson and Young, my co-residents at Leith Hospital, who had also joined the Navy, were both posted to destroyers. Some of these were First World War American vessels; President Roosevelt had exchanged fifty of them for certain privileges in the Caribbean. In rough weather they were nightmares and fraught with risk in proceeding from one end of the craft to the other. This entailed going out on deck holding fast to a cable as the seas washed over the ship. There was a certain mortality.

Young had another problem. He couldn't sleep on trains—but was equal to the challenge. At the end of his embarkation leave, after an evening of gaiety, he crept into his sleeper bunk at Edinburgh station. The drill was simple; he produced from his great-coat the twin bottles of "Douglas's Instant Slumber Wonder". The gulp from the bottle of liquid chloral hydrate was like filling your mouth with hot embers. The fire was at once extinguished by draining the second bottle—which contained water. Six hours of sound sleep then ensued—at least that was the principle

His "sailor's farewell" to Scotland had sadly impaired his dexterity and taste buds. In the gloom of the sleeper, a quick slug of water was washed down by the complete contents of the bottle of chloral hydrate.

Darkness closed in on him as he fell into his bunk. His last thought as the train left for King's Cross was of Professor

Dunlop's "Good safe stuff, chloral, acts at once, tastes like hell—but it's damned difficult to kill yourself with it!"

At dawn, he awoke on a trolley in a London Hospital. He was surrounded by people in white. Somewhat befuddled, he thought he might be in heaven, until he received two simultaneous messages.

"I'm a psychiatrist, why did you try it? Battle fatigue?" and............

"It's your bladder calling, we had ten pints last night! Man the boats!"

Douglas never patented his "Instant Slumber Wonder", but he did manage to join his ship in time.

PART II

NAVAL SURGEON

CHAPTER FIVE

I reached London's Waterloo Station feeling desolate, then travelled onwards to Plymouth and the Naval Base, HMS Drake, where I arrived as an isolated nervous new boy. In my allotted "cabin" the need to change into a brand-new uniform was therapeutic. The stiff white collar cut my soft fingers and my neckwear was streaked with blood when I arrived in the anteroom. The Surgeon-Captain was waiting, gave me a large pink gin—and my orders—in one sentence.

"Report to Medical Inspection room at 0900 hours tomorrow."

The haze of tobacco smoke and the tang of old leather upholstery were reassuring and I felt even better to see six of my medical year steadily absorbing their pink beverages. I joined them, feeling strangely comforted and finished in happy mood.

At 0730 next morning I found a "Wren" in the cabin—holding a teacup under my nose.

Her "Will that be all, sir?" did not elicit the traditional profane student observation which came automatically to mind—but had to be sublimated. I reached the Medical Inspection Room and reported to my Surgeon-Captain—whose orders were clear.

"M.I. room 'til 1700 hours. Fire Drill at 1800, Dinner at 1900."

One of twelve new Surgeon Lieutenants, my job was to make sure that the matelots fresh in from sea were "free from infection". A Petty Officer gave me a high-powered lamp. An endless stream of sailors filled the morning.

"All right? Drop your trousers. Turn round. Bend over."

I gulped the wardroom lunch striving to suppress the memory of a matelot with one large eye tattooed on each buttock who bent over to reveal a nose with THREE nostrils.

The afternoon passed in the same rhythmic monotony; the Surgeon-Lieutenants filled the gaps with an intense series of games of "Battleships" on prescription pads. The Chief Petty Officer shattered the peace by asking them to don gas masks and asbestos suits.

"You crawl, gentlemen, through a blazing tunnel. I let off fireworks—and when—if, you emerge after ten minutes, you'll be well prepared for Hell."

Square bashing was awful but rifle drill was horrific. The Surgeon-Lieutenants trembled before a Chief Petty Officer who had stepped straight out of a barrel of brine.

"Gentlemen, I never saw so many pansies with two left feet. If you handle your own tools the way you handle them rifles, the War is already lost."

But in four weeks I could throw a hand grenade, fire a rifle and wear my cap at the required jaunty angle—and I was rich. £30 a month—of which £10 was allotted to my mother.

Immediate postings now arrived from the Admiralty for the excited new boys. Tom Matheson, my partner as a student—fortunately for me—an intelligent and generous chap and a good friend, was to go to "Warspite". The others were destined for destroyers—except for one—myself. I was to go to Burntisland to a vessel which only possessed a number, K391. Burntisland was familiar as a small fishing town in Fife. "Doctor to a fishing boat perhaps", said Tom, trying to contain his mirth. "At least you will be near Edinburgh and you can borrow my father's fishing tackle!"—I was NOT pleased.

The following day, I was in Edinburgh. The next morning at Leith Hospital I was reunited with Lesley. Oblivious of the scanty traffic, we held each other—in the middle of the road. She didn't smile. Unlike a goddess, she just plain grinned and then her laughter erupted. It was happiness and not my tomato-like nose she explained (I had a large nasal boil!).

Admiralty gave me five days leave. Lesley was "on nights", but remained virtually sleepless as we lived it up. You must leave your birthplace to appreciate it and, during Lesley's brief sleeps, I saw Edinburgh through fresh eyes. A tramcar ride down the Mound early one winter morning started another love affair, but of less intensity, with my city—still smoky enough to merit its nickname "Auld Reekie".

Standing on the quayside at Burntisland, I studied the newly commissioned H.M.S. Loch Killin (K391). She looked prosaic, frail and unaggressive but was certainly not a fishing boat. I walked up "the brow", nervously remembering to salute the quarterdeck. The Captain was beside the First Lieutenant.

Stanley Darling, the Skipper, was a tanned, blue-eyed Australian. Direct and uncompromising he was never to waver in our months together. Saluting and shaking hands he intimated.

"We're doing acceptance trials, Doc, for two weeks. The ship sails at 0900 hours each day, returning to Burntisland at 1700. You can't sleep on board yet, but you may want to "dig" at your home. Edinburgh, isn't it—and travel by train?"

My pleasure at my good fortune must have shown. Captain Darling nodded knowingly at his First Lieutenant.

"Must be love, Number One!"

The tawdry smile he got in reply made the Captain seem even more impressive. Ryecroft, the First Lieutenant, was almost a caricature of a louche tramp steamer officer. Equipped with overactive salivary glands, the excess secretion had dried at the mouth angles in a ragged grey film—like the salt stains left on sea-sand by the receding tide. His teeth were discoloured and matched the brown stain on his upper lip just below which hung the habitual cigarette. Wondering at the disparity between this ill-assorted pair, I listened to the Captain's code of conduct.

"Doc", the Australian said, "I run a tight ship so make your choice before you begin. You'll either be a bastard or a bad officer!"

I could never reconcile this statement with the man, addicted to Beethoven, who had formerly been "Uncle Stanley" in Australia's "Children's Hour" on the radio.

The Sick Bay was a masterpiece occupied by a curly-haired compact Chief Petty Officer of the Royal Naval Reserve, who came from Wigan. Goggins by name, he sounded like something out of a theatrical script; apparently easy-going, there was a steel core in the flexible cable. He was, for fifteen months, to be my guide and friend. He took nothing for granted; nor did he presume on our friendship. One of the world's gentlemen, he was part of the Service's backbone. He never set out to demonstrate his excellence—except in his calligraphy. He could write, in beautiful flowing fashion, with either hand—independently or simultaneously. The message could be written backwards, upside down or as a mirror image. I used to marvel at the unique composition of Goggins' neurological tracts and wanted him to donate his body to some Anatomy Department for dissection. My Sick Berth colleague was indeed unique.

The First Lieutenant appeared as the two Medicos sized each other up at their first meeting. He didn't bother to knock.

"Morning Doc", said Number One. I was about to respond when Goggins beat me to it. Ryecroft, the Number One, spoke in a broad Lancashire accent as he looked appraisingly at me.

"Met the Quack, have you Doc?" Goggins laughed at the puzzlement on his Surgeon-Lieutenant's face as he began to explain small ship jargon to the bemused doctor and Ryecroft vanished in a flurry of overalls, gum boots and oily odours.

"You see, Sir, no warship smaller than Killin carries a doctor. Corvettes and other little tiddlers have only a Sick Bay Attendant and he's addressed as "Doc"! So, in a small ship language, you're "The Quack". Sorry! The Officers will show you more respect."

The Wardroom was equally immaculate and "The Quack" met in turn, Dickinson, the Torpedo Officer; Eason, Gunnery Officer; Trentham, Asdic Officer; Harding, the Navigating

Officer—from New Zealand; Stevens, the Midshipman and Captain's Secretary; and Gledhill, the Chief Engineer.

Gledhill, the only regular RN Officer, had a face hacked out of old red sandstone. At the age of 50, he was obviously the Wardroom father and made it plain from the first encounter that the Admiralty whisky issue of one case per Wardroom each month, was HIS alone. In return for this, he would dispense advice and adopt anyone who needed him. Not always happy because he was, unconsciously, a perfectionist in search of 110% from his life, his high professional standards rubbed off on others—and not to their detriment.

Stanley Darling, the Captain, casually asked (of no-one in particular) if he might enter the Wardroom. Captains have only courtesy use of the Wardroom. He at once moved round the individual officers, carefully enquiring about duties and readiness. With his target pressed against the bulkhead, Darling succeeded in separating me from the flock.

"Everything alright Doc?"

"Aye, aye, Sir" replied the MO. "We can do anything except obstetrics."

The Captain smiled.

"Don't worry about that, pregnancy is strictly forbidden. You'll find most of our 140 are pretty sound. You won't be too busy medically, so I'm making you Cypher Officer, Wine Caterer, Tobacco Controller, Mess Secretary, Mail Censor, Welfare and Entertainments Officer. So, you'll be in charge of this Wardroom and to support you, you'll have the Chief Steward, two very junior stewards and the Officer's cook—he was a bus driver 'til six weeks ago and will need watching. Later on, we'll make a real sailor of you and give you a standing watch—probably the afternoon." I said I would like to think about all this—feeling I could reason with Uncle Stanley of the Australian Broadcasting Company.

"Look here pommie", said Uncle Stanley, "An order is not a basis for discussion. I'm not asking you—I'm bloody telling you! And spare me any non-combatant nonsense. Number One tells me you own a Browning Automatic."

I silently cursed the perfidious Ryecroft in whom I had stupidly confided in a search for .32 ammunition.

"You're not as wet as you look—and neither am I!" The Captain seemed to have inflated—like a bullfrog. I understood where all his uniform ribbons came from, felt a sneaking sympathy for any opposition and wished for the bulkhead behind me to open.

The other officers looked at me sadly as the Captain strode out, decreeing "Report to me in my Day Cabin now, Doc!"

The Day Cabin was alive with cables and speakers. Beethoven's 5th was booming out as I fell, shouting, over the sill of the cabin and the deafening music.

"Won't the music keep the crew awake, Sir—and any U-Boat that's around?!

The Captain smiled as he switched off the apparatus.

"Sorry I rattled you Doccie!" I winced at the solecism.

"This is a new and top secret ship, the first of her class. We've got the finest devices in the world for detecting and killing U-Boats. I'm proud of this ship. I want her in action P.D.Q. You'll help me?"

Warming with admiration and patriotism I apologised for being obtuse.

"That's okay, Doc. Do you like music?"

"Oh yes, Sir. I'm a Bing Crosby fan"

It was the Captain's turn to flinch but he didn't back down. "I'll play your records anytime." He enunciated this like a judge delivering the death sentence. But we parted friends and the doctor felt the Royal Navy was in safe Australian hands.

The Engineer Officer ("Chiefie") passed me a large pink drink as I carefully negotiated the Wardroom sill.

"David, lad, Stanley Darling's rough—but fair—and a damn good Captain. I had ten years on the China Station and as I'm fifty, I've known a lot of Captains. Cheer up. Drink up. Here's the Snottie to talk to you. Offer him a port and lemon—that's his tipple—a woman's drink!"

Midshipman Stevens came over. "Don't be sad Doc. It's your first ship. I know we'll muck in together. Not a bad bunch really!"

The port and lemon appeared in the Junior Steward's grubby hands as the Chief Steward sidled over and drew me a little apart to make his apologies. My nose had been assailed by the unexpected odour of stale urine. Fresh from cruisers and conscious of his responsibilities, the Chief Steward whispered,

"Sorry about the pong, Sir, but he just keeps wetting his 'ammock', you know."

The Snottie heard the mutterings and crimsoned.

"For God's sake, Doc, step in and help. I'll never eat another thing. Thank heaven for peanut butter." The Midshipman's mother had provided enough of this delicacy to see him through "the duration".

Further discussion on the steward's weak bladder was avoided by a bellow from the brow of "Help". Running topsides I found Eason, the Duty Officer, pointing at the Harbourmaster, who had gently toppled on to his face as he approached Killin. Pupils dilated and respiration ceased, the Harbourmaster was beyond assistance—a derisory cigarette still smouldering in his dead fingers—and a small seed of thought about cause or coincidence was planted in my head. But I lit up myself as the police and ambulance began to clear up the fracas.

"Isn't that your first patient, Doc?" enquired Eason as we descended the ladder together and sat on the Wardroom settee. Chiefie and I looked sternly at the Gunnery Officer as he chuckled before vanishing aloft.

"Steward—more pinkers for the doctor, please!" The Chief looked at the departing figure and began a diversion.

"Schoolmaster with a lovely big wife. My oppo in China wouldn't have liked her. Preferred small girls."

"And preferably over the sink!"

Ryecroft had arrived, complete with overalls and oily odours.

"God, Number One, you're crude" growled Chiefie—regretting a previous alcoholic confidence. Stevens the

Midshipman, murmured that the Wardroom was not the place for such talk when someone had just died.

"You'd better watch Number One", he whispered, "He's as nasty as he smells." Unfortunately the First Lieutenant overheard him.

"You're insolent, Snottie", said Ryecroft in his broad Lancashire accent. "I'm right fed up with your remarks—and all that sort of silly stuff."

"Sorry, Number One, I apologise. I deserved that 'bottle'. It's your oily feet. I thought you wouldn't hear me."

"So now I'm not only dirty, I'm deaf!"

I was feeling very uncomfortable when Dickinson arrived. The sudden appearance of his cheerful, cheeky face averted a crisis as he came over.

"Had a run-in with the Captain, lad? You'll recover. Killin will be a good ship—but she'll never be like tiddly little Camellia boy." The Torpedo Officer had served two years in the Flower Class Corvette of that name and he was rightly proud of this.

"Little Camellia, boy" and Ryecroft's "And all that sort of stuff" became catchphrases in the months ahead—nonce expressions when you couldn't be bothered to think any more.

That afternoon the Midshipman was vindicated. Number One fell down a ladder and badly sprained his ankle. Five grey toes protruded coyly from a filthy black sock—which I had to peel off.

"Maybe you need a wife to darn your socks" I ventured.

"Not on your nelly, Doc. I buy a dozen pairs at a time and wear 'em till they burst. Saves dhobeying." I strapped the swollen joint and prescribed elevation and rest of the limb—hoping to ease the Midshipman's predicament. But Ryecroft continued to vent his feelings about "little boys with fancy accents"—until the ship's surgeon felt like stopping the Lancashire invective by plastering Ryecroft's mouth.

Trentham, the Asdic Officer, looked into the cabin to see how things were. He hastily withdrew.

"See you below in the Wardroom, Doc." Then quite unnecessarily he added, "Better wash your hands first."

The verbal barb sailed unnoticed over Ryecroft's head. In the Wardroom the weather-beaten Asdic man—"Ping" to his friends—gave a thumbnail sketch to the new boy.

"I'm a chartered secretary of thirty seven, played rugby for Moseley and I've got four children.

None of the statements was connected but "Ping" didn't believe in wasting words. "Have you met Harding, the Navigator? Solid chap—Kiwi."

I was looking at a pleasantly firm smiling face. My future brother-in-law, a dentist, had made me very tooth conscious. Harding was dentally well-equipped and I was further impressed to see the cheerful extrovert was wearing the insignia of a "mention in despatches" which he claimed, under pressure, to have got "by mistake".

In spite of the pink gin I was feeling estranged by my inexperience. Trentham had been roughed up in HMS Egret; Ryecroft, Eason and Chiefie were also seasoned veterans; "Dickie" had served in "Little Camellia boy", which he modestly explained set him above all other men of the sea. "Camellia" had sunk U47. "Dickie" didn't know that this U-Boat's Captain was Gunther Prien who, in U47, had destroyed the "Royal Oak" in Scapa Flow—when 833 British sailors perished. Awareness of trumping this ace would have made "Dickie" quite intolerable.

The Captain was adorned with the hallmarks of bravery. Only the Midshipman and the Doctor were unblooded.

I voiced this to Trentham who understood my feeling of isolation.

"Won't be long David. This is the new breed of U-boat destroyers; the working officers are handpicked. You could be busy!"

I wondered what on earth I was doing on board but felt closer to the company of this "tight little ship"—perhaps too close and too tight to go ashore at times.

"Right, Doc, the cabin opposite mine."

"But that's my bloody cabin!" shouted "Dickie".

Captain Darling entered the Wardroom. A disciplined silence fell.

"Not any more, pommie. King's Regulations say that the doctor must have his own cabin."

"Waste of a bloody cabin, sir" muttered Dickie.

"Perhaps it'll put a stop to your illicit love life if you share with Harding," interjected Trentham. "Anyway the doctor may have a love life too!"

"Dickie", puce coloured, tore out of the Wardroom and forgot about the sill. There was a loud thud and an oath as there drifted back from the alleyway. "Wouldn't have happened in little Camellia, boy!"

There were derisive replies making it clear that Camellia didn't carry a doctor anyway—and that it was sex, not sleep, which occupied the Torpedo Officer—apart from "nutty"—to which he was addicted—to the extent of acquiring each month most of the ship's allocation of Mars Bars.

So I spent my first night in my first ship. I lay in my bunk looking up at the singular deckhead; had my "jigsaw" sensation and decided I was ready for sea. I fitted in.

CHAPTER SIX

Three days later, Killin, having completed her acceptance trials, headed north from Burntisland and into the Pentland Firth.

The Firth's mood was vicious. Everything was grey—the sea—the ship—the cliffs—the sky—the spirit. Sleepless and bombarded with ciphers (none of which was relevant), I remember only an endless series of retchings and lining up cipher mechanisms on my cabin desk. I crept up to the bridge where the Chief Boatswain's Mate—"The Buffer"—took pity on me and as Killin heaved her way out of the westward end of the Pentland Firth, he added a large tot of Navy Rum ("Nelson's Blood") to the mug of instant coffee handed to me by Douglas the Chief Yeoman of Signals—and a most dexterous "bunting tosser" he was to prove.

It was the middle watch and, as I slumped nauseated in the chartroom, I could see Harding grinning from the exposed bridge while rain and salt spray landed on his protective gear.

"Doc, you look bloody awful" shouted the Kiwi into the tiny cubicle of the chartroom, above the appalling noise. "Wait till we get some real weather! If you're sea-sick Doc, you're frightened you're going to die; at the next stage you're frightened you're NOT going to die!"

I drank the mug of witches' brew which tasted like nectar. Suddenly survival seemed probable and through this liquid experience came a craving as intense as an appetite caprice in pregnancy, for peanut butter. I reeled below to the Wardroom and stole the Midshipman's special jar of peanut butter, made a large salty sandwich and returned to the bridge.

The signalman handed me another cipher.

The weather moderated as Killin steamed, in spring sunshine, down the West coast of my native land. It was a stunning experience and, seeing Scotland from the sea, I felt patriotic, proud and privileged—or was I just relieved that I fitted in?

Skye, Mull, Jura and Islay drifted slowly past the ship as she headed for Fairlie—and the scientists. The Captain had warned us that the backroom boys would be very interested to see what the Admiralty had created out of a composite of imageries. There'd be intense criticism of this prototype.

The cipher traffic eased as the coding office proposed that it would deal with all but the top-secret ciphers. My well-being was further increased by the improvement in my sea-sickness. I determined to improve the Wardroom's quality of service.

But I was thwarted by the Ship's Postman, who acting as a dispenser of life's basics as our "Jack Dusty"—mail, tea and coffee—was surely the most lugubrious man ever to leave land. He emanated doom and gloom. Five hundred letters from 140 matelots were unceremoniously dumped on the Wardroom table.

"Mail for censoring, sir," he said dolefully. "Expect you'll find they're all from Able Seaman Corbett. He over-estimated Corbett, however, for only ten letters were from him.

Many letters bore puzzling messages on the envelope flaps. Goggins interpreted these for me. Viz- ITALY "I think always lovingly of you"; SWALK—"Sealed with a loving kiss"; BOLTOP—Better on lips than on paper"; BURMA—"Be upstairs ready my angel." "Shall I go on?" said Goggins. "They get worse!"

After the first hundred letters had been chopped up by my scissors I, the censor, had learned many things. The ship's company was actually happy but extremely indiscreet; not only were there vivid accounts of an erotic nature in encounters totally foreign to the Pentland Firth in March, "The Doc" I learned was a great guy, but "The Quack"—me—spoke with "a plum in his mouth"—when he wasn't being seasick. The Captain was "fair"; most of the officers were "gents" but Number One was a real.....................!"; while the food was "as poor as haddock water".

As the vessel neared Fairlie the five hundredth letter was also from AB Corbett of Liverpool. Five of Corbett's letters were identical proposals of marriage—to five different girls. Corbett, a fine looking fellow, was gently asked to explain.

"In strict confidence, Corbett, I've noticed in the mail your five proposals to five different ladies." I realised that his mental ability was less than his physical endowment.

The AB's face remained as expressive as a bollard.

"Well, you see, Sir, I've been away from home for a long time and I love them all, especially because of what's coming to us.

"What's coming to us, Corbett?"

"The big test, Sir; the Admiralty will send new and secret ships where it's tough. Do you think we'll make it? And, while I'm here, Sir, could you help me with my spots?"

Corbett, with all his good looks, carried on his face an extensive crop of acne. I had just read an article in a medical journal on the successful use of oestrogen—the female sex hormone—in his skin disease.

"Corbett, you can certainly be helped. One tablet a day and you won't know yourself."

Corbett was delighted and left, firmly reassured that neither in his naval service nor his treatment was he in any sense an experimental animal.

But the Welfare Officer—me—sought out the Captain.

"For Pete's sake, Doctor, don't tell me his name. Release the letters—but tell me the outcome. One way or other, he'll die in action!"

I remained unsure whether I was being offered a threat or a prophecy.

The persistent querulous nagging of the Asdic's searchings is incessantly audible throughout submarine hunters. No human being can imitate it. It pings and penetrates and if the note or rhythm changes, you are at once on the alert—even though you've been asleep—or addressing the Captain. And the Captain heard the alteration in the echo first.

"Captain to Bridge, you've picked up something. Sound Action Stations!"

The Medical Officer wasn't sure where his action station was but I felt safer on the bridge where I was at once confused by Darling addressing a general question.

"Any British subs. In the area?"

The Chief Yeoman of signals and the Navigator said "No!" together and firmly, with confidence which they couldn't really feel. I wondered how they could possibly know. Looking for'ard I saw Number One's crewmen taking the canvas covers from "The Squid". This well-named device consisted of a pair of triple mortars which pointed petulantly ahead of the ship. Trentham and his Chief Petty Officer, Gent, were shouting out ranges and bearings to help turn Killin's bow towards the source of the echo. Louder and louder grew the noise and the "pings" came closer together until they were almost continuous. At this point the target was precisely three hundred yards ahead of the frigate.

Darling gave the order to fire. Six three hundred pound bombs looped lazily through the air and slid gracefully, like porpoises, into the sea.

Harding crept out of the charthouse and I cornered him.

"It all looks a bit ineffectual but it's certainly elegant."

The Kiwi grinned. "David," he said in the seemingly endless interval, "it's like nutcrackers. Three bombs explode above the U-Boat and three beneath her. In theory, the target gets squashed in between by hydrostatic pressure. Notice that we've stopped in case we get blown up too. Principle—good—experience—Nil!"

We lit cigarettes and then came the eruption. The sea boiled and bubbled ahead of us. A white geyser rose a hundred feet in the air as the ship convulsed from stem to stern.

"My God, it works" gasped the Captain as the cigarette fell out of his mouth.

"Slow ahead together." Trentham's pink face appeared in the doorway of the Asdic cabin.

"Echo's gone, Sir. Must have been a shoal of fish."

"Balls!" came the retort but as the Captain continued to berate Trentham, about two hundred dead fish reached the turbulent surface of the sea and Eason arrived on the bridge smiling broadly.

"Expensive fish supper, Sir, but it's all perfectly fresh. Shall we launch the whaler?"

"Well don't thank me, thank him", replied the Captain, indicating Trentham's Asdic cabin.

Within an hour Killin had become the largest fish and chip shop afloat.

Unaccustomed to violent death by unsporting methods, I neglected my portion of conger eel, compensating with a double dose of the inevitable "Brown Windsor" soup.

Darling joined his officers. Fully recovered, he said to "Ping".

"Well, it was worth a try and we shall learn from our experience."

Trentham agreed and, much relieved, ate the doctor's piece of conger eel—and chips.

CHAPTER SEVEN

Fairlie is as pleasant a place as its name. The "boffins" boarded the frigate as soon as she tied up to the buoy. Six scientists came up the ladder—each quietly dedicated and expert in his own field—radar, Asdic, engines, squid or surface armaments. In garb they varied from the traditional "bowler" or cloth cap with a waterproof to crisp traditional uniform. Each expert gathered round him a portion of the crew and set about them with a will. Feeling excluded from all the mystique, I asked the Captain what speciality I could be involved with.

"All fixed up, Doccie, lucky bastard you, you're doing cipher training with the Wrens. Row yourself ashore each morning in the dinghy at 0800 hours, do your cipher work, exercise the ship's dog and collect milk for the Wardroom", replied Darling.

There followed a week of this bizarre activity. The Wrens were patient, the milk and the dog excellent—but the rowing was sub-standard.

The "working officers" struggled to conquer scientific mysteries—amid the breathtaking scenery of the West of Scotland. The frigate's crew was dissected by the experts—being constantly reminded that the difference between life and death was a margin of a fraction of a second.

And so it turned out to be.

It was as well that excellence had to be attained before they'd let the ship depart.

Killin was released after seven days of intensive tuition, investigation and assessment and, in confident mood, we sailed north.

"Fairle for fun, Tobermory for terror" had been a small ship slogan for two years. The Captain was strangely quiet when we reached Tobermory Bay and not because of the beauty of the scene as we rounded Calve island to enter the harbour where the sunken Spanish galleon still waits in its muddy grave.

The White Ensign fluttered from HMS Western Isles as the frigate tied up to a buoy. An Aldis lamp flickered from the floating Naval headquarters. Chief Yeoman Douglas reported to the Captain.

"Message reads, 'Now go back and do it again!', Sir"

Cursing seamen released Killin from her mooring. The frigate went briefly astern and repeated the manoeuvre.

"That's better!" ordained the Aldis lamp of RNHQ Tobermory.

On the quarter deck Dickinson groaned dismally, but quietly—in case Admiral Sir Gilbert Stephenson overheard him he said as he looked pathetically at the doctor.

"This is where they work you until the wax runs out of your ears."

I had never heard of "Monkey" Stephenson and was ecstatic about the beauty of Tobermory on May 1st. The evening light shining on this ethereal township would have awakened the sleeping bard in any Celt.

"Monkey" was aboard five minutes after we tied up. Small, wrinkled and with great tufts of hair sprouting from his malar bones, I realised at once that I was looking at a wartime phenomenon—a creature generated at just the right time for a portentous purpose—like Churchill, Montgomery and Patton. It was chillingly tense and the entire ship's company was watchful and wary. Even the Captain was clearly under the influence of this ancient mariner whose demeanour made one feel vaguely apologetic towards any opposition. I had the impression that if I touched "Monkey", I would get an electric shock. Although old by Naval standards, Admiral Stephenson was very much a modern living legend. His professional objective was to train novices for "the real war". However, most of those who took a ship into Tobermory found the enemy infinitely less troublesome than "Monkey's" stressful ordinances.

Although sympathising with the "working officers", I continued my Fairlie routine of dog walking—in the Aros estate—and buying milk for the wardroom. The sun beat down on magnificent "roddies". It was wonderful—but it couldn't last. Admiral Stephenson picked on me when I was obscurely positioned on Killin's bridge.

"What do you do my boy?"

"Sir, I'm the doctor." I had it in mind to offer my twelve other official positions in the frigate—but decided otherwise.

"Right! There's a man in the crow's nest with three bullets in him. Action!"

Looking up fifty feet I saw the pallid face of the officers' cook peering dolefully down at me. Obviously "Monkey" had set up this situation to test out the medics. At once I sought out the imperturbable Goggins.

"Worry not, Sir, dressings, a rope and a Niall-Robertson stretcher is all we'll need."

The two docs reached the crow's nest taking with them the means to immobilise and lower the reluctant "casualty" to the deck below.

"Look sir, I'm not going down there! I'm a married man with three children", groaned cook.

"Balls! You're seriously wounded with three bullets in you, so get into the bleeding stretcher", shouted Goggins. Secured—fixedly—like an Egyptian mummy, cook was lowered erratically to the deck. I had been hoping the cook was adequately insured but became less caring when Goggins remarked—"At least if we drop him you'll get better food in the wardroom. They say you live on peanut butter."

The Admiral was lavish in his praise as I realised once again that the Services ran on their senior non-commissioned ranks. "Monkey" rewarded me with a Mars Bar.

We proceeded with gunnery practice in the Sound of Mull. The 4" gun on the foc'sle was expected to hit a target two hundred yards behind the towing tug. The first shot was a near miss on the tug which vanished in a cloud of spray. "Monkey" Stephenson tore off his cap and jumped on it as he called down the wrath of God on Higgins, the poor gunlayer. But the next shot hit the centre of the target and the Admiral, always fair, sent for Higgins and congratulated him. Higgins was also given a Mars Bar. The Admiral dispensed these to the successful.

That evening the ship's motor boat took the liberty men ashore. The officers went to the Western Isles Hotel where, in great comfort, while blue-jackets with fixed bayonets protected the entrance, the wine flowed freely. Petty Officers and crew went to the Mishnish Hotel where the surroundings were more austere, more vigorous and less formal.

The last liberty boat left the pier at 2300 hours. In the hotel bar at 2255 Chiefie glanced at his watch.

"Time gentlemen" he shouted as he led the charge down the black precipitate 109 steps to the pier head. As I reached the last turn in the 200 foot descent, I tripped and took off into the darkness. I came to saluting the quarterdeck and feeling a large lump on my forehead.

In the morning, however, I rowed ashore with Goldie, the ship's dog, for our usual walk to Aros House. I looked over at the Western Isles Hotel and felt my bruised skull as I released the cocker spaniel to pursue the black rabbits of Aros amongst the towering rhododendrons in the most beautiful place I had ever seen.

Stephenson's final party in the Western Isles Hotel was really a reparation for the month's ordeal by fire. The human side of Killin's tormentor was exhibited as he said goodbye to me in his small office.

"I'm not difficult, doctor, and naturally, I like to be liked—but I have a job to do and dammit I'll do it."

A sensitive human being had popped out from the tough carapace in which it hid. This brief revelation of the true character of "The Terror of Tobermory" impressed me. Involved with these arcane thoughts, I tramped down the 109 steps to the pier head convinced that the outcome of any war hinged on 1% of the combatants. I appreciated that I had already met a few of this tiny proportion—those whose initiative and leadership would ineluctably encourage their hurt.

It has always been so.

HMS Loch Killin left Mull on June 1st 1944 with her company totally confident in their ship, their shipmates and themselves. The enemy had to be less troublesome than Admiral Sir Gilbert Stephenson!

The doctor fell asleep to the haunting petulant questings of the Asdic—musing on the irony of war which always culls the best and bravest of a nation.

That next day I wasn't seasick. My semi-circular canals could now adapt to Killin's roll—and to her pitch. But if the two movements co-incided to produce the shape and feeling of a maritime corkscrew—there was a clear limit to physiological tolerance.

Thirty six hours later Killin tied up in Liverpool. We were ready for war.

"The Buffer" went home to his wife to leave behind the ship's dog while I made my number with the doctor of the frigate alongside—HMS Mourne—one of the "River" class—elegantly comfortable, with a panelled wardroom and a piano. My colleague was Dr Evans—handsome, experienced and ebullient—who gave a graphic account of the wrecking of the wardroom when their piano broke loose in a heavy Atlantic swell.

At dinner the Chief Engineers of the two ships went deep into the esoteric lore of malt whisky. The Mourne's food was excellent. In the relaxed atmosphere Evans and I gradually shed our non-combatant shells. Service doctors hate to be left out of the aggressive aspects of war and the two young MOs agreed that ahead-throwing weapons had a more perceptive anti-U-Boat effect than treating acne or constipation—and infinitely more glamour. Evans described Mourne's "Hedgehog" which hurled mortar bombs ahead of the ship. His enthusiasm was qualified only by the experience of a sister ship which had, by a slight miscalculation, blown off her own foc'sle. The "Squid" was my personal ace however.

The following evening, June 5th, the mail arrived on board Killin—with it were Dr Evans and the complete wardroom of HMS Mourne. They came for drinks and stayed for dinner—and to allow me to demonstrate the Squid to my colleague—under Number One's watchful eye. There was much talk of the Second Front and the Invasion. The dinner was a disaster. The steaks looked beautiful but no knife could penetrate them. The stewards were upset and, when Mourne's Captain asked for a fresh napkin, the junior steward stood at the serving hatch and threw it at him. The lad was formally charged. But he was to mature rapidly—and soon.

Evans, defeated by the steak, heard the incredible story of AB Corbett's five marriage proposals. Chiefie had found his fellow whisky lover and the Chief Steward told the two doctors that Corbett would be up all night answering his mail.

"Why?" Evans enquired.

"Because four of his girl friends are now engaged to him!"

At 2200 hours Chiefie asked me for a stretcher party to transport his colleague to the ship alongside—Mourne.

"Can't understand it Doc, we didn't drink much more than a bottle!"

Evans, Chiefie and I carried the incapable officer aboard his ship. Chiefie muttered

"He'll be mourning in the morning."

The prophecy was to be fulfilled.

At 2230 the Captain appeared in the wardroom and said he had received, by hand, an urgent signal to proceed at top speed to the Western Approaches of the English Channel. Mourne and three other frigates were to accompany us.

"Second front, Sir?" enquired Surgeon-Lieutenant Evans.

"Right Doc" said the excited Darling. Evans rose languidly and shook hands.

"I'm glad I got married before it started," he said.

"I should have—but I hadn't enough courage" I replied.

I saw my guest over the side and descended hurriedly to a pile of mail for censoring. There were four identical letters from Corbett delaying his wedding ceremonies until there was peace. The Ship's Censor scribbled a note to his goddess and the mail was dumped on the quayside as the frigate cast off.

Chiefie's engines began to pump and Killin manoeuvred slowly out to sea.

CHAPTER EIGHT

In a few minutes it would be June 6th 1944. The five frigates steamed south, making all speed in line abreast. Mourne was next in line to Killin. Nobody slept. The war games were over. It was difficult to relax—wearing a life belt over one's clothes—which concealed a whistle, an identification tag, a torch and a first aid kit.

As dawn broke I gave up the struggle to sleep and clambered up to the bridge and looked across to where the likeable Dr Evans would be. But I couldn't see Mourne on our starboard beam. Where was she? I turned to the Captain who was controlling the zig zag. The Chief Yeoman handed over a signal. Darling, wordlessly, passed it over.

"Mourne torpedoed and blown up at 0630 hours; three survivors on raft" Evans was not on the raft.

A mere thirty six hours earlier we had performed "Barnacle Bill" and "Eskimo Nel". Now U-767 had snuffed out our friends.

I took refuge in the Asdic hut where Trentham was complaining.

"Doc, that dinner last night was terrible!"

"Shut up Colin", I snarled. "You can be the bloody mess caterer. Incidentally Mourne was torpedoed an hour ago.

Even the disciplined Trentham looked stunned.

"Seems all wrong. We saw them only a few hours ago—and we are—were, next to Mourne in the line."

By dint of "knocking hell out of my engines", Chiefie got Killin in position with her consorts a few hours after the D-Day landings began. Our mission was to keep the U-boat packs away from the landing beaches.

For three weeks we patrolled and zig-zagged as far south as the Bay of Biscay where we joined Captain Walker and his legendary 2nd Escort Group.

Killin's Captain's pleasure was unconcealed. Johnnie Walker's 2nd Escort Group, which he led from the sloop HMS Starling, was the scourge of U-boat commanders. The war had thrown up Captain Walker when his country most needed him. Having lost his son when the British submarine Parthian failed to return to port, Walker began a personal vendetta against U-boats. He had developed a "nose" for finding them and his contributions were astonishing.

During those sun-baked days in the Western Approaches the U-boat hunters had heard and seen a lot—but experienced nothing. Johnnie Walker's arrival on the scene was a recipe for treatment rather than prophylaxis. He attracted trouble they said. They said truly. But in the absence of the enemy he tried to provoke the Nazis by sailing his Group first into Ushant and then into Brest. Through binoculars we could see German soldiers peering back at us. They signalled "Good Evening". Walker replied "Sieg Heil" and then something unrepeatable. Their coastal guns remained silent. I was scared stiff being aware of the awesome reputation of their 88mm guns.

Walker's staggering impertinence was beyond my comprehension. The Group watched and waited in a sunblest morning which seemed endless.

U.333 (Captain Fiedler) had left La Pallice on July 31st 1944. Her former captain was Peter Cremer, known to our Admiralty as a U-boat ace and worshipped by his crew who were confident of survival if they served in Cremer's "Three Little Fishes". (The average survival time of a German submariner was only 42 days). Three weeks before we encountered U.333 Cremer had been given command of the new U2519.

Trentham picked up the ill starred Fiedler as the submerged U333 crossed our bow at the correct range for Squid and I reached the bridge as the familiar six projectiles were ejaculated 300 yards ahead of Killin. I was wondering whether the adjective was "orgiastic" or "orgasmic" as the explosion sent Fiedler to the bottom.

"Killin" had slowed to six knots, her black attacking pendant hanging down "as limp as a eunuch" according to No. 1. We dawdled along the bearing coming from the Asdic hut—with Trentham intoning "stationary on the bottom Sir".

As the Squid was reloaded "Starling" ordained that she was going in with depth charges. This done Killin repeated the first attack. The mortar bombs slid into the water as Darling shouted "Stop engines. Slow astern both." "Won't be hoist with our own petard eh Doc!"

Stevens the midshipman was unusually pale. "To think they're still waiting down there for us to pass over them and drop depth charges. Thank God for ahead-throwing weapons!"

When the explosion came even I knew there was something different about it. Anything which was unsecured shuddered, jumped about or fell over. Killin was distinctly lifted as jets of water, air and oil reared upwards from the target area. This was no ordinary "Squid" explosion.

"Echo stationary on seabed; much noise of air escaping!"

"She's blown up!" barked Stanley Darling. "Slow ahead both."

Killin tip-toed decorously through the turbulence. Oil! An Officer's cap; papers and then a significant sighting—a piece of somebody!

"Away whalers crew" was piped and the flotsam of war was brought inboard. I was handed a mass of bloody tissue—a human lung. Surprisingly I felt nauseated. The other Officers' voices were muted—as if at a graveside. U.333 had been sunk and Mourne avenged.

The first Squid sinking on 31st July 1944, was a tiny fragment of naval history—made by HMS Loch Killin.

"Splice the mainbrace" flashed Starling. The crew got a special issue of rum—Officers get no rum ration however, but Chiefie came to the rescue. He was so relieved that his ship had sustained no damage that he produced a bottle of whisky—peevishly complaining "What in God's name were you lot doing up there?" "That explosion frightened the wits out of me. Thank God the ship's alright. Do you ever think of the boys in the engine room?"

Chiefie's words struck home. Being trapped below would be terrible. I couldn't stand slowly drowning in an enclosed space as the sea came in.

In the U-boat war there was seldom anything between 100% disaster and surviving all shipshape and Bristol fashion.

I was brooding over the number of surgeon-lieutenants who had been trapped below and looking thoughtfully at the ship's side when I realised that Goggins was speaking.

"It's yet another hand infection. Corbett—penetrated by wire—as usual. I think we'll have to open him up. It's like all the others."

This posed no problem thanks to Ben Murray's training. The medics of Killin had perfected a logistical sequence of surgical action for hand infections.

After Pentothal was injected intravenously into the sound side, Goggins began the inhalation anaesthetic as the doctor elevated the affected limb of the unconscious patient and applied a tourniquet to ensure a bloodless field. The operation then went ahead—with any heavy work or additional help being given by a Wardroom volunteer.

This lay help was not dependable, however, and seemed invariably to be found lying horizontally on the deck. Harding, the Kiwi Navigator, was always keen to assist but invariably succumbed.

"I don't understand it", said the Kiwi. "I can kill Germans in anger but when the knife goes in—usually with some tasteless joke, it's all too much for me."

Goggins comforted Harding with a yarn about a V.C. who was terrified of mice—and women. But I could have done with one of Admiral Nelson's "lob-lolly boys" to help us—though I recalled their reputed addiction to amputation!

CHAPTER NINE

Quinn, the port look-out on the bridge was feeling the effects of his rum ration. Quite unfairly, perhaps, I distrusted Quinn whom I regarded as a surly recidivist. Captain Darling, who never seemed to sleep, shouted out to his look-outs that they must keep awake and I encouraged him particularly to supervise Quinn whose binoculars were raised less and less frequently as his afternoon watch progressed.

On the 6th August we encountered U.736 (Captain Reff) at 47N 04W. A week had passed since we blew U.333 to pieces and now, three hundred miles from land, we were about to retrace our sweep with the Second Escort Group.

On August 6th Biscay was as smooth as a baby's bundook. The sun fried the crew and the Chief Yeoman was doing his favourite trick of making scrambled eggs on the steel deck.

I was now a watch-keeping officer sharing a standing afternoon watch with Eason (Guns) who gradually indoctrinated me into the mysteries of boxing the compass, setting a course, and taking a bearing. The ship's M.O. was confident about zig-zagging, moving the ship's head twenty points every two minutes so as to confuse torpedo aim. It was a proud and responsible feeling marred only by the incident of taking a fix on a piece of land which suddenly moved—as banks of fog do!

Too hot to sleep the Captain had come up on the bridge and chided Quinn for dozing off. I looked disdainfully at Quinn and realised he was peering, transfixed, through his binoculars at something in the clear unruffled sea. His mouth was wide open but no sound was emerging.

Suddenly it came. "Red 30—periscope!" Darling thumped the Action Stations' button as we all looked thirty degrees on the port bow.

"Bearing first then report the sighting" "Monkey Stephenson had drilled this into us and in so doing he'd saved us from certain death.

About three feet of "broom handle" was projecting from the sea, proceeding so slowly there was scarcely any wash.

Within seconds Trentham was shouting a bearing, a range and that there must be a U-boat. The Squid fired its six projectiles almost immediately—the U-boat lay fortuitously and fortunately at the range of the weapon. As the projectiles angled into the water I noticed two parallel tracks heading for Killin's port side.

"Oh God," I prayed! I know what's happening." Trentham bellowed "Torpedo noise sir!" and I began to run down to the quarterdeck towards the torpedo tracks. Bravado obliterates reason. "Monkey's" mantra for medics was "First on the scene; last to leave it—alive." So I had some vague compulsion about being on the spot—and had forgotten that I was heading like the torpedoes, towards Killin's magazine.

But by the grace of God the U-boat Captain had chosen acoustic torpedoes, "Gnats", which were homing in on the noise of the ship's screws.

Killin's mortar bombs, exploding when the acoustic torpedoes were only twenty feet from her side, countermined the U-boat's missiles. A great wall of water washed over the frigate. "You obviously blew up" Alex. Cherry told me later. I reached the quarterdeck in time to see Dickie, who believed we'd been sunk, swimming strongly for the ship's rail. Killin cleared herself of the tons of vibrating seawater like a dog shaking itself.

Dickie surfaced. "Good God, Doc, I'm still alive. I thought I was drowning. I'm nipping off to change."

He waded off through the flood as I reassured the depth charge crew who looked settled if, like me, saturated. They hadn't yet appreciated that they had missed certain death by the merest fraction of a second. We had indeed been touched by angels. Quinn's cry had given us the vital vestige of time.

The Mourne was very much in my mind because it was a replica attack, but I suddenly realised that I was looking at a U-boat's conning tower less than two feet from the quarterdeck rail and two hundred miles from the nearest land. U.736 (Captain Reff) had surfaced under our stern. The hatch opened and a head appeared which vanished in a hail of Oerlikon fire.

"Cease fire" came Darling's voice over the loudhailer. The hatch opened again and one by one the Germans began to step on board Killin's quarterdeck. Not a word was said until the junior steward, the one with the weak bladder, wailed.

"What do we do, sir?"

I pointed a finger at the Germans. I couldn't think of anything else to do.

"Get a rifle son. Cover them with it. If they move—shoot!"

The steward found a rifle and levelled it at the group of survivors—who were simply walking from the U-boat on to Killin's quarterdeck. I noticed that they hadn't even got their feet wet as I mistook their shocked state for composed aggression.

"Will they rush us, sir?" enquired the steward as the rifle barrel convulsed wildly. "I can't fire. I've no bullets!"

"But THEY don't know that, steward. Keep pointing the gun."

And so they remained, palsied by their disbelief until Dickinson leapt back into view like a pantomime demon springing through a trap door on to a stage.

Somebody laughed. The tension broke and the mood changed from hostility to farce. The half-drowned Torpedo Officer bristled with weaponry—suggesting a Christmas tree which had gone to war.

"Right lads. I'll take over now" muttered this comic figure. "What the hell are you all laughing about?"

"Nazis! TEN-SHUN!" The U-boat crew at once sprang to attention. Nineteen dry uninjured Germans were shepherded into the Engine Room Flat.

Higher and higher in the water rose the U-boat until Killin's screws were clear of the water. H.M.C.S. Iroquois came over to see this astonishing sight. Cameras were trained as her Aldis flickered.

"Looks quite indecent from here!" Get off!"

Killin was now helpless—her stern and propellers high out of the water. She was sitting athwart a surfaced U-boat whose open conning tower was now right alongside Killin's quarterdeck guard rail.

I was wondering how much previous experience the Royal Navy had of this situation when it occurred to me that the frigate made a wonderful target. For many months U-boats had been hunting in packs and, somewhere out there must lurk another U-boat with its Captain glued to the periscope as he spied on a madman's image of maritime procreation.

Captain Darling remained unperturbed by the stalemate and spoke on the Tannoy system.

"As long as we are clung to by the U-boat we're safe. The rest of the Group are protecting us from possible revenge attack."

After five minutes of immodestly exposing Killin's bottom to an enthralled audience, the U-boat slowly fell away. Killin's stern descended to its natural element. U.736 (Captain Reff) gurgling and puffing, slipped down to a watery grave carrying some entombed men. Their cries were appalling but nothing could be done for them. I was distraught until the sea and total silence closed mercifully over the scene of the action at 47N. 4W.

There was a brief period of complete stasis as the combatants peered at each other in the Engine Room Flat. Chiefie made his Damage Control Report to the Captain as I returned to the bridge.

"One propeller is out of true, sir and I've got two leaking glands."

I offered a medical opinion on the glandular problem but failed to get through to make my own report. I returned to the captives.

The prisoners in the Engine Room Flat looked warily at the British. Not one German was even scratched. I requested an issue of tea and cigarettes and reported to the Captain, now in the Wardroom, who was dispensing similar comfort to the two surviving U-boat Officers.

"You should be dead" one said. "We torpedoed you—but your ship rammed us."

"Yes, we're very fast" Darling replied—with his face quite expressionless. The U-boat Captain twitched nervously.

"How many men were saved? How are they?" He was reassured that all was well with the 19 of his crew who had walked over the gap between two vessels interlocked in a naval impasse.

I controlled myself as I assessed one survivor who loudly announced that English cigarettes were hellish, the food was worse and anyway he wanted coffee not tea! The other Germans looked at their shipmate with a mixture of fear and apology. I had enough German to learn that the complainer was the U-boat Gestapo man. Midshipman Stevens wanted him quietly dropped overboard but Dickie, as an ex-butcher, proposed a particularly radical surgical procedure—without anaesthetic. But he qualified his statement.

"The Quack will get him anyway. The bugger will never see land again."

But he did. Killin escorted by Iroquois, limped into Liverpool. With all hands at "Harbour Stations" there was a hero's welcome as a hundred sirens sounded their approval. The Second Escort Group had done it again! Elation was tempered by the arrival of a photograph from H.M.C.S. Iroquois of the mating rites of Killin and U.736.

It was AB Connolly's birthday and, as tradition ordained, every man in the mess passed his tot of rum to the "birthday boy". The protocol was strict, and, on your birthday, you took from the other nineteen tots of rum "sippers" not "gulpers". Conolly was only 18 and failed to observe the unwritten rules. He was turned into his hammock at 1300 hours and three hours later the doctor was called.

I examined the sagging, vomit-spattered corpse. An overdose—of rum—Admiral Nelson would not have been pleased!

Two days later as repairs were being finished I was called to the destroyer alongside. Their doctor was on leave and life comes in lumps.

"The Petty Officer's down in the rum locker doctor." The captain's facial expression took away the surprise if not the shock of finding a discoloured P.O. face down on the deck of the rum store. I was uncertain. Had he died from asphyxia or the absorption of too much rum by inhalation or by ingestion? It was academic anyway. He was posted as "killed in action." I was beginning to believe in "case clustering"—a bunching or conglomeration of unusual medical incidents.

And how many ships—and good men—have gone down because of the Senior Service's traditional rum issue?

As we sailed from Liverpool I voiced this thought to Captain Darling who advised me not to investigate the matter further—well, that was the essence of the advice although the phraseology was more unsophisticated.

The sea was calm and it seemed an ideal time to begin the three statutory lectures on health which every ship's company had annually to endure. The topics were "Feet, First Aid and Venereal Disease." The crew, according to Goggins, had altered the title of the last lecture to an alliterative alternative.

The first intimate talk, "The Care of the Feet", was broadcast from the bridge Tannoy. The Captain, formerly part of the Australian Broadcasting Company, felt professionally involved and stood by his doctor during the afternoon watch as I rambled on. Most of the crew had their heads down anyway and the sombre tale of Athlete's Foot and Plantar Warts was only halfway through its pedestrian platitudes when Killin met a persistently unpleasant swell. The combination of the corkscrew motion and the image of 140 pairs of diseased feet proved too much for the M.O's stomach. The Captain who was being sprayed by Brown Windsor soup, shouted

"For Chris' sake Doc. Do it down wind!" The M.O. apologised for being sick over the Captain and reeled below to the sanctuary of the Sick Bay—only to find "Doc" Goggins deep into a game of cribbage. Always the perfect gentleman, Goggins would not discourage his medical colleague.

"That was very good sir," he said.

"Bloody liar, you switched him off" replied his 'oppo' or 'winger', the Chief Yeoman. Goggins coloured.

"'Fraid it's true sir, but I'll be all ears for lectures two and three when they come up—like your lunch! I expect the Captain was upset when you spewed over him! That cook of yours will kill the entire Wardroom!"

The second lecture was on First Aid and focussed on burns, fractures, head injuries and missile wounds in general. I had gained much vicarious experience of war and laid it on thick—getting carried away in a tide of entrails, blood, brains and splintered bones. Captain Darling again stood by his doctor on the bridge until his professionalism overcame him and he grabbed the microphone.

"Right, Killin, to sum up the M.O.'s excellent talk, if you see someone with a hole in him and red stuff is coming out, stick something in the hole. This is known as the "Arrest of Haemorrhage.""

"Doc" Goggins was pleased with his M.O.

Killin's war now assumed a pattern. Four to six weeks at sea were followed by a few days in port for boiler-cleaning and minor repairs. The first two days of each patrol reduced me to a walking talking seasick corpse—a grey apparition of nausea fuelled by coffee, Brown Windsor soup and peanut butter sandwiches. Day three of each patrol brought a tenuous normality which snapped if the ship corkscrewed or shipped it green too much for the tolerance of my labyrinth.

But there were experiences in the monotony to capture in a box of memory and preserve forever; events which remained indelible—such as the preparation of the third lecture—on venereal disease. I was conning up on my notes. It was the afternoon watch.

"Bridge—doctor" snapped the Captain down the voice pipe. "Get up here now, one of the 'Queens' is on the starboard bow." I reached the bridge within seconds to see the "Queen Mary" approaching at full speed. Her bow wave curled high as the Asdic lamp flickered.

"Beautiful isn't she doc? What's she saying Yeoman? Why would she call us up 200 miles from land?"

"Well sir," said Chief Yeoman Douglas. "She's noticed our pendant number and wants information."

"Got it! What is doctor's name?" Darling laughed.

"All is now clear" Yeoman, please reply as requested."

Chief Yeoman growled "I can't really believe this. We're 200 miles from land and Queen Mary replies. "Captain's name is also Illingworth" "The Queen" winked again at us and the Yeoman handed the signal direct to the doctor.

"Greetings from the Captain, David, are you till being seasick?"

There was a familiar figure waving from the starboard wing of the massive bridge as the huge Cunarder, packed with American troops, glided past the tiny frigate.

"How's he taking it Doccie?" asked Darling. "I mean the Curacoa disaster. I know your father was in command when the ships collided."

I weighed my answer carefully "The Curacoa" crossed the bows of the Q.M.—due to her Captain's wrong helm order. She was cut in two and hundreds of men died. The Cunarder had a slight dent in the bows and my father's feelings can be imagined—although he was blameless."

Thus was dismissed one of the great sea disasters of all time.

The M.O. (and the Captain) continued to contemplate the lecture on V.D. as Killin's head turned 180 degrees for Plymouth. It was rough. The bridge was open to the elements and seawater poured frequently from the bridge down into the wheelhouse as the ship yawed and heaved. "Fiddles" were placed on the Wardroom table; those with bunks tried to secure themselves with the employment of their leeboards, while stepping over a sill was an athletic feat.

Halfway home to Plymouth Killin was flashed by an M.T.B. —"Have you a doctor on board? We have a casualty." I was ferried across by the ship's whaler and found the Commanding Officer looking at his mutilated foot.

"Christ doc, thanks for coming over. I was cleaning my revolver when it went off!"

I attended to the foot and its large tissue gap—and then asked the relevant questions.

The C.O. of the M.T.B. made no bones about it.

"Doc, I'm "chokker" and I was wondering how much more I could take when the gun went off."

I understood and did my best to counter his stress.

"These accidents will happen with firearms. Set course for Plymouth and leave it to me." The C.O. of the boat heaved a sigh and smiled. I made the appropriate report to Captain Darling.

Killin headed off for Plymouth to tie up alongside HMS Wren. Goggins got two days leave, a large stirrup cup from his colleague, the MO, while Killin got a visit from Captain Johnnie Walker R.N. Forty-eight years old and the manifest apotheosis of the Royal Naval Captain, Walker presented to the doctor as a handsome, slim muscular weather-beaten man—somewhat tired after twenty-four hours on his bridge. How could he find time to be interested, charming and humorous? He shook hands with me and I understood why the Second Escort Group would follow Johnnie Walker through Hell and back again. Here was charisma. Here was leadership.

But Captain Walker died of a sudden devastating "stroke". I tried to decide whether the hero Walker died a natural death or was killed in the service of his country. I opted for the latter.

HMS Starling (now Commander Duck R.N.R.) sailed the following day, leading the Second Escort Group to the sound of Walker's aggressive theme tune "A hunting we will go". The group's depression was lessened by a ragged cheer from onlooking ships' companies.

The third lecture went out the next day. The entire crew was awake for "Sex and Venereal Disease". Even on the bridge there was standing room only as the doctor made it clear that reporting sex problems would bring only understanding and NEVER consequences, only confidential advice.

Captain Darling inevitably produced a Catonian epilogue which made me shudder. "To control V.D. you have to control yourself—and if anyone in my ship gets this infection I shall order the M.O. either to cut it off or sew it up."

I was unhappy. "This is counter productive, sir. We must help—not punish."

The Captain's reply—"This is a warship not a whoreship!" left me rather confused. I went below.

And there I found several enquirers who had disregarded the Captain's awful threats.

The first supplicant was the archetypal stoker, "Tomes the Tattoo" whose trunk and limbs were covered with pigmented erotica.

"Will I be punished if I tell you I'm squeezing up, sir?"

"Squeezing what up, Tomes?"

"IT, sir" Goggins was almost speechless.

"He means he's got a urethral discharge, sir" croaked the Sick Bay attendant.

"May I see the affected part, please Tomes?" A patterned privy member was produced and we made a smear from the pus obligingly squeezed up by Tomes.

"Will it be cut off, sir, as the Skipper said? Bet he was joking but perhaps I wouldn't mind—it's so sore!"

We stained the smear and saw the organisms of Gonorrhoea under the microscope lens. Curiosity overcame discretion.

"Tell me, Tomes, wasn't it very painful being tattooed there?"

"Very sir, but at times it takes a real trick" and gave the doctor a lecherous wink. The last of the queue of six was a wireless operator with a stammer. It crossed my mind that if we got into real trouble he might never get beyond the "S" of S.O.S. before we blew up. Tormented by groin ringworm and fearing the worst he was very apprehensive.

"No sleep for weeks sir; I know I've got it!"

"Well Nimmo, I doubt it. When were you last with a woman?" Nimmo's emotional barriers crumbled as he released his tensions. He began to sob.

"Two months ago it was. We're engaged, see!" Goggins interjected,

"Tell the doctor what happened."

"Well, we went to the 'chummy seats' in the pictures", wept Nimmo who had totally lost control of himself.

"And then what happened," persisted Goggins—neither medic could use the vernacular approach.

"Well we held hands and I proposed. Now I've got this. Must have got it in a lavatory." Goggins clutched the patient's shoulder.

"Bloody stupid place to take a woman! For God's sake son, this is 1944 you don't get V.D. from holding hands. You've wasted half an hour of our stuttering time! Off you go!" Nimmo protested.

"The Officer asked me if I'd been with a woman and I told him the truth—because I can't get married with my gentiles all red."

I patted Nimmo on his trembling back.

"Doc and I both admire your honesty and decency. We're proud of you and now we'll cure your Dhobi Itch. We've all got it and we'll fix you in a Dog Watch." Goggins handed Nimmo the Whitfield's Ointment and Nimmo left smiling at Doc's –

"Keep it off your 'gentiles' lad or else you'll have to hang them in a tumbler of cold water. That'll cool your ardour!"

No. 1 walked straight in as usual without knocking.

"Doctor, you're five minutes adrift from captain's rounds!"

Each week all accessible parts of the frigate were visited by the Captain, Number One, Chiefie and the Doctor. The quartet had no respect for privacy and the two seamen "misbehaving" in the ship's heads were put on a charge.

Still learning about human nature I was puzzled by two men holding hands as they emptied their bowels.

The problems of ringworm and verrucas were discussed yet again—and this time the M.O. got his way. The sodden duckboards in the ablutions disappeared for ever and the incidence of two irritating problems dropped dramatically.

"Life comes in lumps" was a favourite aphotism of my future partner Dr Lamont. This belief was pre-empted on the 9th August. At 46N and 02W U.608 (Captain Reisener) was in the Bay of Biscay. All seemed peaceful when the Germans popped up for air. The heat was sweltering as the hatch was opened to reveal a sea as calm as the undertaker makes the face of death. Reisener swept the area with his binoculars and as he looked astern he peered into the trembling field glasses of the lookout in HMS Wren's crows nest—five miles astern.

"Crows nest—bridge, dead ahead U. boat"

Wren's No. 1, Alex Cherry, an American banker who had joined the Royal Navy in July 1940 was one of many Americans who had joined the British Services long before the U.S.A. became formally involved in the War. He was on watch on the bridge and reacted immediately.

"Action stations" Dead ahead—U-board on surface! Range about five miles."

The startled German mariner vanished down his conning tower for an emergency dive. The twin turrets of the Bird class sloops of the Group began to slam away. Even the first salvo was close but the third salvo produced a cloud of spume, smoke and spray.

"Looks like a hit," said Darling above the sharp crack of Killin's single four inch gun which was firing more in hope than expectation. Five minutes later Wren was in Asdic contact.

"God, she's attacking!" yelled Harding.

Wren was streaming her black pendant to indicate that she was going in with depth charges. A creature of beauty and aggression she drove at top speed through the expressionless blue water, the burgee parallel to the sea and a white moustache sprouting from her stem. Over the site of the echo the port and starboard throwers hurled their deadly drums of explosive as the stern charges began to slip away from their ramps. The sloop bustled on ostentatiously and stood not on the order of her going.

The silence seemed endless. I watched the area where hundredweights of explosive were slowly sinking beneath Wren's wake. Suddenly the plug came out of a watery volcano. Plumes of water soared a hundred feet high and Killin shuddered down to her last rivet.

Within a few minutes some calm returned and U.608 appeared in the seething cauldron left by Wren's attack.

In a sudden diversion a Liberator aircraft appeared out of a hovering cloud and dropped a depth charge. Fifty one Germans—the entire crew- abandoned ship and were rescued from a calm Biscay by Wren and Starling as the scuttled U-boat rapidly sank.

Two days later (August 11th) U.385 (Captain Valentiner) received exactly the same treatment from Starling and the Royal Australian Air Force.

Killin made only one attack in this action.. We now know that Admiral Doenitz had made the mistake of ordering all U-boats to make a daily report. Bletchley Park pinpointed the enemy for us through these signals. And I was at the "sharp end"—deciphering their messages—bewildered by "B.P."'s insight and accuracy and in total ignorance of its existence.

This war winning ability of the top secret "B.P." was not known until 1975—except to 30,000 dedicated and unique women and men (whose discretion and silence were absolute!) who worked in this esoteric system of code breaking—telling us where the U-boats were. The source of our extraordinary knowledge was revealed only after 30 years of peace.

We were directed to Plymouth. Killin had in six months taken a tremendous pounding. High explosives and heavy seas had left their mark and she was dry docked. Stem to stern she was checked and re-checked in five days. How much stress could this new class of frigate take? She had certainly been tested to the limit—and yet the damage seemed minimal. Was this due to Scottish skill, good luck or a benevolent Creator?

But I was angry. I had carried out a routine check of my first aid boxes in our lifeboats and rafts. All the containers which had held morphine and dressings were empty. I couldn't reconcile the sturdy crew of the ship with such an act of treachery. Why?

However a vast amount of mail had to be censored. Each letter reflected a comradely pride in the ship—even those of the amorous seaman with four potential brides—A.B. Corbett, who felt it unwise to leave the security of the mess deck.

The ship's emptiness and quiet were strangely depressing. Like an empty theatre it was drab, cold and spiritless. Light and power were unavailable most of the time and the Wardroom had the stale atmosphere, which is the aftermath of a successful party. Chiefie, the Engineer Officer, remained on board to supervise damage repairs. I was also shipbound—to keep the medical services running; it was Chief Sick Berth Attendant Goggins' turn for leave. The Captain kept awake the surviving population of Plymouth—those who had escaped the devastating German bombing—by pumping Beethoven at them from his miraculous music machine and, later in the evening, Chiefie and I would sneak ashore to tour the hostelries of the area. We even managed to hire a car for three days and do a brief tour of Cornwall which seemed to be empty—although near Fowey, we met another motor car and stopped to speak to the driver who turned out to be the local doctor.

In late September 1944, Killin, all shipshape, left Plymouth and led four Colony Class frigates North. Ryecroft was scathing about our consorts.

"They don't even have rivets and that sort of stuff. They're welded! In America! They'd do better with some of The Quack's sticking plaster."

We reached Scapa Flow intact and together—in spite of No. 1's fearful warnings that welded ships would burst asunder if somebody passed wind. In spite of a violent storm and driving rain I went topside to see the legendary barrenness. Through occasional clear patches in the curtains of rainwater I glimpsed a small motor boat. The seas were breaking over it and the occupant was either mad or the bearer of vital news. The tiny boat pitched its way round to the lee side of the ship and a

middle-aged man, in oilskins, somehow clambered on board.
Before he could speak I shouted above the wind.

"Took some risk didn't you?" With water running down his
face the visitor replied.

"Well it's worth it. I see you're the doctor so you'll
understand."

I waited for the life-endangering problem which had brought
the little man out to this watery torture chamber.

"Go on, please."

"Are there any Catholics on board? I'm a priest."

I gaped at him and tactlessly replied

"Yes—but all this just for --------------that."

"My son, if it helps them it's all worthwhile. A wondering
doctor guided him below. My experience of Catholics was
limited to the knowledge that they usually died more graciously
than the rest!

"Use the sick bay, Father." This was the only possible
courtesy I could bestow as I was left humbled by the courage
and devotion of the tubby little cleric.

Off Iceland in early November with Dominica on our
starboard beam, in a heavy swell, Killin was called up on the
radiotelephone. Dominica's Sick Bay attendant was worried
about a seaman with abdominal pain. After ten minutes "over-
and-outing" I still couldn't exclude appendicitis. I thought of
the R.C. Chaplain in Scapa Flow. Thus fortified I asked Darling
if I might go across and look.

Stanley Darling said, "Waves twenty feet high, Doc, and the
weather's deteriorating. We'll try getting you over but I won't
risk bringing you back. We'll take care of your "ditty box"—the
container in which I kept my personal treasures—"until you get
back."

In my "Pusser's Bag" from Naval Stores there were packed
anaesthetics, instruments and a toothbrush, while "Away
whaler's crew" was piped. The Chief Petty Officer shouted,

"For God's sake, sir, don't fall between the ship and the boat
or you're dead. Jump in "on the rise" and when you leave us,

catch Dominica's ladder on a wave crest. We'll throw your things up before we return."

"Thanks Cox'n" said a tremulous doctor and, as the whaler rose alongside Killin's quarterdeck I stepped, or fell, into it. I sat aft in the whaler, gloomily contemplating my approaching athleticism "on the crest of the wave".

The whaler sliced through the swell towards Dominica.

The Coxwain grinned encouragingly and roared above the noise,

"Remember, sir, jump for the ladder at the peak of the wave. I'll give you a 'ready' and then it's up to you. But if you slip, God help you, sir."

"Well, this is the test and I'll make it—someone's waiting for me," I thought.

"Ready, sir. Now!" and I found myself hanging onto Dominica's ladder with Killin's whaler's crew two storeys below me. On the next crest, up came my bag—before I'd saluted the quarterdeck and the Captain.

Dominica's Captain shook me by the hand while I could only think how near Lesley might have been to drawing a widow's pension.

Dominica was a remarkably good sea-boat and the "appendicitis" was rapidly cured by an enema. The Ship's Sick Bay Attendant, who was a sound, stable chap, was worried in case he had risked me unnecessarily. He was rapidly reassured then got a bonus by the discovery of a seaman with a monstrous axillary abscess. We agreed to operate on what was really an infection of last century standards—but the ship was corkscrewing madly and it was difficult even to stand up.

In the Sick Bay, in spite of vertigo, I hit the vein of the good arm with Pentothal. The Captain held Dominica steady into the wind, but as the scalpel touched the skin over the abscess, the operating table broke loose from the deck. It was the patient who opened the abscess as he unwittingly became the victim of a giant wave and slid along the blade on his unconscious trip into the bulkhead twelve feet away.

Half a pint of pus hit the deck. In went the rubber drain. Up came the Sick Bay Attendant's lunch.

One month later H.M.S. Dominica still had Killin's M.O. living in luxury in the Captain's Day cabin. Being marooned wasn't all that bad—and I enjoyed the change of food and company. At the same time I helped in tidying up the various minor ailments of Dominica's crew—until one day the Captain drew me on one side.

"Just a quiet swell Doc, do you want to go home?"

A Breeches Buoy was nothing compared to Squid, gunfire and torpedo. Gladly I took off into space for Killin, my aquatic home. Sadly the mobile block on the buoy hit me on the head and I arrived at Killin not a little concussed and far from brave after a hair-raising trip as a human yo-yo.

Goggins was glad to see me—and reported one septic hand and a dental abscess. I took first the easier problem and, recalling Lesley's brother's advice, pushed and twisted out the offending molar—instead of trying to PULL it. Why do medical students miss out on dental education? The Yeoman's hand had been septic for seven days. Pentothal slide into the vein of the healthy arm; Goggins slipped the mask over his face; the Navigator slid under the table. He was replaced by the Torpedo Officer—who likewise disappeared as the tendon sheath was laid open and the rubber drain inserted. Ten minutes work ensured a useful hand for the future and convinced me about my destiny as a surgeon.

But my injured head hurt; I felt unwell and turned in after sending a message for Chief Petty Officer Goggins to visit.

"Doc, I feel I may be slightly concussed, but the important thing is that the Captain says that there's a signal diverting us to Lerwick." Goggins grinned.

"That's good news sir. We've had five rough weeks in the Iceland Gap in a tin box and a run ashore would do the boys good." The rum ration had just been dispensed and from the seamen's mess below my cabin arose a chorus of bawdy songs and slogans.

"Sorry about the noise sir. Five weeks non-stop in Northern waters is a lot for the lads. You can hear Corbett—the one with the four fiancées and the hot-groin syndrome." We listened in mutual astonishment at the chorus—led by Corbett of the undisciplined hormones.

"We want jiggy jig! We want jiggy jig!"

Doc Goggins shook his head and slid shut the M.O.'s door.

The five frigates tied up in Lerwick Harbour and the Provost offered an open invitation to the Saturday dance in Lerwick Town Hall. It was a precise recipe for trouble with five men for each girl. Peace was maintained for ten minutes before the first blow was struck. The gold braid fled and, in the haven of the ship, Goggins and I prepared sutures and dressings. Two hours later we had inserted thirty sutures and as I told the Captain that we had justified ourselves I was rebuffed.

"Christ, M.O. what a lot of bloody animals! We're sailing at dawn!" Depressed and angry the Captain sent the Provost of Lerwick a message of apology on behalf of his Escort Group.

We headed South to Govan for boiler cleaning and tied up alongside two days later. When we stepped ashore there was a welcome from various Glasgow "Aunties", whose fluttering hankies meant to each ship's company a comfortable bed and good food. The five ships emptied rapidly for three days' leave. Killin's officers accepted an invitation to a party in Anniesland and arrived there carrying small cipher bags marked "Top Secret" which, with military precision, they had marched past the Dockyard guard.

There were six bags. Each one held four bottles of spirits. And so began the ultimate, or worst, of social occasions for the five most junior officers. I went along—as the father figure—but in truth I was glad to get my feet on solid ground.

At midnight I realised I was sitting alone by the gramophone repeatedly playing Bing Crosby as we sang along together—"Beautiful Dreamer, queen of my song!"

There was no reply to my shouts as I observed two uniformed pairs of legs behind the settee. I looked down on two fellow officers who had passed out and felt a qualm of conscience. In the master bedroom I found a couple in bed, the host and hostess of the party, snoring loudly with a sick basin between them. Increasingly aware that things had got out of hand I crossed a large hall and found a lighted bathroom.. A young woman was kneeling over the toilet bowl. I tapped diffidently on the doorpost and got an instant if rather muted response.

"You're a doctor, you've got red on your sleeve. I've just been sick and my top denture is down there in the W.C.! Please be a pal and get it back for me."

If ever I had any spare libido it was vitiated as I explored the plumbing to extricate the upper denture of the fallen angel—which was washed and restored to the owner.

"How can I repay you?" asked the now gleaming smile. My response was tactful—I was recalling the 21st birthday present of a complete dental clearance—not uncommon in Scotland.

"Help me collect the bodies—and I hope you're not disappointed by my answer. There were twenty when the party began and I've got to get MY lot back on board in a few hours."

We sat and shared a mug of coffee. I was reflecting on how awful Scottish teeth were and how many young people had to wear full dentures when my ally suddenly came alive.

"Got it, they were playing 'Sardines' so they'll be in the most unlikely part of the house—the servants' quarters. I'll take you."

At the end of a stone-flagged corridor we found the absentees lying in a large bed like netted fish. There was an aroma of sweat, perfume and hormones as I hastily switched OFF the light and began to think how to get my shipmates onto the first morning train to Govan docks.

Stanley Darling, the Captain of Killin and the Commander of the Group was visibly upset when the wanderers returned. He singled out the M.O.

"What the hell do you think you were doing arranging all this arsie-tarsie in Glasgow? I know you're the Entertainments Officer but you've reduced most of my officers to a state of disability. Look at them. Even for pommies they're in bad shape and three of them are still as tight as farts!"

I clutched my splitting head.

It got out of hand, sir—and I'm sorry."

The Captain then rubbed salt in the wound:-

"You are, after all, our doctor and I expect a good example in spite of your immaturity. But perhaps at 22 years not too much should be anticipated. Carry on!"

A very worried doctor stumbled over the sill and leant over the rail. A few minutes later Stanley Darling was beside me.

"There are worse things, doccie. You might have been punished. I could have sentenced you to a course in the music of Gustav Mahler."

The Captain winked, patted my shoulder and smiled.

"Your sins are forgiven, you pommie bastard! But don't let it happen again!"

I was left wondering who Mahler was—and how fortunate it was that war discovered people like Stanley Darling.

CHAPTER TEN

The group headed South, commanded by Killin, a ship now over a year old in active service. These were familiar waters. The captain was as sensitive and enigmatic as ever. His doctor decided that the skipper had never recovered from some emotional disaster. This theory had a romantic fitness about it.

My afternoon watch over, I got my head down and looked at the deckhead to try to assess Darling's psychological problems. It was rough and the ship rolled and pitched so much that I put up the leeboard of the bunk to keep my body in place. When Killin reared up on end and I was thrown over the protective rail on to the iron deck I had only one thought, "This is it!" and waited momentarily for the end. When nothing else happened I raced up on deck, automatically checking that I had a lifebelt, name tag and whistle—although I knew that small ship doctors usually went down with the vessel—trapped below getting out the injured. Having prepared for a hero's death the spectacle up topside was farcical. Killin's bow was buried deep amidships in a trawler and an explosive burst of bad language was emanating from the trawler's bridge. Only months ago a U-boat had raised Killin's stern to heaven—where now her bow was pointed.

"My God, we're going up hill this time" choked the midshipman recalling our last collision at sea. The little ship was almost cut in two by Killin's sharp stem. Probably the trawler would sink as soon as her assailant moved astern—if she could. Amid streams of further profanity the trawlermen were taking to their life raft to paddle across to the frigate.

"Were you feeling lonely Skipper? You crossed our bow, didn't you?" were the ill-chosen words of the Chief Yeoman of Signals as the trawler Captain reached Killin's bridge. Captain

Darling rebuked the Yeoman sternly and turned to the Officer of the Watch—who was grey of face.

"Board of Inquiry inevitable laddie! I'll relieve you. Leave the bridge to make the fullest possible notes NOW!"

"Dead slow astern, both engines." And with the easy grace of a well-behaved afterbirth, Killin withdrew herself from the embarrassment of her missionary position. The trawler hesitated momentarily, as if pondering her inevitable fate and then heeled over as the sea poured into the gaping wound. But her bulkheads held and we took her in tow for Portsmouth.

After generous hospitality the towed trawler and crew were transferred to another frigate which was returning to Pompey for engine repairs. Killin and the rest of the Group meandered on, thoughtfully pinging in their search for the unseen enemy. Then we reached Start Point!

In the middle watch I was hauled out of my erotic dreamings by a change in the incessant Asdic murmuring. The note altered from a repetitive request to a petulant elegy. The bridge was reached in bright moonlight as Trentham's face appeared in the frame of the door of the Asdic hut and the alarm sounded.

"Clear target across our bows; no question what this one is, sir!" he rapped out. The other ships in the Group were sharply outlined as Darling contacted them. There was a brisk breeze as the frigate ambled towards the target, streaming her black battle pendant—a stridor of Asdic, speed and bearing directions and radio-telephone distortions. The inevitable night action brought a new dimension of fear and my guts twisted and my mouth dried as the searchlight was switched on. The surface of the sea over the U-boat's position was clearly lit up. My childhood fear of the dark enhanced my riotous imagination. I had been through this before. Even now there might be acoustic torpedoes homing in on us. Was there just time to shut down all sources of noise before the reckoning arrived to claim us"

The echo was now painfully loud and almost constant. At 300 yards Stanley Darling nodded vigorously.

"Fire Squid!" The six missiles glided up into the moonlight.

"Stop engines! Slow astern!"

I was praying voicelessly with an intensity equal to my apprehension. Had we struck first? The ship shuddered and the sea boiled. My nails came out of my palms when the Squid missiles exploded. It was the darkness full of imagined moonlit menace which signalled this as the most frightening five minutes of my life and one could only stand still and wait. There was nothing to occupy the mind. The tension broke as Trentham shrieked in a strange castrato falsetto,

"She's blowing her tanks!"

A sudden turbulence appeared in the middle of the searchlight's beam to prove him correct.

"She's surfacing" yelped the Captain. And she did. The bow of U.1063 appeared at an angle of thirty degrees and the rest of the vessel slid gracefully onto the surface. She looked like polished silver in the combination of natural and artificial light. There was a moment's total tranquillity as Darling kept our bow pointing at the U-boat's side so as to present the smallest possible target as our 4" gun was brought to bear.

The frozen image suddenly melted. The conning-tower hatch opened as the Germans erupted on to the U-boat's deck. As hypnotic as pantomime demons they popped up and trained their surface weapons on Killin—clearly silhouetted by the moon. I was feeling distinctly insecure but the Germans' disgorgement from their craft's innards had coincided with—

"All guns—open fire!"

Higgins, the gunlayer was good at short range and his first shot hit the centre of the U-boat's conning tower. Unfortunately they had carelessly left in the gun's breech a solid projectile for target practice. Like a crossbolt the missile went straight through the U-boat creating a vast shower of sparks. Oerlikon and Pom-Pom fire swept the U-boat's deck as Higgins, who had changed from crossbolts to explosives made repeated hits with the 4" gun.

The noise was beyond belief and obliterated all volition and initiative. My ears, carefully trained to detect the soft murmurs of a heart and the whisperings of active lung tissues, were now being racked by the pulverising din of battle. Still unoccupied I anxiously watched Killin's gunfire sweeping the U-boat's superstructure. We were close enough to witness among the emerging Germans, a moonburst effect of blood and body tissue from the systaltic pounding of our guns. Thought was impossible in this frenzied tumult of noise.

Then I remembered my colleague below.

In the Sick Bay 'Doc' Goggins grinned cheerfully. Did nothing disturb this man?

"What a bloody noise and it's so much worse when you've nothing to do. Let me go topsides and have a look, sir!"

"Go and see it. You'll never see the like again Doc. The Jerries are really being hammered."

"And about time too, doctor. Remember I served my time in small ships!"

And Goggins vanished up the ladder. A few moments later I reached the bridge once more.

Killin and the U-boat were about 75 yards apart as the moon went behind a cloud. There was still some small arms fire from the U-boat and one or two lines of tracer were barely clearing our bridge to emphasise the Captain's advice. "Keep your bloody head down, doctor!"

I thought I'd check for casualties aft and I found the Torpedo Officer on the quarterdeck with his depth-charge crew repeatedly ringing the bridge telephone. The din of gunfire defeated his wish to get involved and, on his own initiative, he adjusted the depth charge of the starboard thrower to a surface setting. As the frigate and the U-boat drew closer our crew fired the canister which arched alongside the U-boat and exploded with shattering effect amongst the U-boat men in the water.

Its bow portion destroyed, the U-boat began to sink—grudgingly and with admirable reluctance. Goggins and I looked on from the quarterdeck.

"By God, we're not the only ones who can build ships" grunted the Chief Sick Bay Petty Officer. The noise murdered the future silence and the quietness which then descended was almost as painful as the gunfire.

In the sudden calm the moon reappeared, the frigate stopped and all boats and scrambling nets were made ready to help the enemy survivors.

"I suppose we could steam away and leave the buggers to drown in their oil—or shoot 'em as they do us." shouted No. 1. "But here we are playing the game as usual and by God it's hard work!"

The British worked to the point of exhaustion, forgetful of revenge attacks from other U-boats. Every German visible in the water was being brought on board—alive or dead..

I thought we had brought inboard all the Germans near the quarterdeck until I heard a faint cry "Hilfe!" Calling for help and hanging onto the scrambling net was yet another oily survivor. Leg wounds prevented his climb to safety. I found that the sea in April is very cold, but with two pairs of strong arms—his and mine—he reached security to be grasped by Nixon, Dickinson's replacement as Torpedo Officer.

But Killin had drifted away from me and, in my saturated clothing, I couldn't reach the scrambling net. I could only think "If the Skipper starts the engines to avoid a revenge attack with torpedoes I'll have a long swim ahead of me!" But Nixon, inevitably, was equal to it. As his cheery face appeared over the guardrail he threw a line and pulled me in.

"Couldn't leave you! For once you'll be useful.!" "And you're five minutes adrift!" called the man from Milngavie.

The sea suddenly became choppier and the Germans were being caught between the rescue boats and the frigate's side. Numbed by cold or injured, several couldn't help themselves and the whaler, tossing in the swell, trapped them as helping hands stretched down. Their skulls made a dissonant noise, sickeningly like the cracking of hazelnuts at Christmas as the counter of the whaler crushed their heads against our steel side. This sharp obscenity was clearly audible through the merciful screen of darkness. No wonder I am still troubled by nutcrackers!

War's imprints on remembrance are indelible. Violence gives a special clarity and permanence—as if the high power lens of a microscope has been activated—to make the images not only larger but more sharply etched on the cells of memory. I can't forget any of it.

What was the word for the task ahead of me?

"Triage." That was it! A sorting out—of the bodies—motionless, twitching or retching on the steel deck, distinguishing the dead from the living—black, choking with oil and slippery with blood or vomit. The medical department of two began the demanding process of separating a foetid melange of humanity.

On the quarterdeck lay 10 dead. Seventeen of the Germans were still alive and two more severely wounded, were hurried to the Sick Bay. The dead were decently covered; the living were all in shock. It had been a bloody encounter. Hysteria was not far away and one young German—a confusion of oily rags and blood, ran down to the mess decks and clung screaming to the hammock bars. We couldn't get him down. The German repeatedly yelled "Kapitan." Corbett, now a "killick" (Leading Seaman) proposed the ultimate solution—Corbett was biased however—he had been hit.

Finally we got Captain Stefan from the enemy U-boat U.1063 to deal with the gibbering submariner.

"He is my steward and he says he thought I was dead; he'll be O.K. now." And he was.

The Sick Bay contained wounds reminiscent of Leith's casualty Department. Shrapnel had done much damage, driving clothing deep into tissue. Pain relief with haemorrhage control was the priority and I remained totally confident. Whoever stocked up Killin had done a wonderful job. Intravenous containers were hanging about like Christmas balloons. And Ben Murray had trained me!

There was only one who puzzled the medics. He had a lot of metal in his abdomen and Killin's corkscrewing was going to make surgery very difficult. I found Captain Darling in the Wardroom talking to the two surviving German officers, one the U-boat Captain. Shocked, but otherwise uninjured, they sat in their survival gear and blankets.

"We didn't expect to be blown up! You made us surface—and after that _____ "

Stanley Darling's face remained enigmatically bland as he saw the doctor.

"Just as well we were first to think about the nutcracker principle" Both Nazis smiled politely—the concept of a weapon which killed submerged U-boats from afar was beyond them—even had it been discussable. The secret was kept until 1975.

"Hello, doccie, are you in trouble? You smell horrible! If it's about the wounded, before you start butchering them I can make Falmouth in 24 hours. Does that help?"

It did, in spite of the phraseology. The dead were buried at dawn with proper ceremony. Chief's engines rose to the occasion once again and Killin discharged the wounded and prisoners at Falmouth the next morning.

By serving together in this lucky ship, ahead of her time, our crew had altered. They had a mutual pride which fastened them together into a formidable fighting unit. They were undoubtedly going to win through. I even began to think about the medical future. After the Navy, perhaps a thesis—"The Psychiatry of Combat." No, not psychiatry, I was a "blood and guts" man—and I had no illusions about myself. I had always known that I was never destined to stalk the corridors of eternity—as was Thomson my boon companion—killed in Italy. And Maclachlan, the brilliant mathematician—shot down over Bremen.

As we arrived at Gourock for a boiler clean, came the worst news of all—long delayed. Lawrence Hall, my alter ego, had experienced a direct exclusive personal hit by an 88mm. Shell. He had been taking his landing craft into the Flushing beachhead. I could hear his voice,

"To cope with me they had to use a particularly large and lethal missile, laddie. One for me alone!. They must have been hellish scared!"

But my co-explorer of adolescence had gone forever and the tears were real and unashamed. I was desperately confused,

"This won't do. I must get a grip on my life. I must take some action—now that God has got it all wrong. Let me compensate for the extinction of those who were so much superior to me. If my close friends die does this canonise them in my mind? War takes the best, the most unselfish and those who lead—by going first. Have I not also known the ultimate in fear? What will buttress me in my muddle and distress? Funny how it has taken mortal terror for these private revelations of the truth."

The train reached Waverley station in Edinburgh and I stepped out carrying the famous "pusser's bag" from Naval stores.

"Sorry to ask you again sailor, where are we going?" asked the cab driver.

"Leith Hospital please cabbie." Ten minutes later I was confronting the Matron—Miss McKee.

"It's all highly irregular, doctor and the off duty is made up. But if all you want to do is buy a ring, go and get Lesley now. She's in the Medical wards. You've got two hours. My good wishes doctor."

The Scots are such a controlled people that, in spite of this commonplace utterance of felicitation, I felt touched—glad, moreover, that I was going to make it legal. Just how glad I realised two minutes later! We are not as the comedians call us "God's frozen people!"

Lesley, bearing a covered, and therefore used, bedpan, appeared from behind a screen in female medical. In spite of the absence of ethereal music and in the olfactory presence of a urinary infection, the reality of our meeting far exceeded the expectation. Sister came in, and took the bedpan from Lesley.

"You won't need that where you're going. Matron's just 'phoned me."

In two hours we had bought a ring (second hand), visited both mothers and arranged an announcement in the Scotsman. As the taxi returned to Leith Hospital we separated—with great difficulty!

"Anyway, it's official" said Lesley. "And they can't take it away from us now—even though you have to go back."

"Why not come through to see the ship at the weekend?"

Somehow it became possible to have two whole days in the Tontine Hotel, Greenock and in the ship to which so much had happened.

Goggins coloured a little when challenged.

"I hope you like her, Doc."

"Indeed I do, sir, she's a find, O.K. "A very special bint!"

The Chief Yeoman who was still struggling to beat his 'winger' Goggins, at Cribbage interrupted.

"She's a nice little judy! Oh sorry, sir, I thought you'd gone!"

Captain Darling was called ashore for briefing on the evening of Lesley's departure and brought all Officers to the Wardroom early next morning.

"Information is that the U-boats will make one final attempt. Observations have been made in the shallowest of waters around the West coast of Scotland—in the Sound of Mull; off Jura, Islay and Iona. They're lying close inshore where they're almost inaccessible and that's very dangerous. Several sighting are on record and our job is to work round every island in the West of Scotland. The Navigator will have his work cut out and the doctor had better stand down—apart from spectating from the Bridge. He tends to zag instead of zig!"

I was relieved that I could not now be responsible for parking Killin on Oban esplanade or having Chiefie Gledhill and his engines scraped off the seabed. There followed six weeks of hide-and-seek amongst the bays and cliffs of Western Scotland. The sun beat down monotonously as the frigate probed with meticulous care—and not a little apprehension for the inshore U-boats. The crew's boredom was relieved only by games of housey housey.

Not an echo, an image or an alarm spoiled the dreich perfection of our coastal cruise. Wherever we wandered we saw the characteristic shapes of the Highland distilleries. Off Islay, I realised we were looking at Bruichladdich distillery—which made the finest single malt whisky in Scotland. I found the Chief on the quarterdeck peering fixedly ashore. I spoke—though Chiefie remained mute—in a religious trance it seemed.

"So this I how a Muslim looks at the first sight of Mecca."

"Don't laugh David, this is a holy place. How the hell do we get ashore?" His face again illuminated into a congealed rapture after he muttered,

"I'm chokker! The whole crew's chokker. You should speak to the Skipper about morale. We all need a run ashore and I know where I'm going—even if I swim there."

Half joking I intervened with the Captain.

"It's really a shrine, sir. Couldn't we lower a boat and pay a courtesy visit? Suppose German submariners are holding the employees prisoner?"

Darling laughed like the proverbial chief stoker.

"Christ, Doccie, what a bloody good effort! But what an imagination! You must think I'm as wet as a scrubber! Tell Chief to eat more "nutty"!"

We sailed on, but the idea wasn't all that stupid as the Captain later admitted. After a month of constant tension and monotony the average matelot's appreciation of the beauty of nature was less than nil. He wanted a run ashore and some mail. Boredom is destructive of discipline. And Chief thought little of the Skipper's advice to eat more chocolate.

The oppressive heat had produced its inevitable torpor. Yet none of the eight Officers in the Wardroom could disregard the Coxwain's entrance, through the for'ard door and instant exit via the after door. Attention sharpened further as Leading Seaman Corbett did a repeat performance—carrying a knife. The Sick Bay attendant followed the Chief Steward in flitting in turn across the stage.

Number One rasped "I'm seeing things. Am I ill" and peered at the doctor.

But it was no use pretending that something unusual wasn't happening. The Doctor joined the pursuit, vaguely hoping to give the matter an air of medical respectability. The chase went on merrily through one mess deck and twice round the engine room flat. Just as the spectators were thinking about wagering on the Coxwain's survival, Goggins, who had played the Rugby League Code in Wigan, tackled the seaman from behind. The great lover of Killin—L.S. Corbett—semi-conscious and much troubled, was dragged into the Sick Bay, shoved into a bunk and heavily sedated as his head was bandaged.

By the time authority was allowed entrance by Goggins, Corbett was slurred—but rational. He looked up at the Coxwain.

"Sorry Cox'n. I just went "berersk" when you said I'd a wife in every port. Corbett was held in the Sick Bay for a week—as a case of "battle fatigue". As he had been wounded in action no charge was brought. After fifteen months in the same small ship it was extraordinary that no more sinister indication of the need for change had occurred.

Leading Seaman Corbett had for long been obsessed with his Acne Vulgaris—here a facial pimple, there a disenchanting blackhead. Months ago I had succumbed to Corbett's cosmetic needs and initiated the current therapy with female sex hormones. The trouble was—it worked! Worse—I forgot to stop treatment and Corbett had been allowed to continue to feminise himself. Goggins was embarrassed.

"He was so pleased with his appearance that he persuaded me to keep him on the pills, sir. His face is as smooth as a baby's bottom. He hardly ever shaves—but there's a snag." I waited with trepidation.

"It's not all that bad really but he's a lot less randy—not so manly if you know what I mean, sir. Perhaps that's why he broke out as he did." Goggins looked happily apologetic as he continued. "In confidence, he's worried. He hasn't had a wet dream for weeks. What's more, doctor, he's grown a bust!"

"And Coxswain's ribbing him."

Contemplating the wonderful balance of nature, I struggled for words.

"Tell him, Doc. That, as from next month he will become exactly as he was before. He may even get back his acne!"

It was April 1945 and the Group's last sweep South and West to the Channel approaches was enlivened by the Yeoman handing me a cipher marked "Top Secret and Immediate". I fled below to the cipher books—which I repeatedly checked as I transcribed.

"Five German destroyers, probably 5" armament, heading towards you on same bearing, range 30 miles."

The Cypher Officer's fingers were unsteady as I passed the signal to the Captain.

"Five 4" against thirty 5"." I groaned.

Killin made "Maintain course and speed" to the other four ships in the Group. The range closed to fifteen miles and I kept thinking of Wilfred Owen, the poet who was killed just at the end of the previous holocaust.

"How miserable to die now!" thought the doctor, cipher officer, censor, entertainments officer etc. I was frantically scanning the horizon for topmasts when the Germans suddenly altered course for Brest. The British bluff had paid off and the enemy nerve had cracked first. Darling grinned.

"Bet your pommie boots they knew we were there. Reckon they overestimated us? Were you praying again, you bloody Scots Presby?"

Past the old beach-heads, through the Channel and North to Rosyth, Killin tied up alongside to learn that German resistance was almost over. Twenty minutes later I began seven days leave in Edinburgh, full of introspection and something close to guilt when I heard the latest casualties. It seemed that I had scarcely one friend left alive. My mother who had constantly asseverated that it was "nothing to the first lot," was rattling off a list of FIRST World War annihilations when Lesley appeared. She not only looked good, she smelled good. How evocative and primitive is the fragrance of women!

On May 8th with the unconditional surrender of Germany I was rapidly recalled. Killin was transformed. Captain Darling and his music machine had vanished. The Wardroom contained only Chiefie and Trentham. There were other faces but I didn't know them and was feeling isolated until the new Captain seized me by the elbow.

"I'm Hancock the new Captain. Feeling strange?" It was a good beginning although I felt as though someone had sold my home over my head. There was a slight initial resentment. A common cause, a mutual fear and shared experience had welded Killin into a tight ship. This little warship, this small floating island of democracy, could never be the same again.

But I was wrong! The ship immediately headed for Norway to show the flag. It was a mission of gratitude to express indebtedness to a remarkable people. And we were laden to the gunwales with whisky and corned beef; Admiralty had got it just right and for two weeks we flitted in and out of fjords so narrow that we could lean over and shake hands with our allies living in tiny places with unpronounceable names, and play Santa Claus with corned beef and whisky.

Captain Hancock sent for me. "I'm being offered command of one of the new Bay Class frigates in the Far East, David. Would you and Goggins come with me?"

We shook hands and agreed on a party to signify the inevitable end of Killin's present service when we reached Greenock.

"See the Chief Wren, Doc, as soon as we tie up, number one uniform—and best bedside manner. We'll have a dinner party to end all dinner parties for Killin's sake." And I did my stuff as I spoke to the Chief Wren.

"Ma'am, I'm Killin's doctor. We're going out of commission and request the pleasure of six young ladies for dinner to-night on board ship. Of course, Ma'am you must come yourself. Safe return at 2300 hours I will personally guarantee and I accept full responsibility as a doctor."

To my astonishment the Wren Officer agreed.

"Things have been dull for the girls with the German surrender. It's very good of your Captain and you."

Little did we know that the doctor in the sloop tied up outboard of us, was shortly to employ the same tactic.

At 1900 hours there were TWELVE bewildered Wrens in our Wardroom and the cook and stewards were frantic. A boarding party from the sloop's Wardroom solved the crowd problem by carrying off the six best-looking ladies. Nevertheless the six who were left became progressively more beautiful as the evening wore on. Chiefie had produced two bottles of Black Label and the Cook's Brown Windsor soup had never been better. He reached new heights of excellence with his corned beef hash and Devils on Horseback.

After dinner Captain Hancock slipped away to telephone his wife. One our guests enquired about the presence of hammock bars in the Wardroom.

"Oh" said Nixon "we exercise on them when we're tied up in harbour." An incredulous Wren was astonished to see Nick hanging upside down from the deckhead and by the time the Captain returned Nick had been joined by two Wrens also inverted.

"Doctor that's enough!" advised the skipper "Thank God they're wearing 'black outs' or should I say passion cheaters?" And suddenly it was 0100 hours and I cursed myself for breaking my promise. Luckily the Officer of the Watch had marshalled three taxis in double-quick time and the Wrens were bustled across the planks which made up the brow. It was high tide so that when one of the girls fell between the ship and the pier she was easily rescued with a boat-hook. It was a bad omen, however, and, having made sure that two Officers accompanied each pair of Wrens, I watched the convoy move off along the jetty. To my horror the leading taxi pulled up after a few yards and one of our guests leaped out and relieved herself in the glare of the headlights. The Duty Officer said poetically,

"It's like a full moon peeping through black clouds. Pity it's raining, it spoils the effect!"

The following morning a refit was ordered and the entire ship's company went on leave. Gallant little Killin went out of commission—with a loud bang and a memory of a wonderful dinner party. I went to say goodbye to Goggins.

"I'm staying on board one more day, sir—just to fix things up before we meet again in our new ship out East."

"Thanks for everything Chief", I replied—rather surprised at my emotions. Final plans for the first atomic bombing were made that day and history was being ruthlessly altered. Not that I could have grasped the significance of nuclear fission—even had it been explained.

CHAPTER ELEVEN

Lesley, who had been winkled out of Leith Hospital, was facing a purposeful fiancé.

"It's now or perhaps never; I'm being posted to the Far East and I must have you to come back to."

Once again our parents showed total opposition.

"What if you're killed?"

"Suppose you go missing. How could you tie each other down?"

"All right then, we'll live in sin!"

"That's just stupid; people like you don't anticipate marriage."

"Anyway you'll be cheapening the woman you love."

In 1945 these arguments had force. Morality prevailed, somewhat uneasily. There was a small degree of comfort, perhaps, in the thought that there was still something to experience together. Or were we deceiving ourselves and gutlessly doing what was ordained?

Such tormenting problems have a way of settling themselves and the wavering couple had the decision made for them. Admiralty's telegram arrived on the third day of my leave and directed me forthwith, to London—with tropical kit.

Not having been in London since the days of V1s and the V2s I found the city strangely peaceful. It was remarkable how much of it was still standing—as significant as the quiet pride and humour of London's people who epitomised the country's years of struggle.

After a night in the Officers' Club in Piccadilly I was directed from Admiralty to a special bus which travelled rapidly to R.A.F. Lyneham in Wiltshire. As dawn came we took off and headed East.

The York aeroplane was full of military achievement. It contained virtually nobody below the rank of Brigadier. Who on earth could see any priority in the transportation East of one Surgeon-Lieutenant from small ships? Eventually I fell asleep and awoke near Malta to find myself firmly grasping the hand of the Brigadier beside me. The Brigadier loosened my grip and cut short the apology.

"I've left someone behind too, my boy; perhaps I've just had longer to get used to it. Still don't like the separation, however. Tell you what, I'll show you round Malta."

Malta was comfortable and amiable but our next stop, Cairo, was merely an oasis for the night and much bad temper. It was cold and wet and the York's sanitation had to work hard all the way to Karachi. Rameses' Revenge had struck and this great leveller of rank laid low together the crowns and pips and my paltry pieces of gold braid. Still fondling this idea of the democratic effects of mass diarrhoea the York landed me at Karachi.

In the Transit Camp I had a tent to myself and a servant who laid out my tropical uniform—while I sought out the Paymaster. There seemed to be endless hooks, eyelets and buttons on this new rig and I was glad of the gloom as I headed for the Officers' Mess. Bravely shouldering my way to the bar, with my epaulers reversed back to front, I was at once penalised for "going astern" and had to buy a round of drinks. But happily I met Dr Stewart Rae—a school friend—now R.A.F, who became a golf companion ten years later—small world!

With the next dawn we took off on the last leg of the journey to Colombo. All my personal gear had vanished during the night. Unwashed, unshaven and with a foul-tasting mouth I tried to dismiss my initial impression of the East—there had to be more to it than dirt, dishonesty and dysentery.

Colombo was the delightful city described by relations and friends. Hastily winkled out from the other passengers I was transported by truck from the airport to a Naval Transit Camp—H.M.S. Mayina. In the tradition of the Service this camp was described as "a stone frigate"—although on dry land it had to be designated as a ship.

It was August 14th 1945 and Mayina exuded an aura of anti-climax and bewilderment. I soon learned why. The Americans had dropped "The Bomb". The war was officially over and all activity ceased until those involved assimilated the pattern of power.

Meanwhile there was unlimited travel and swimming with days of exploring Colombo, hours surfing at Mount Lavinia—the finest beach I had ever seen—and the glories of Kandy with its Temple of the Tooth, elephants and tea estates. For three weeks I and my cabin mate, Lawrence Evershed, became lotus-eaters. We even investigated the mysteries of the Shanghai Omelette of which we could never eat more than half each. Then we discovered that the recipe began—"Take twelve eggs......."

Quite suddenly the situation crystallised. Moved up country to Kurunagala where a Royal Marine Base Camp was being built, I found a C.O., who was a regular Major, his Adjutant, a sergeant major, four other ranks and a cook.

The jungle had swarmed over this former estate. There was a tiny old brick bungalow in which the Officers slept and a collection of huts for the others. The job was to create a Royal Marine base for those heading home for demobilisation. We spent three weeks keeping order and discipline as best we could. There was no running water and as the privy was fifty yards from the bungalow it was fortunate that the intense heat evaporated most of our body fluid. The medical work was virtually nil and the long evenings were whiled away on the rickety old balcony. Oil lamps gave some light but I blessed my clinical torch—especially at night when we felt very isolated. There was an infestation with Kraits—little snakes—like bootlaces—they tended to doze under your pillow or in your shoes. The C.O. insisted that each pillow be lifted at "lights out" and each shoe, or boot, tapped out at dawn. Kraits are highly venomous and one night when the Adjutant forgot his routine, something emerged from under his pillow and slithered across his throat. While he claimed that this situation could only be met in the total darkness by absolute self control and immobility, he ultimately conceded he'd been scared stiff and couldn't even breathe.

A few days later a King Cobra took up residence in the wood pile which the cook had carefully created. Having laden himself with logs, the cook was not a little thoughtful when the elegant creature emerged one morning and proceeded to dilate its neck. As he said,

"We don't 'ave things like that in 'ackney so I 'its it wif a stick—right on the nut; and the bleeder drops down dead."

The Adjutant and the Doctor congratulated him and returned to their bungalow with the snake.

The C.O., a man with a sense of humour, was still asleep as his Adjutant arranged the deceased cobra in the small lobby. The creature's pose was most life-like as it lay outside the C.O.'s "cabin". Halfway to breakfast there was a yell and several shots. As we dashed back to the bungalow the C.O. choked out,

"Cobra, by God, but I saw him first. He's dead alright!"

"Well done, sir" said the Adjutant. "Quick thinking."

I pointed out quietly to the young Marine that the spot in the hallway where the bullets hit the snake wasn't where we had left the cobra.

"You mean, Doc, that I was carrying a LIVE snake?"

"Lucky the cook had stunned it first!"

The Adjutant paled and refused to return to breakfast. The C.O. in his ignorance smiled tolerantly.

"No battle experience these young officers."

Bereft of words, I was condemned to spend hours hearing the C.O. recite the tale of his battle with the cobra. Neither of his audience of two could say anything in contradiction.

The oil lamp was useful for Krait pillow drill and nocturnal travels after beer sessions but I came to bless the lamp—and the C.O.

Creeping gently across the hallway, in sandalled feet after my last trip to the privy, my right sandal hit something hard. In the lamplight was the largest scorpion I had ever seen. It looked like a lobster—but infinitely more frightening. My cries brought the C.O. through the doorway, plus lamp, plus gun, plus shouts to keep still. I froze as the C.O. shot the creature dead centre. Thus died the great grand-parent of all scorpions and with it went any possibility of my coming to terms with this environment.

Kurunagala's Royal Marine Major was never accorded more deference than during our brief future time together. However, the M.O. now thoroughly phobic about the order of Arachnida as well as the entire class of reptiles, made haste to Naval Headquarters, Colombo. The Surgeon-Captain listened patiently to the account of the hasty trip by air from England followed by a paradoxical posting which, it was claimed, would produce physical and mental atrophy of a would-be medical paragon. I rambled on.

"Anywhere at sea, sir, or with the task forces and naval parties—which must be going out to fulfil the Japanese surrender. Anything at all, sir, as long as I get away from hornygolochs and creepy-crawlies. I really can't stand these things in the jungles of Ceylon."

The Surgeon-Captain smiled in a bemused way under the deluge of youthful phobias.

"Do I understand you, are you actually volunteering for something which might be even worse than those horned things you're complaining about? Don't you know that one should NEVER volunteer for anything?"

It was my turn to be nonplussed. I picked up my cap and apologised for wasting my senior's time.

At the office door the Surgeon-Captain recalled me.

"I'll see what I can do. I promise you it won't be dull."

He was as good as his word and two days later, a replacement and old friend, Dr Mark Marlborough, arrived at Kurunagala. Having said a rather sad farewell to my C.O. I left for Colombo where I boarded a Tank Landing Ship. After H.M.S. Loch Killin this vessel seemed of vast proportions.

The First Lieutenant met me as I boarded, showed me my cabin and the Wardroom and solemnly suggested a bath before we sailed.

"L.S.T.'s roll like bitches." Having matured in frigates in the Atlantic I nodded patronisingly and entered the Wardroom to see another Surgeon-Lieutenant blissfully having a zizz and smoking a pipe. One of Ronald Fisher's eyes opened and then closed again. He adopted this air of lethargy to conceal his considerable grey matter.

"Java bound too I suppose. I'm Fisher. How's your Bridge?" Weariness then overcame him again, before his natural grace reasserted itself and he explained tersely.

"Two Naval Parties on board; ours goes to Surabaya after we drop your lot off at Batavia. Pink gin O.K.?"

Fisher gradually surfaced and the lubricating effect of the spirits and Angostura bitters did away with his staccato speech. We ate together and formed a Bridge four after dinner. By midnight Fisher, now crisp and incisive, had dominated the game. The L.S.T. was beginning to wallow grotesquely—like a playful hippopotamus and I was losing the place. A bath and my bunk seemed indicated. Number One was sadly correct with his weather forecast.

Without a lock the door's sliding mechanism operated every time we rolled and, like a grotesque peep-show, I was briefly revealed to passers-by. One of these was Fisher who glanced in and commented on my strong resemblance to a bespectacled walrus. I sprang at him out of the bath and reached the sliding door as the ship rolled again. To Fisher's delight the head of his new friend was pinned firmly in the jaws of the trap. As the door opened to release its hostage's skull it was plain that I had sustained a double fracture of the spectacle leg. It was a memorable way to enter one of the darker, dirtier phases of my life.

The next bath was many months away and chaos was to become the norm.

Over the next three days Fisher, Illingworth and partners played Bridge, pausing occasionally to eat. Jones, the First Lieutenant of our party, kept us well informed as news rolled in. The Dutch had taken control of Java but the Indonesians were resisting. The Japanese had surrendered but when they found themselves being slaughtered with their own weapons, started the war again. As Jones had it,

"Gilbert and Sullivan are still alive and working in Java." They were prophetic words from an officer who contained much Welsh poetry. In the early hours of the fifth day he winkled me out of my happy dreams to show me the volcano Krakatoa as we passed through the Sunda Strait between Sumatra and Java. Jones, his head packed with history, recalled in his rich Welsh accent how in 1883 the glowing mountain had exploded to kill over a hundred thousand people. In an earlier existence Jones, the archetypal Welshman, would have been a wandering bard.

It was good to be back at sea.

Tandjoeng Priok is the port of Batavia, now Djakarta. There is an eight mile avenue between the two. It is, fortunately, a straight road—not conducive to ambushes perhaps but, at that time, a route through swampland and vast wastes of uncontrolled vegetation. Its traverse, without incident, led invariably to feelings of relief. Lined with Poinciana trees, brashly aflame, the Royal Navy promptly and dramatically designated it—"Deception Street" because of its misleading tranquil appearance.

The L.S.T. entered the harbour of Tandjoeng Priok through the rusted desolations of 1942. She tied up alongside amid a confusion of orders from the Dutch, the British advance party, sign language from disarmed Japanese soldiers and requests for food from malnourished Indonesians.

I could see the edges of the enlarged livers and spleens; here was a leper; there a case of Yaws, while the Tropical Sores defied description—their severity ineffectually disguised by a pathetic piece of filthy rag supposed to keep off the flies.

The senses were assailed by the humming of winged insects and the sweet-sour stench of decay and rotting unmentionable things of eastern exotica. If this wasn't exactly "The White Man's Grave" it was certainly not a place conducive to a good healthy appetite.

Farewell then to Dr Fisher and the Surabaya party; into the trucks we clambered and on, through unguarded dockyard gates, to report at the Port Offices—now to be known as Naval Headquarters. The Truck's final stop was the Seamen's Mission where the Naval Party was disgorged. It was the largest of a series of four sturdy bungalows which constituted the Wardroom, the Petty Officers' Mess, the Naval Sickquarters and the Seamen's Mess. The Officers' mess was entered from a balcony and was about 150 feet long and 60 feet wide. This was to be the Wardroom and it opened on the right into a similar room which would become a communal cabin. It was some minutes before I appreciated that the windows were devoid of glass.

On the left side of the Mess was a small room for the Dutch Liaison Officer. A large craggy man, Jonge, spoke excellent English and somehow held the view that the Doctor would run the Wardroom Mess and take all responsibility—apart from matters military. Within an hour of arrival he pulled me on one side.

"Life is not safe here for anybody, doctor. There is shooting all the time and the rebels have Japanese weapons. Please be sure that your officers understand that the insurgents do not know the difference between the forces here. I think they recognise the Japanese and they kill them—of course. But they wish the Dutch to leave here and if we will not go happily they will make us go." I managed to drag up a sickly smile but this only encouraged the Dutchman to continue.

"Please tell your friends that life here is cheap. They must be careful—even you must carry a gun. You are not safe because you are a doctor."

This last warning was accepted with some doubt. The idea of a gun-toting doctor was hilarious. I could just hear Goggins of Killin:

"So it's cure or kill, sir?"

I walked down the seventy-five yards to the Harbourmaster's office—now to be the Royal Naval Sick Quarters, Batavia. The three Sick Bay attendants were already installed and were encouraging Japanese prisoners to erect beds and mosquito nets in its three separate buildings. The impassive Japanese clearly felt that if they co-operated with the British they would be protected. They were also aware that the British had medicines to help reduce their appalling mortality from Malaria and Dysentery.

By sundown the Royal Navy had become part of the background. In the Officers' Mess the bar was open and in the cabin two dozen beds were in position. When the Captain called to assess progress there was some confusion. Captain Edward Cooper was a tall, impressive, much decorated man. He had commandeered a large house in Oranje Boulevard in the city of Batavia, the main office at the pierhead, now designated as "Office of Naval Officer in Charge, Batavia" and several cars.

"What about the troops?" he enquired.

This was received in silence until he noticed the scarlet in my epaulets and instantly made towards the bar.

"Ah, there's the doctor! Come and talk to me."

I was nervous, never having hosted a four-ring R.N. Captain. I ordered that finest of all drinks—pink gin. Struggling to remember the names and duties of those already installed at the improvised bar, I took the easy way out.

"Please tell the Captain your name and job—it saves time."

Sub-Lieutenant Greasby, R.N.V.R., for example was rather older—a shy tubby man who described himself as a "technical officer" as he said to the Captain,

"I can make anything, sir. Tomorrow we're even shamfering up an old godown as a theatre. And we're making a hoarding for the Doctor to signpost Sickquarters."

The Captain appreciated the little man's unsuspected depths.

"Build us a theatre from a godown, Greasby, and I promise you I'll have it used."

I was contemplating this revelation of human versatility when I realised that Captain Cooper was looking at me.

"You're very much at home, doctor, you're drinking MY drink. Don't worry, I'll have another. Basically I want to allot accountability so you have your assignment also. YOU are the

Port Medical Officer—responsible to me. The Navy is in control here and tomorrow the prison camps are to be destroyed except for those we require for the Japanese. Don't be over sympathetic with the Japs. Remember that the price of a rat was one Guilder (about two shillings) and that live bayonet practice was a regular feature!"

Captain Edward Cooper, R.N. departed in his limousine, standard flying. I returned to corned beef hash, fruit and coffee. Greasby began to create a theatre from an empty warehouse.

Bedtime was a revelation. Sandwiched between two officers praying on their knees as the cicadas choired in the blackness, I tactlessly touched one on the shoulder.

"Look chum, it's not all that bad!"

My cabin mate looked at me rather sadly.

"Of course it isn't, but it helps. Try it!"

I despatched my medical prayer as I made certain that the pistol under my pillow was loaded and the latter—"krait free".

Just before lights out the Provost Marshall, Major James Powell of the Royal Marines arrived by jeep. This hero of the Madagascar campaign had a film star gloss about him. Lean, athletic, blue eyed, tanned, his hair was as black as his teeth were white. He loped into the cabin and presented himself to the fully-dressed Illingworth.

"Captain Cooper said you might still be about." And we set out together in search of a mug of "kye" or cocoa—the navy's panacea for all ills of body or mind. All the Services were riddled with the repetitive jargon jokes of that time, inspired by Tommy Handley's radio shows. Not even cocoa was exempt, as Powell proved.

"Well, Doc, how do you like your cocoa?"

"Same as I like my women, Major—hot, sweet and stirred up!"

"Very good sir, brown or white?"

In the event the brew was strong and bitter, but the cocoa and the witless catch phrase broke down the barriers. Powell leant across confidentially in the gloom and said in clipped tones,

"Doctor we shall be working together. I'm the law and you keep the men in good order. We're sitting on a volcano which is not as inactive as it seems. In addition our camp is NOT guarded; it seemed best to present a low profile—but we may not get away with it. God, I must clean my teeth after that cocoa!"

So it was that this strange pair finished up in the lean-to behind the Mess, where there were two wash-hand basins. I, who had been trained by my fiancée and her brother—a dental student, to regard teeth as holy objects, was fascinated by the Major's oral technique. Powell brushed very slowly, always towards the cutting edge of the teeth and used the tooth-brush in his left hand for the right half of his mouth. It was a learning experience for me which was to influence my future working life. The major looked slightly put out by the scrutiny and muttered some apology for being "dentally obsessed". However it became clear that while his teeth did not rule his lifestyle, the results justified his rigid rules of oral hygiene.

In two days Greasby and his craftsmen had built the theatre inside a deserted warehouse. The Captain was as good as his word. What if the only two films projected were "Random Harvest" and "Laura"—which ran on alternate nights for six months? On two occasions we even had a live vaudeville show from enterprising matelots. These innocent distractions kept the British reasonably contented during the early days of the fragile understanding between opposing forces.

It was the age of the slogan—some foolish familiar statement, some nonce words which had no real meaning—but could be applicable in any situation. Such phrases, by their sheer irrelevance and irreverence, became humorous through constant usage. In this category were such utterances as, "War is Hell" and "If only Mother could see me now!" Some of these shibboleths were lengthy and complex. Childish under normal circumstances, their repetition in tense situations diminished fear through laughter—and improved morale by introducing a distracting mockery and ridicule.

Tom Kelly's bunk was nearest the light switch and at "lights out" he would say in the sonorous voice of Quintin Reynolds, the American war correspondent,

"The lights are going out all over Europe."

If this didn't work he launched, in his thick Irish brogue, into a monologue which expanded into a chorus of verbal nonsense. Shouted, in unison, in the tropical blackness, it may have mystified the indigenous population—but it made the dormitory's spirits soar above the dreadful environment.

> "A shot rang out,
> A woman screamed,
> The lights went out
> Her guts fell out –
>   I went out!
> "........staying in there!"
> The lights then went out.

CHAPTER TWELVE

Three weeks after the landing everything began to go wrong. At 2000 hours the Provost Marshall, James Powell, hustled into the Wardroom and doused the lights.

"Trouble, chaps" he shouted, "there's shooting beginning all round the camp perimeter!"

We were used to a sporadic shot. Now we could hear machine gun fire near us. This was audible to me as I treated my "prickly heat" in the washroom with a purple dyestuff and some tincture of iodine. I entered the darkened Mess wearing only a towel.

As Powell said later, "I switched on my flashlight and there was our doctor, clad in a filthy rag; specs on the end of his nose; hair sticking up in the air. In his hand was a gun and his body was painted purple and yellow." The silence in the Wardroom was embarrassingly palpable until it was disrupted by Kelly's strangled Irish brogue.

"God in Heaven, is that not the most frightening sight I ever saw? Put the bugger out front and shine a light on 'im. That'll stop this bloody nonsense!" And as the bullets began to whine through the glassless windows, a howl of derision went out into the night. It was, of course, entirely coincidental that the firing ceased at that moment and the telephone, hitherto dead, came alive again. The Dutch Liaison Officer 'phoned in to say the affray was over; the lights went on. Twenty-five pairs of eyes peered in astonishment at the doctor.

"Ye Gods!" said Mackenzie, the Captain's secretary. "So it is true—these heathen Scots DO paint their bodies with woad."

On the night when the M.O. was credited with quelling a rebellion, James Powell had slipped away to see the Japanese Commandant. At dawn they awoke to find they were being guarded by armed Japanese troops. Powell had had them up all night manning the perimeter.

When cornered, the Marine Major was reluctant to admit the truth but finally answered the million-dollar question.

"How do you persuade Japanese prisoners of war to guard British combatants?" In reply Powell said,

"Well of course, you can give weapons—without much ammunition. Then you do a deal. I told them that if they kept us safe we'd help them medically. You see they don't have ANY drugs and they're dying like flies."

When I claimed that I had now experienced the ultimate absurdity, Powell berated me for ignoring the enormous addition to my medical practice!

Sick Quarters was always open for business. It possessed two requisitioned cars, a brand new ambulance and a treasure house of medicines and instruments. So well equipped were we that a godown in the dock area was taken over as a Native Dispensary. Soon we were struggling in an avalanche of pathology—leprosy, yaws, tropical ulcers, and syphilis. A hundred patients a day were passing through. The stock treatment was intravenous arsenic; the drug and the diluting water were mixed in a tin sterilised by flaming methylated spirit; the infusion was then pushed into a vein. With this coarse approach, cleansing and dressing various appalling sores, we had some dazzling successes.

After a month the Dutch called. They required the building for other reasons and the Dispensary must close. Very angry, I faced the Dutch Liaison Officer.

"What about my native patients?"

The Dutchman replied gently,

"Doctor, do you not save them from disease only to allow them to die more slowly—from starvation?" The logic was unquestionable and the feebleness of our pious medical gesture was underlined the next day when two emaciated native corpses were found behind Sick Quarters.

The following morning I drove my Ford Mercury the hundred yards from the Wardroom to my consulting room. As the car swung in between the pillars fronting the flight of stone steps leading into Sick Quarters I pressed the brake pedal. Nothing happened. With a crunch and bump the vehicle climbed up the steps and almost deposited me in my chair behind the desk.

Petty Officer Talbot, the engineering wizard who ran the transport pool, heard the crash and sprinted down from what he called "his shop". A little shaken, I got out of the car and ruefully surveyed it. Talbot had always worried about the doctor's ignorance of mechanical matters. He had even lent me textbooks because it troubled him that someone really affected to believe that the propeller at the front of the engine pulled the car forward. Now his worst fears were realised. Surely the doctor didn't believe that automobiles could climb stairs. But Talbot was never depressed by human ignorance—or anything else.

"Wot, no brakes, sir?" was his cheerful greeting. "Or was it too hot to walk up the steps? My God, you've really done it!"

He looked under the crazily angled car and grunted, "Pipe's been cut; no brake fluid. Someone had it in for you!"

Not knowing the proper response I said,

"Ah."

Talbot looked serious. "Good thing you weren't beating it up on the Batavia road!"

After the morning consulting session came the ward round. The seven beds were always full. The Sick Bay Attendants, full of enterprise, had fitted out a tiny room as a laboratory. Here I practised frontier medicine, staining blood films for malarial parasites: spotting gonococci in urethral discharges: even, with dark ground illumination, demonstrating the sinister helix of the spirochaete of syphilis.

Medically self-sufficient and splendidly equipped, Tandjoeng Priok was a professional delight. It was, however, a disaster area. Things became progressively worse. My replacement car was immobilised by sugar in the petrol tank. Shootings and other forms of lawlessness escalated. People looked over their shoulders all the time—for some invisible source of violence.

Unusually innocent in my ways, I found myself entangled in a mesh of intrigue, subterfuge and malice. The ultimate affront to my ingenuous nature followed shortly. In the port area was a group of Javanese interpreters. They were charming, beautiful young Eurasian ladies who acted as contacts with the Dutch, the insurgents and the Japanese. No one was quite sure where they came from. Rootless detritus of the war, they seemed to vacillate between the camp, the Captain's Office and the Wardroom. They spoke all necessary languages and were useful from the intelligence viewpoint as well as being decorative. Nobody enquired about their antecedents. The world was too uncertain and impermanent for people to stop and assess even their own environments.

Of this glamorous corps Kim was, perhaps, the most delectable. She arrived at the end of Sick Parade and said quietly that she had a lump in her left breast. She was led into a private room. Having learned that the swelling was recent I asked Kim to remove her brassiere. Good doctors never watch females disrobing; it embarrasses both parties. I looked out of the window abstracted by mental images of the Pentland Hills and the seductive couthiness of a beef steak pie created by Lesley's mother.

My right hand was suddenly seized and pushed against Kim's left nipple. I returned hastily from the beef steak pie land to the undoubted fact that I was holding the turgid left breast of a naked lady. Kim was all bosom, arms, legs and sighs as she clambered into me. "Ye Gods!" I thought "Is this rape?"

Hippocrates must have been alerted. Suddenly perched like a guardian angel on my shoulder, his silent warning coincided with a wail of dismay from the young doctor. The Sick Bay Attendant, normally shockproof, threw open the door and stood, gaping, on the threshold as Kim scooped up her clothing and glided past me.

"Are you O.K. sir?" asked the S.B.A. "She wasn't trying something, was she?" I could only nod. The S.B.A. looked wistful.

"She might have tried ME. Wonder if I would have yelled for help!"

Three weeks later the S.B.A. wept as I confirmed that he had on his genitals the primary lesion of syphilis.

My Presbyterian standards were coming under attack. I had always regarded doctors as inviolate human beings. From which quarter would the next affront come? On myself or on my rigid beliefs? Sorely troubled I sought out James Powell for an emotional catharsis. I was too young and too raw to be in the position of the authority which I held. "Simpatico" was the best description of Powell. The Provost Marshall was on the same wavelength as myself in that we could communicate without weighing what we said. Unthinkingly and uninhibitedly we talked. James Powell gazed deep into his pink gin as if he were studying a crystal ball. Finally he looked up from the "embalming fluid" as he called it.

"You're a self-righteous bastard."

I winced.

"Negotiation, tolerance and compromise is what the world is all about. But you presume to project your own beliefs onto other people You even endow them with your own pious qualities because you lack an understanding of human frailty."

The miserable disciple of Hippocrates and Galen was gradually shrinking as Powell continued his remorseless analysis.

"My world is one of compromise. Poor old Doc! I quote you from my student days—and not very accurately—it's something about bad intentions with hovering angels and good intentions with unpleasant overtones."

Correct source and version James? I asked eagerly. But Powell was floundering. He couldn't remember! And to me it mattered!

"You know exactly what's meant anyway—so stop confusing the issue."

"I suppose it's the difference between James Powell who's twenty-six and David Illingworth but twenty-three years old and vainly struggling."

"You certainly struggled with Kim! Have some more pinkers lad."

It said much for our friendship that it was strengthened by the older man's brutal and humorous frankness. The languid drawling Major had unsuspected depths and philosophies. We talked deep into the small hours. To Powell it was apparent that the native population would not accept the resumption of Dutch rule. The World used to smile at the jibe that wherever the British went they created a Civil Service. In the East Indies, the Dutch had integrated and intermarried with the indigenous population but had failed to establish any substantial system of self-government. They could not accept that the Indonesians now rejected them.

The insurgents' approach was quite simple. If your face was white you were "one of them". The Indonesians had Japanese weapons and the city they called Djakarta was lawless.

Hearing that there were bargains in textiles at the market I drove into the city one morning. Standing beside me at a stall was a Dutch Naval Officer. When the shots came the Dutchman's spotless whites crimsoned fast and the two fugitives who had shot him were running—towards my car. They leapt into the car to find the ignition key was absent. When they sprang out again they saw the owner bearing down on them with a gun in his hand and his Murrayfield voice at full volume. Not a pretty sight—yellow with Mepacrine and red with Dutch blood, the attackers didn't stop to discuss the problem but vanished up the nearest alley. Suddenly realising I was alone and vulnerable, the pursuit lapse.

I was glad the engine fired first time.

Dawn came and I opened one eye. In the moment between sleeping and waking I thought I must be dreaming. I tried to sleep again—but still the area between the beds at the bottom half of the dormitory was criss-crossed by long bamboo poles. Immobile I watched in fascination as the clothes of my neighbour, Mackenzie, were skilfully lifted from the bedside chair and proceeded in a graceful arc towards the glassless window. Mackenzie was a light sleeper and stirred at the sound of the first warning whisper from his neighbour. One second later two nude figures sprang out from their mosquito nets waving guns and shouting. The bamboos were dropped as their holders turned tail at the sight of a naked prickly heat victim with a purple body and 140 pounds of pure white Mackenzie standing 6 feet 3inches in his bare feet. This successful defence of property was exceptional. So skilled and bold were the natives that they could steal your underpants when you were still inside them.

And everywhere the corpses; bodies in ditches, bodies in the canals—mutilated, arms and legs tied. What nationality? Which sex? As the days passed the Royal Navy felt more and more beleaguered. Two of the original twenty-five officers were shipped out with nervous breakdowns as the situation steadily deteriorated.

But then the Army came and I stood by my car and watched them disembark—not without relief. Two officers of the Royal Army Medical Corps broke ranks and ran up to me. Both doctors had graduated with me and shared a minute of disbelief before vanishing back into the column. It was not reassuring to learn that most of this force was destined for the interior of Java which was a hive of insurgent activity. However, some remained in Batavia and turned its best hotel, The Hotel des Indes, into a military hospital. They set up specialist units and to my pleasure volunteered to see any sticky problems from the Royal Navy.

For two weeks the Naval ambulance occasionally took sailors into Batavia for consultant advice. Initially there were only occasional shots at British vehicles on the port road; then the unforgivable occurred. My naval ambulance was machine-gunned and hit in several places. Thereafter we used smaller, faster vehicles and only for urgent problems. Further inland tensions boiled over when an Army jeep was ambushed near Bandoeng and its occupants ruthlessly gunned down. The only survivor was one of my friends whom I had seen disembark a few days earlier and who appeared to die dramatically as he fell into a roadside ditch. His 'death' was convincing enough to make the rebels concentrate on purloining the jeep. This episode removed any chance of co-operation with the Nationalists—and the British sought only to survive thereafter.

The Dockyard was guarded by a unit of Gurkhas. There was no more comforting sight for the Royal Navy detachment than those fierce proud warriors. Passes were issued to those who had business in the dock area and I had one made out in my magnificent title as Port Medical Officer. My services were available to all ships in the port—not that many called!

"There's an Indian with spots—on board the first freighter to arrive carrying rice. Probably nothing, Doc, but I'll drive you down in my jeep," said the Provost Marshall.

When we arrived at the gangway a line of railway trucks was being shunted alongside to collect the precious cargo. Nobody had bothered to clean up the spillage of oil on the quayside. Powell braked the jeep, muttering darkly. We slithered smoothly on past the gangway. After twenty feet we were still sliding helplessly towards the reversing trucks. The jeep vanished under the rear truck. Suddenly it was pitch black on the floor of the vehicle as it was shoved inexorably backwards.

Eventually the Captain of the freighter persuaded the engine driver to halt and they looked underneath for the mangled remains of the visitors. Powell emerged between the wheels of the wagon. He straightened himself as he stood in the oil—and fell flat on his back. From this position of disadvantage he saw the train begin to move again and bellowed in his best parade-ground voice.

"Stop that bloody train, the doctor's in there!"

I finally wriggled clear and the pair of us who by now looked like "Christie Minstrels", descended disapprovingly on the Captain who took us below to the crew's quarters where lay a Goanese steward—desperately ill. He could only mutter in an interpreted reply to the doctor's questions.

"Yesterday came back from city—feeling bad. Got lift in Army truck."

Smallpox had come to Tandjoeng Priok! The ship was quarantined: all services and forces were alerted; the Goanese steward died within a few hours and James Powell drove me to the airport to collect as many thousand doses of vaccine as could be gathered from all available sources in the Far East.

For forty-eight hours the four medics enthusiastically vaccinated everybody they could find—Powell swore that he had been "done" thrice. On the evening of the second day the Provost Marshall accompanied me in my repaired Ford to the house commandeered in Oranje Boulevard by Captain Cooper, the Naval Officer in Charge, who was being vaccinated at 1900 hours. He needed a report from us both before speaking.

"Doctor, there's a curfew; it's now dark and dangerous outside—especially on that port road. Tell Powell you're both here for the night and don't argue." I wasn't going to argue anyway—but Powell came into the lounge and suggested that we should leave at dawn.

"It's not only the troubles at Tandjoeng Priok, sir. The Doctor's worried about several hundred doses of vaccine going bad in the heat." N.O.I.C. Batavia nodded assent to this remarkable fabrication.

"Put your vaccine in my refrigerator, Doctor, and report to me tomorrow."

Powell and I strode out to find the Captain's steward directing us to our room. At the bedroom door he told me that the refrigerator had broken down and informed the dentally obsessed Powell that he couldn't get him a tooth-brush. The Provost Marshall grasped my arm as soon as the door closed.

"Look here Doc, this is a crisis. My teeth and your vaccine will be rotten by morning. We'll crawl through the garden and if you go like a bat out of hell we'll cover the eight miles to the port in ten minutes."

He quietly opened the window. Into the blackness we went with the vaccine. All that was visible was one lit bedroom window with curtains only partially drawn. That was how I found Powell again—peering through the aperture.

"Hey, doc," Powell hissed, head clearly outlined against the light, "Look at Old Sodface; our second in command!"

"James, for God's sake keep down or else you won't have a head," I replied. Powell disappeared, sniggering wickedly. I risked my brain momentarily, gasped at what I saw and wriggled after Powell to the rear of the house.

"You saw it too, didn't you, Dock?" "Old Sodface was having a grind with Kim, that luscious Javanese interpreter. Yesterday he told me he was very upset by the matelots' morals!"

Powell was crawling, Hollywood style, into the car for the getaway. I followed with the ignition key. The engine fired at once and, as the doors closed, the car, without lights, rounded the front of the house. There were hoarse challenges from the sentries when we careered into the empty boulevard but we made a difficult target. Only one or two street lamps were functioning but we found the port road without incident. We hurtled along it, showing only parking lights, never dropping below 80m.p.h. A watery moon had appeared to help us and out of the corner of my eye I glimpsed the Royal Marine—slouched in his seat. He was wearing a bush jacket, shorts, an Anzac hat and soft kid boots. Any impression that he had stepped out of a comic opera was destroyed by the fact that he had wound down the passenger seat window and a Sten gun lay across his knees.

In ten minutes the vaccine was safely cold in Sick Quarters; in fifteen minutes Powell was waging his personal vendetta against dental decay.

Inevitably the N.O.I.C found out about this escapade, but one of his Staff Officers—"Old Sodface", no less, had a visit from the Provost Marshall to discuss the moral standards of the Task Force. Powell suggested that the Naval Officer in Charge might forgive the coltish enthusiasms of young officers; furthermore the vaccine had taken precedence over personal safety—and that was reasonable. No more was heard.

The Army now gained a General Officer Commanding—Christison by name. He was concerned to deal with the Indonesian Supremo—Soekarno—a devilish clever little man. Christison was also worried about the soaring rate of venereal disease. A committee was formed which included James Powell, myself, the Naval Chaplain, "Old Sodface" and a

Colonel from the Royal Army Medical Corps. Its remit was to study the causes and control of sexually-transmitted diseases in the area.

General Christison, as Chairman, welcomed the Committee and defined its role. When he asked for opening remarks James Powell did not hesitate.

"As an initial comment I'd like you to know, sir, that there are two main sources of infection. There are the brothels in the port and there are the railway trucks on the perimeter of our base."

Christison was puzzled.

"What have the trucks to do with V.D., Major?"

Powell became faintly pink under his tan.

"Well, sir, the sailors visit the trucks from time to time."

"Major Powell," I interrupted, "means that the sailors are having relations with the women who live in the trucks."

General Christison's tolerant smile vanished as he pronounced judgement.

"Very well, gentlemen, the Provost Marshall and the Naval Doctor are appointed to supervise the railway ladies who dispense their favours on the lines—(he paused to let the appalling pun take effect) indicated. Dr Illingworth will become Medical Officer in charge of Brothels in Tandjoeng Priok."

As the meeting concluded Powell came over to congratulate his friend. He shook me warmly by the hand.

"God, I'm proud of you lad. M.O. I.C of brothels. If only your mother could see you now! When do we start work?"

The following morning we went up to the line of six railway trucks, making enough noise to allow the customers to escape. We rounded up twelve women and coaxed them gently down to Sick Quarters. The "patients" giggled constantly—even during the examination. When it was all over the ladies sat on the verandah while their slides were prepared in the small laboratory. I was interrupted by Powell's troubled face and choked voice.

"I have a horrible feeling that they expect to be PAID for this. One wants money, another cigarettes—and a third keeps on chanting, "Cup of bleeding kye, Jack'" Powell was visibly shaken.

"In that case they believe, to put it as nicely as possible, that we're a little unusual. O my God!"

I was quick to comfort the perturbed Royal Marine by completing my list of diagnoses.

"Actually, James, THEY'RE a bit unusual—six have gonorrhoea, one has primary and one secondary syphilis—while another poor soul has an advanced cancer."

And so the trucks were moved.

The village contained three brothels. The Provost Marshall and the doctor used to visit each one twice weekly. Little was concealed by the mosquito nets and some of the clientele were identifiable. What is the correct protocol when you meet one of your comrades in a bordello? Once or twice we encountered an effusive greeting which, with its apparent warmth, signified a plea for understanding. It was tacitly agreed by the two brothel supervisors that no-one was ever recognised during their inspections.

By Christmas 1945 the strength of Indonesian nationalism was being increasingly felt. Even during our calls on the pleasure houses, a quiet indefinable discomfort was apparent to this sensitive pair of inspectors. Were the natives around the door slower to make way for us? Were the native knives—the parangs, more in evidence?

"Tell me, oh wise physician, why we inspect these places. What are we looking for? Are we doing any good? Do we not dignify illicit sex by having a law-enforcement officer and a doctor present during the adulterous act? And why did the nape of my neck prickle this morning?

So we asked N.O.I.C. to put the village out of bounds.

Captain Cooper acted on this advice at 1000 hours and a barrier, bearing a warning sign, was erected across the road. After dinner that night there were shouts and screams from the other side of the barrier. At dawn we found the mutilated remains of two sailors. They had not died a rapid death in spite of the sharpness of their assailants' parangs.

To Powell and me such an incident was highly significant of a tilting of the balance of power away from the Dutch. A few of them reacted violently to coloured faces and assumed that Europeans were above the law. Outside Sick Quarters a native approaching a Dutch Officer did not immediately stop when ordered. He took four bullets in the chest as his murderer faded into the expressionless background of the dock area. The killing was motiveless but symptomatic of a Dutch feeling of increasing insecurity.

A small number of Netherlanders believed that the only good native was a dead one. They found the Gurkha sentries on the dockyard gates a constant and irritating paradox. Armed guards they were—but they were not white and therefore had no authority. How could the British honour these little coloured men?

Four Dutch Officers attempted to walk past one of the Gurkha sentries—who reacted quite properly.

"Your passes, please sirs." The leading Dutchman then made the greatest mistake of his life. He shouted at the sentry and struck him across the face, calling him a stupid backward native. It was the ultimate insult to a proud soldier—who immediately shot his attacker. The other three Dutch officers tried to draw their weapons. They were all dead before they hit the roadway. The Gurkha stood surrounded by four corpses. Perhaps he felt that his own survival might embarrass his superiors. Maybe the regiment was more important than he. The muzzle of his gun entered his mouth.

"God in heaven," cried the M.O. in Charge of Brothels, looking at the carnage. "What on earth happened?" A Gurkha officer answered me.

A few brief logical unemotional sentences sufficed as thousands of flies homed in to feed. I might have vomited but I saw the Provost Marshall's jeep stopping near me. Powell listened to the account and said tersely,

"The one thing you never do is hit a Gurkha. These four men committed suicide. 'Nuff said! I'll tell the Dutch Liaison Officer."

CHAPTER THIRTEEN

Every day was abnormal. Idiosyncrasy became the conventional.

When the Red Cross arrived in Batavia their leader was Edwina Mountbatten. She looked startlingly bleached. Morale soared—especially after thé dansant which rapidly became a pink gin flamenco. What started as a welfare enquiry became a great social event. Dutch ladies liberated from the P.O.W. camps mixed with "Japanese interpreters". James Powell produced four jazz musicians from the Army as the British created a nostalgic oasis of serenity and normality in the middle of a swamp of decay and malice. At the end of the occasion Edwina Mountbatten, who must have been exhausted, drew me to one side after we had danced.

"Look doctor, you've put on a good show—but the Navy here is having a tough time. Right! Where are we? Spell it—Tandjoeng Priok? I won't forget you." She remembered.

Ten days later Powell and I drove to the airport at Batavia to collect a large case and brought it back in triumph along the port road.

We opened it in Sick Quarters to find 240 tins of asparagus. James Powell became hysterical.

"My God, David, can you see the Senior Service facing up to that lot?"

I disagreed.

"There are all sorts of things you can do with asparagus, James."

"Like what, lad? It can't be good for you. It makes your water smell like hell!"

"Well, there's asparagus sandwiches, asparagus soup, asparagus rissoles and asparagus fritters. You can even eat it raw. Look at our consumption of bananas. It's like the monkey house at London Zoo—a staple diet! Some of the officers are even banana-coloured (due to Mepacrine—the anti malarial). How could anyone refuse this delicacy from Edwina Mountbatten?"

One month later the doctor solemnly presented 200 large tins of asparagus to the Japanese Prison Commandant. There was quite a ceremony—which was repeated two days later when three Japanese Officers responded with an elaborately wrapped parcel. Some inner sense told me not to open it as it might have contained a bomb—or even a tin of asparagus! Later I found that the package contained a medical book—in Japanese.

Little Ena was eleven years old and unconscious with cerebral malaria when her mother carried the limp brown body into Sick Quarters. A frail elderly man accompanied them. He spoke a few words of English.

"This Ena; she one child; she die."

I instinctively bent over the comatose girl. She was indeed deeply unconscious. I turned to ask a question of her companions but there was no one there.

The Sick Bay Attendants at once came to the rescue and secreted Ena on a corner of the rear verandah where she was not visible even to the seven Naval patients in the Ward. Stealth and cunning, combined with the awareness that they were doing something highly irregular and risky, gave a clandestine excitement to their efforts. Two days of intensive care and constant vigilance saw Ena return to consciousness (under a mosquito net marked with a skull and the telling phrase—"Danger! Keep out").

On the third day she sat up in bed and vomited profusely. The vomit was a mass of round worms. As she gasped two large worms emerged from her nostrils.

After forty-eight hours Ena was eating ravenously and had been de-wormed.

One week later the two adult Indonesians materialised again in the consulting room as suddenly as they had disappeared. The elderly man said simply,

"We go now." He opened the rear door to collect Ena from her obscure corner of the back verandah.

For nine days there was silence. On the tenth day this odd trio and a berobed priest who had quietly joined the assembly, re-appeared at Sick Quarters. Ena wore a yellow robe and a headdress. The old man uttered a quick spurt of dialect and then spoke in slow, carefully rehearsed English as he pointed at the small saffron-robed child.

"Ena is for you. Mother gives Ena to you—to be your wife."

I looked aghast at my prospective Mother-in-law and shook my head. This action clearly caused great distress amongst my would-be relations. The Chief Sick Bay Attendant recognised that rejection of such a precious gift would cause much offence. He stepped forward.

"Tell 'em you're already married, sir. No, I'll do it."

The great pantomime which then ensued almost convinced me that I was responsible for several wives and dozens of children and couldn't possibly enlarge my harem any further. The marriage ceremony was cancelled and honour was satisfied. I shook hands with the visitors who bowed low and withdrew. They were never seen again.

Each day brought death to someone. Almost invariably it became clear from the circumstances or the general appearance of the body to which faction the corpse belonged. Demarcation disputes were rare therefore. However, just before Christmas, the main canal by the dockyard was an interesting scene—but only for those of gastric fortitude. The canals were alive with alligators but there was still a large volume of bloated flesh remaining on this particular body. Firmly tied, hand and foot, and grossly mutilated, putrefaction had advanced to the extent that it was difficult to tell whether the thing had been British, Dutch, Indonesian or Japanese. A vigorous argument flared and was only controlled when someone said the equivalent of,

"When in doubt ask a policeman or call a doctor."

They got both.

Powell with two of his Royal Marines stood with me and two Sick Bay Attendants. We peered at the putrid mass as the other contestants in the heated discussion all vanished.

"As usual the British are left holding the baby. Some baby! Load him into my jeep and we'll take him round the various headquarters," said the Provost Marshall, his face a grimace of distaste. No-one moved until Powell produced an old tarpaulin from his jeep and tried not to breathe when he spoke.

"O.K. don't touch him. Slip the cover underneath. Can't leave him here. What a BLOODY smell!"

The improvised hearse moved off on a round of headquarters. The Dutch brusquely rejected responsibility; the Ghurkhas said the deceased was too large to be theirs; the Japanese pointed out that they were starving and had no-one over 50 kilos—but could they please have some Mepacrine?

As it darkened the horrid truth became evident. We were left in possession of this awful trophy. The jeep swayed on and, in the gloom, we came to a small lane which led to a large clear area of ground beyond the camp perimeter. Powell drove the jeep into the centre of the clearing and in a few minutes, using the entrenching tool in turn, we had fashioned a shallow grave. The tarpaulin and contents rolled in and a thin layer of earth went over the remains.

There is no twilight in the tropics and suddenly it was quite dark and we were not alone. There were several dim shapes all round us. My flesh began to crawl. These must be insurgents.

"Don't shoot first!" Powell said crisply to his undertakers.

A torch flashed on. Its holder laughed softly.

"Good thinking! We're Ghurkhas! Thought you were hostile. We had you cold!"

In daylight Powell and I found the grave again. It was bang in the middle of the front garden of a beautiful bungalow. In the evening Powell was uncontrollable due to his macabre vision of a civilian Dr Illingworth quietly burying troublesome patients in the dead of night in the front gardens of Edinburgh's sanctimonious suburbia.

Christmas lunch was corned beef hash, fruit and Indian beer—preceded by "Powell's Pink Preservative and Preventative". In the middle of the meal a small party of carol singers arrived led by an officer carrying a lantern. They were all drunk but the officer was also plainly mentally disturbed, showing all the features of overt religious mania. Clearly hallucinated, he was chanting nonsense as the tears poured down his face. Sick Quarters answered my call at once and the ambulance arrived to take the patient away. He was flown out the next day, heavily sedated. Others were to follow this example of mental breakdown or "The Post Traumatic Stress Syndrome" as it is now labelled. The constant pressures of a hostile environment were taking their toll.

That day there was a visitor—Surgeon Lieutenant Jack Wilson walked into Sick Quarters. We had started school together, graduated together and shared the experience of Leith Hospital and joining the Navy. It seemed impossible—but Jack's ship had now docked in Tandjoeng Priok—and here he was!

My delight was qualified by his casual acceptance of danger. I didn't want him shot and felt very responsible for him. I was relieved that he couldn't stay long as I had already lost so many friends.

If lunch was an ordeal, Christmas dinner was a disaster. One Petty Officer stabbed a messmate in the face, and, but for a fringe of nostril, the nose had been cut off. I had had less gin than the Petty Officer had rum. Loading the area with local anaesthetic took half an hour before the Sick Bay Attendants began to hand me the tiniest of needles and suture material. Two hours later the organ was back in place—and working. After two months the Petty Officer's proboscis was the pride and joy of Sick Quarters. The site of reunion had become a faint linear scar—and it was generally agreed that the incident had enhanced the victim's appearance. It was also suggested that no anaesthetic was required because of a mutually high blood alcohol—which unfortunately had made the doctor replace the nose upside down.

The New Year came in and with it an appendicitis patient. The sick man, the previous day, declared he had seen a forceps-waving naval doctor running down the road after a terrified Chinese—with toothache. Though in pain he courteously declined my operative help—before it was even offered—and it was decided to take him to a specialist Army surgeon. For transport we chose the ambulance as it would permit the sick man to lie down. There was also the illusory protection of the Red Cross marking strangely contrasting with the bullet holes in the vehicle. As an additional insurance two Sub-Lieutenants had volunteered to increase our fire power as we rocketed along the beautiful avenue of flame trees which stretched from the port to Batavia city.

The sun and the quiet breeze made the scarlet luminescence of these ethereal Poincianas dance and flicker. Even I, hunched over the steering wheel, could not fail to contrast that profusion of natural grace and beauty with the brutish behaviour of unseen men lurking too close to the road for comfort.

Having prepared for the worst, as so often happens, nothing significant occurred during our journey. The patient was left safely with the Army and the ambulance returned to the Port Sick Quarters. Its crew, relieved and relaxed, tumbled out and entered the Consulting Room as they removed their weapons. In one unguarded, unthinking moment a pistol caught in its holster. One of the Sub-Lieutenants fell with a bullet in his abdomen. The only sound was the whimpering of the culprit.

"God, what have I done?" he cried repeatedly.

We turned the ambulance, lifted in the injured man and headed inland once more along the avenue.

By the time we reached the reached the Army Hospital it was plain that the patient was bleeding internally. Rapidly transfused and anaesthetised, the laparotomy revealed an abdomen full of blood, a shattered spleen and the bullet buried deep in the right lobe of a torn liver. Next day he died.

The Naval Padre had become ill and been flown out like so many others. The letter to the dead man's mother came from me who penned the usual clichés interspersed with a few justifiable superlatives. Naval doctors have to be very flexible.

The dead officer was replaced two days later by Andrew Cockle—a Gourock lad and a talented musician. I welcomed him into our quarters but he had eyes only for the piano and sat down at it to play "Clair de Lune". It was a beautiful moment for us both and I was transfixed. Andy said "It's been six months since I saw a piano."

But I should have warned him of life's uncertainties before a machine gun opened up on the Wardroom. I dived under the table from where I watched Cockle concluding his Debussy, quite oblivious to the metal flying around him and the solitary applauder under the table.

The Dutch had re-opened the Box Club in Batavia. A magnificent outpost of empire before the war, it was hoped to take up where life left off when the Japanese invaded three years earlier. Gaiety was unrestrained—if forced—and here the pre-war ritual of Dutch colonial life was rigidly observed in a facsimile of paradise which contrasted strangely with the enclave of alligator-infested swamp in which the Navy resided.

The Box club had a surplus of ladies released from the Japanese prison camps. All abnormally thin, they each had a story to tell—but with some prompting. Clearly they wished to banish from their minds these terrible three years of imprisonment; to forget such things as trading in dead rats, live burials, beatings and bayonet practice on prisoners.

They wished only to begin again—where they left off in 1942. But they were wishing for the moon.

Five miles by sea from the port was an idyllic tropical island. Some palm trees, a bungalow and a superb beach provided a tiny capsule of bliss to which we occasionally escaped on Sundays in a fifty-year old, four knot "puffer". Anybody could come and Greasby had created a small bar and provided a gramophone and six records. We anchored off the island's beach and forgot about bullets, bacteria and alligators as we swam and dived in the deep, pellucid water. It was balm to strained spirits. The native helmsman repeatedly uttered two cautionary phrases which became standard fill-ins for conversational gaps.

"Stand on a sea urchin, foot full of spears," became adapted to cover any situation where sensitive people had to be handled with tact.

The second literary gem of our native philosopher was, "Barracuda bite off soft bits". The English equivalent was "Guard your vulnerable areas!"

I had particular cause to remember the second aphorism when, fifty yards from the shore, Powell's parade ground voice shattered our peaceful paradise.

"Watch your groin, Doc. Barracudas!" I swam the distance to the seminal sanctuary of the beach in record time with dozens of these hideous fish splashing behind me. Gasping for breath I collapsed beside Mackenzie, the Captain's secretary, who, now bronzed and thin like an Indian holy man, lounged on the sand.

"They nearly spoiled your married life, Doc. Barracuda bite off soft bits!"

A stranger to expediency and compromise "Mac" was one of the pair who knelt to pray at night. Even he, however, was overwhelmed by his encounter with something on the beach. He leant towards me.

"Doc old chap, look what's in my hand." Out of the sand he pulled a human skull.

"Is it European?"

After a moment's examination, "Mac" got his answer.

"Yes it is. And is it the only one?" A little digging revealed that the entire island was a graveyard for Caucasians. Imagination took over. We never returned to our tropical paradise where the massacre had occurred and Jonge's words about "vanishing people" had a new nauseating significance.

In February 1946 N.O.I.C. sent for his First Lieutenant and the doctor. "President" Soekarno was already in the Naval Office. Ostensibly the discussion was to be about the health of the swamp-dwellers but Soekarno was quick to indicate that his "nationalists" held the vital centres and were determined to oust the Dutch. I liked the Dutch as people but was sure they were wrong to reassert their colonial status by force of arms. Already the venture had been costly in terms of human suffering and casualties. The sailors I served with were unwilling to fight the insurgents except in self defence. THE enemy, German, Japanese and Italian had been dealt with. Why should they now fight for the Dutch? They hadn't joined up to do that!

Soekarno sensed both the strength of his position and the lack of British commitment. The little man smiled and extended his hand to us as we entered but the First Lieutenant was peering fixedly out of the window at the pier adjoining N.O.I.C's office.

"My jeep can't be moving. I put on the handbrake!"

I looked down and saw the empty vehicle moving slowly but ineluctably along the pier. The First Lieutenant clattered down the stairs and returned to view as a blur of white uniform pursuing the runaway—which reached the pier's edge and launched itself gracefully into five fathoms of water.

Its breathless owner re-entered the office. Number One was clearly upset but restrained himself as he faced his Captain and the Indonesian President.

"Sorry, sir, my transport's just been sabotaged—pushed off the end of the pier. No sign of the culprits." In unison the three officers turned and stared accusingly at Soekarno, Captain Cooper peered down at the Indonesian like an eagle assessing a rabbit. He didn't measure his speech.

"Mr Soekarno, I must assume that one of your nationalists has just destroyed one of my jeeps. I must account for all such valuable pieces of equipment. It would increase my respect for you if you were to replace the vehicle in question."

Soekarno may not have understood all the words but no-one could remain insensitive to the frigid factuality of this withering blast. The Indonesian's soft voice emerged from a smiling face.

"It's very difficult to make a distinction. To you we are all coloured men; to us you are all white and we intend to throw you out."

Next morning, however, another jeep was delivered at Naval Headquarters. The significance of the episode was not lost on the Wardroom which was henceforward convinced that the Dutch had no more than a snowball's chance in hell of regaining their colonial possessions.

On waking I was more interested in my body pains and severe headache. The mirror reflected the customary pale yellow face of the Mepacrine consumer. I couldn't really have Malaria therefore—but why was my skin so hot?

Two days later the M.O.came back to reality in his own Sick Quarters—in the private room where Kim and Hippocrates had tussled for my immortal soul. Or was it my body? Either way I felt so weak the point was only academic. As vision cleared I focussed on N.O.I.C. and standing alongside him was Surgeon-Lieutenant Dugald Kemp a contemporary in Medical School. It all seemed like a hallucination until Dugald spoke.

"Came in on board our landing craft and tied up. The Captain's Secretary said you weren't well so I came along. Imagine finding that the M.O. was David Illingworth! God it's a wee world!" N.O.I.C. broke in.

"You've had a sharp dose of Dengue Fever your colleague tells me, and he advises two weeks off. Poor old Powell got smashed up on the port road—sutures, concussion and so on. He's to go with you two days from now to Singapore to convalesce. Kemp will cover for you. It's all arranged—but both of you should come back soon to help with this ill-fated venture. To be honest, doctor, we need both of you."

It wasn't much, but in many months I hadn't felt so gratified.

Youth is resilient and Dengue rarely killed anyone; by next day I was up and around to receive James Powell whose head was swathed in bandages. He appeared to be wearing a turban on the top of which his bush hat sat precariously. The head-dress made him seem at least seven feet high but he looked pale and thin. He casual drawl hadn't altered however.

"Bin swingin' the lead eh, Doc? Strange coincidence us nearly croakin' together! N.O.I.C. is flyin' us out day after tomorrow—to a convalescent home in Port Dickson, Malaya. Can't say I'm sorry. Good of your friend to cover for you. Why not give him a party?!"

The following day the M.O. discharged himself from his own Sick Quarters and sought out James Powell. We invited Dr Kemp and two dashing young bachelor officers to entertain six of the ladies who had appointments as "interpreters" at Naval H.Q.—those smiling attractive Eurasian girls, whose origins were unclear. Powell had removed his turban and his sutures were concealed by strips of plaster as he delighted his companions with tales of derring-do interspersed with illuminated accounts of the Madagascar campaign and motor accidents. It was a most successful evening. At 2300 hours the ladies were escorted to their billets.

Twelve hours later Powell and I reached Batavia Airport where we boarded a weary old Dakota—without seats. Gathering mail and personnel this loyal servant hiccoughed along, first to Palembang and then onwards to Padang in Sumatra. The two invalids lay on the aircraft's floor except at two stopping places where we spent the night.

Sumatra was delightful after our paludal months. On the second morning I emerged from our hut and stretched myself, saying to Powell, "Hope Dugald will be OK with those six interpreters."

"Don't worry David, Dugald's a hard-headed Scot, he'll probably open a Highland Brothel and make a pretty penny. Anyway, you're an authority on brothels!"

The discussion ceased as we landed at Singapore and were dropped off at the Adelphi Hotel near the Cathedral. After Tandjoeng Priok the Adelphi was the last word in sophistication. For three days we shared a superb room. Powell's sutures were removed and I was rewarded by a most recalcitrant form of Athlete's Foot which the Provost Marshall had contracted in Madagascar and which I still have.

The invalids were then driven to Port Dickson to become the first occupants of the Officers' Convalescent Home. Situated in a luxurious beachside bungalow, we found ourselves in a state of tropical indulgence. Each patient had a cabin and the outfit was in charge of a timid white steward. Two other junior officers arrived that evening minus their appendices—but the

Boys from Batavia imposed an authority born of experience. The Navy had installed a fully stocked bar and Powell, as Senior Officer, soon had it open for the service of his pink embalming fluid. Not in the least dependent on alcohol yet he could dignify pink gin with majestic alliterative titles. The most ornate was "Powell's pink palliative, preventive, preservative potion and paregoric panacea." Only I knew that, at parties, if he couldn't recite this full verbal description, Powell switched to Angostura bitters and water.

Within twelve hours a totally hedonistic routine had developed. At 0700 hours we staggered out of our cabins onto the verandah, down its wide wooden steps to the beach and plunged into the sea. The swimming was magnificent but we never ventured near the reef which was the haunt of venomous sea snakes. A full breakfast at 0800 hours was followed by writing or reading. At 1000 hours we swam again until coffee at 1030. Between 1100 and noon we kept the bar steward busy. After lunch we slept until 1500 hours when we drove in our small bus to Seremban and wandered round the traders' stall. The Boys from Batavia were enchanted to walk about unarmed and safe from attack.

Hot showers led to a further sojourn at the bar—in proper mess uniform. The Royal Marine far outshone his compatriots who refused to accept his explanation that it was all about keeping mosquitoes away.

After dinner we lay on the verandah, smoking, fantasising and sipping long cool drinks until sleep overcame us.

This lotus-eating existence continued for two weeks—when the Subs. were recalled to Singapore. Time had never passed so quickly for any member of this strange relaxed democracy in which illness had been the great leveller.

After the Subs' departure the remaining two decided to test their stamina with a day's shooting. From dawn to dusk we trudged along jungle tracks in search of wild pig. Perhaps it was as well our rifles were not used; there seemed to be a high density of beaters wriggling about in the undergrowth and the arrival of a wild pig would have caused casualties amongst the hunters and their ancillaries.

Our wanderings finally brought us to the superb beach of Cape Rocado where transport awaited. On the return journey to Port Dickson, Powell drawled in his casual relaxed voice,

"We've tested ourselves out, my revered healer, and we seem to have recovered. Is it not a little strange that we have heard nothing from Singapore? My guess is that they've forgotten about us. If we haven't heard by the end of the week we really should drive down there and enquire. Otherwise we'll either be left up here till Doomsday—or be shot as deserters." When nothing disturbed our idyllic existence we packed up and, two days later, reported to Naval Headquarters, Singapore.

The Provost Marshall was first to explain himself. He was congratulated on his rapid recovery and emerged with orders to hitch a lift by air to Batavia. We then walked into the Medical Department and I reported to Surgeon Commander Silver, R.N. who at once exploded,

"Are you the stupid _____ who's been ordering tons of drugs for the entire population of the Dutch East Indies? You've been requesting supplies from Colombo as well as from here and created the most God-awful confusion. How many hundred thousand people are you treating? How are you disposing of all these medicines? Now for Chris' sake man explain yourself before I call you a stupid _____ again!"

It was a savage, noisy attack which silenced the entire office and filled me with disgust. I tried to acquaint the suffused Silver with the chaos and confusion of the East Indies. I should have saved my breath. My two minutes on the difficulties of swamp life, bullets and smallpox weren't being heard. An oblivious Silver was simply thinking out the next stream of vituperation to heap on the head of his hapless junior.

"You silly young _____! Go back to your bloody swamp and never trouble me again."

A greatly disturbed Powell was waiting.

"I heard it through two doors, David. That man must be crazy and I want you to bring a complaint against him. He had no reason to make such a vile attack on you. I've never heard language like that from an officer—but you'll find I make an excellent witness.

I calmed down my loyal friend.

"Thanks, James, but it means more trouble and more time. In any case, as the philosopher Powell would remind me, 'Nothing is wholly bad'—and it is such episodes as this which influence our future decisions."

Silver's public display of obscenity and injustice had helped clarify my future. Fiercely proud of the Royal Navy though I was, I could not contemplate a career which entailed contact with such men as Surgeon-Commander Silver, R.N. Escape I must! And when, some weeks later, I was offered a permanent commission and told I was "Fellowship material" this promise of security—with further training and assured prospects, meant nothing to me. Silver had destroyed any inchoate inclination to become "permanent". I shall never understand or forget this incident—a milestone in my career.

CHAPTER FOURTEEN

We hitched a lift to Singapore Airport. James was good at coping with such trivialities as flying a few hundred miles. He vanished into the control tower and reappeared ten minutes later.

"The Americans are delivering a new Mitchell bomber to Batavia and there's room for us."

Probably fated to become a maverick in peacetime, James Powell was the man for the hour—an ideal companion in troubled corners of the world. When the Mitchell took off, I sat behind the American pilot who spoke constantly for half an hour then suddenly said,

"O.K. you fly it Doc."

These few minutes in the co-pilot's seat were entirely different from an afternoon watch on Killin.

One hour later we landed at Batavia. It seemed impossible to travel such a distance so rapidly. When he and his co-pilot were thanked the American pilot said he was glad of the company. Clearly he hadn't been unaware of his passengers' origins and solemnly asked –

"Why don't officers in the Scotch Navy wear kilts? Real cool in this climate. Nothing underneath!"

At the airport we picked up a lift to Tandjoeng Priok. As we hurried along the avenue of Poinciana trees, I thought of the foul-mouthed Silver with some irritation; my prickly heat was already reasserting itself.

I reached Sick Quarters, took over, appreciatively, from Dugald and walked with him back to his ship. Dugald suddenly said with a tired smile,

"You are a rotten old dog. I happily volunteer my services so as to give you sick leave and you reward me with the company

of six comfort girls from Japanese brothels. God, David, I have
my pride!"

An Army Officer walked into the consulting room the
following morning. He carried with him a box containing three
pairs of nylon stockings. These had emanated from Ronnie
Fisher my bridge partner in the landing ship and my counterpart
in Surabaya. A note was enclosed. This confirmed the bad news
which had for some time been filtering through. I always
reckoned I'd been lucky in the draw as regards postings.
However, the letter and the officer's first hand report made me
appreciate the degree of my good fortune. British casualties had
been considerable. Again I heard the account of how our
defined enemy, the Japanese, had capitulated months earlier and
yet the British were still fighting—to re-establish Dutch
colonialism.

He told an initially sceptical doctor that, in Surabaya, some
of the British troops had refused to obey orders. Even worse
was his mention of trouble on board a British cruiser. It
appeared that the ringleaders had been quietly rounded up and
shipped to Singapore. No word of this 'mutiny' and mutiny it
was, was ever to reach the media. In retrospect the cause of the
revolt was fatigue—an exhaustion of spirit produced by the long
years of war, followed by a rapid loss of motivation. Germany,
Italy and Japan had been defeated and yet, the war won, the
British forces were still isolated in a strange land, constantly
vigilant and struggling to survive against an unseen and cunning
enemy endowed with nationalist fervour. They were involved in
a combat without patriotic appeal which could never result in
the restoration of Dutch power in the East Indies—no matter
how profound the effort or reasonable the justification.

Those who returned from Indonesia (and many did not)
never spoke of the rebellion. Their silence was due either to a
sense of embarrassment or, more probably, to a conviction that
such strange and contradictory events would not be credible in
the cold light of a British day. As for me I felt caught up in a
ridiculous fantasy; a second-rate Victorian melodrama which

was not entirely without humour. At least I had three pairs of nylons to send home.

The end of my role in this futile but deadly farrago came swiftly. All agonising was cut short by the British government's decision to set up a comprehensive National Health Service on the foundation laid down by Lloyd George in 1913. Inevitably this caused the recall of medical manpower to Britain and somebody in the Admiralty remembered a sweaty yellow medico in an Indonesian swamp—me.

Mackenzie, N.O.I.C.'s secretary, who had served twice as long as the doctor, smiled wryly as he handed over the signal.

"Surgeon Lieutenant Illingworth to join Royal Fleet Auxiliary, Dewdale and proceed Portsmouth for demobilisation."

My reaction was an ambivalent mixture of embarrassment and pleasure. To my surprise my replacement was again Mark Marlborough who had relieved me at Kurunagala in Ceylon. Mark's reappearance was a great joy; once more we talked of Ceylon, of the East Neuk of Fife and of our golden days of tennis. Was it only ten years ago?

James Powell appeared in Sick Quarters—vigorously complaining.

"What's all this I hear about your leaving me to perish in this bloody hole of desolation? You're not even married, dammit, and your erotic fantasies are restricted to steak and kidney pie and doughnuts! Why go home?"

The Provost Marshall insisted that the hero of Tandjoeng Priok should not return home empty-handed. His generosity was magnified by the pink gin the trio had been attacking in the Mess.

"I will personally call on Dewdale's Captain tonight and arrange that the spoils of war are shipped home. Our doctor, in spite of his aberrations, will sail with his ambulance (complete with bullet holes), a 1941 Ford car, a clock which doesn't go and an X-ray machine which he won't approach in case it cooks his gonads. (What's 'gonads' anyway?) These will be crated and loaded tomorrow morning—or my name's not Powell." He arose and drove off to the docks.

At lunch next day he reappeared, looking a bit rough, but still able to speak.

"Dewdale sails at 1500 hours for Bali; I have persuaded her captain to accept a few crates. God it's hot. Where's that miserable farrier—the doctor?"

Lunch was a silent meal. Goodbyes said, James Powell drove me to the ship and waited, with a bottle of VAT 69, while I reported to Dewdale's Captain and was allotted a single outside cabin. The luxury of it was overwhelming, yet only the traditional comforts were there: a couch: a bunk: a mirror: a table. But above all there was privacy and air conditioning.

Two hours later Powell stood up in my cabin, grasped the empty bottle and set off for the gangway. I followed. We shook hands. Nothing could be said. The Major leapt into his jeep and, without a backward glance, returned to the swampland.

Ten minutes later Dewdale sailed past the wreckage of ships, warehouses and humanity. It was mid-April 1946. Another part of my life had ended. But I can't forget the unforgettable and the unbelievable. So I often wonder what happened to my car and X-ray machine—last seen standing forlornly on the jetty as Powell's potion took effect on my memory.

CHAPTER FIFTEEN

Dewdale's vast bulk cleared the harbour entrance and I had a last glimpse of the volatile, dangerous and unreal area in which I had survived. The Captain came down for dinner and indicated that the ship would travel round the East collecting people for demobilisation. He was unable to say when we would reach home and was concerned more with the time of Sick Parade than with the date of the doctor's wedding.

During the voyage to Bali, I had time to reflect on the irrational world of Java which had held me in thraldom for so many months—as unbelievable events succeeded the indescribable. Briefly I fretted for friends of recent memory as they sweated to survive the grim theatricals of Tandjoeng Priok. Short is the memory of youth, however; Cormack, the Radio Officer, was always eager for a game of chess; the invariably damp areas of uniform were now dry; the food was good and Bali was on the horizon and here we met more trouble.

We left Bali as darkness set in to cover its untold infamies. As we sailed westwards, each revolution of the engines brought me nearer to home.

Singapore welcomed Dewdale with an influx of humanity—impatient for home and demobilisation. I experienced a long forgotten feeling at seeing the Wrens in their tropical uniform. I hadn't seen a British woman for some time. They looked strangely pallid.

Suddenly bashful, surprised by my reaction, I sought the sanctuary of my cabin to examine my Calvinistic soul. I was behaving like a schoolboy. Lying back on my bunk, drawing in the smoke of a cigarette the shelf above my feet caught my eye. On it lay the carefully wrapped gift of the Japanese Prison Camp Commandant, to whom I had given so generously of drugs—and canned asparagus. The parcel which had been opened with care and the hope of finding gems of oriental philosophies. contained "A Textbook of Tropical Diseases"—in Japanese! It remains unread.

Besotted by the prospect of seeing Lesley I dozed off. As a student I had translated and written a brief life of the physician Galen (A.D. 130—201)—A Greek who had carefully recorded his medical life amongst the Romans. Wrongly labelled a homosexual, he wrote a love poem which applied particularly to a lovesick doctor returning from abroad to marry. My translation remains central—many years on. I was recalling it as the demanding shrill of a Wardroom party brought me back to reality. I wrote down what I remembered before joining the throng—so dense that I could scarcely get in the door and was at once pinioned by the mob.

DAWN ELUSION (after GALEN: 148 A.D.)

Come back into my dream
I woke before I touched you.
The mistimed sounds of bird
Dissolved the wraith I almost grasped
And left me hollow –
Full of memory.

Experience like this
Diminishes the dawn and clouds the early sun.
My day is bleakened, meaningless.
I cringe within
Demeaned and low.

But if I close my eyes
Perhaps in drifting I can reach you
Though images like this
Will never satisfy
They keep the longing sharp
The recollection clear.

If want is gain –
To stretch for magic and eluded be:
To be apart and ponder what is mine
Then dreaming presence gives you real dimension
And magnifies the wonder of my love.

Thus, till reality replaces vapouries, come back
Come back into my dream.

There were glasses on the piano; there were people on the piano; there were people under the piano!

Immobilised by pressure I found myself wedged against a striking-looking woman of about thirty whose patrician gaze was cool yet disturbing. Without any hesitation she introduced herself.

"I'm First Officer Truebody and I'm in charge of all this."

She indicated with an inclination of her head the surrounding turmoil of female hormones.

"Obviously," she said looking at my epaulets, "you're the doctor. We need your help, please. It's the usual problem—which I'd solve if you'd give me a lot of cotton wool and gauze."

Up on deck she explained herself, maintaining her direct approach. She leapt from menstrual requisites for her flock to her observation that I was "very yellow and staring at her as if I'd come from a desert island." I stammered slightly "I'm sorry I stared at you. Actually you're absolutely correct, only it wasn't a desert island, I was in a swamp. I haven't talked to a British woman for months. I'd even forgotten how nice they smell!"

"My God, doctor, you're not going to ravish me, are you? And surely not in the Sick Bay?"

The idea made me wince. For doctors celibacy is not difficult. We are conditioned by the iconoclastic experiences of the anatomy room and the purifying effect of clinical gynaecology and obstetrics. Such influences soothe the flagrant libido of youth.

On the first night out of Singapore, dinner was a rather fussy affair. The Captain made 'True' sit on his right. I was next to her while a well-upholstered Wren—childishly pretty and vulnerable, sat between another Scot and myself. My countryman was Tom Robb. Tom, from the West of Scotland, was a constant source of Glaswegian humour. He played the piano (and Contract Bridge); drank "Bass" before breakfast and, at the drop of a hat, would render such soulful ballads as 'The Hearse Bumped into the Gutter' and 'They're Digging up Father's Grave to Build a Sewer'. On Tom's right was a Wren Third Officer, Winifred Fullerton—a Dundonian who, much to our pleasure, confessed to sharing our enthusiasm for cards.

Tom Robb arranged a bridge marathon with 'True', Winifred and me. This quartet became an entity for the weeks ahead. Yet the relationship, for all that we were young and normal, remained platonic. Each had a private life waiting at home. Emotion was only generated each evening from 8 pm to midnight, or beyond, when we entered the card-playing world of Ely Culbertson. The game was played with intensity and cunning; the only reward was the intellectual satisfaction of crushing the opposition.

The Radio Officer had eschewed chess forever, having fallen in love with his Wren who devoted her time to treating his acne and once destroyed lunch with,

"I simply adore taking out his blackheads."

'True' asked on what they would base their relationship when the supply ran out!

Tandjoeng Priok seemed light years away as Dewdale sauntered into Colombo to collect even more personnel and supplies. Its streets were, as usual, stained with splashes of red—spat from the mouths of betel nut chewers. The card fiends played merrily on but there was a pause, between rubbers, to communicate with loved ones at home. My cable was brief and pointed—a simple request for a wedding in early July.

A Welfare Officer came aboard in Colombo to ask if we needed any comforts to pass the time. A gramophone and some records were at once requested and each interested passenger was allowed one choice. The repeated playing of this eclectic group of records planted the seed of a permanent involvement with music. I defected. Glen Miller and Mr Crosby were supplanted by spreading arpeggios and scintillating cascades of notes. New to high-stepping pianism I was deeply moved by Rachmaninov, Tchaikovsky and Cesar Franck. Bach and Leoncavallo also touched me but it was the sad and languorous brilliance of Rachmaninov with which I really identified. The composer seemed to have insight into the mood of his listener and removed inner barriers of understanding by creating a harmonious empathy.

It was a dazzling and long overdue revelation. Having no technical insight I could make no analysis; I only knew that I loved this extraordinary sound which was nothing other than an elegant, arcane from of personal communication.

Unfortunately Dewdale was again diverted—to Trincomalee where the golden sands proved a solace for psychological solitude and a healthy diversion from the obsessions of the bridge table.

After another two days R.F.A. Dewdale left Trincomalee behind and meandered across the Indian Ocean into the Red Sea. The card players paused briefly—to examine the Suez Canal. Dewdale entered Port Said at dusk.

'True' was determined to use our four days in port to the full. Next morning we were inside "The Greatest Store on Earth"—Simon Artz, where one could buy everything from a pin to a stuffed elephant. The tales of my wandering relatives had always made Simon Artz a household name in my home in Scotland. I really felt as if I were in a shrine. Standing in that cavern of serendipity and shrewd business, I recalled the generations of my family who had made a visit to Simon Artz sound like a trip to a small boy's concept of heaven.

Realisation exceeded expectation, as did the journey to Cairo next day by train and then, with a homicidal taxi driver, to Mena House Hotel at Giza. Tom and I shared the bridal suite; rode round the Sphinx on horseback and by camel: visited the Great Pyramid and dined at Shepheard's Hotel.

'Shepheard's', like 'Simon Artz', had ancestral connections and their ghosts must have looked on in astonishment as the two young lions attacked that innocuous-seeming innovation from the U.S.A.—'Rum and Coke'. It had been hot in the desert. I was sadly dehydrated. Six drinks later, we entered the dining room with a corrected fluid balance but a disturbed co-ordination.

It was bad timing. We ordered spaghetti and by the time the plates were empty the pasta had become more a form of apparel than a meal. Tom leant over gravely.

"With yon string head-dress on, son, you're just like Lawrence of Arabia."

Next morning at breakfast on our balcony, the bridal pair were still finding pieces of spaghetti stuck in odd places. Undeterred, however, we proceeded to absorb the dreadful social disparities and contradictions of Egypt, visiting the Fort and the museums. We shopped madly and badly for our ladies; agonised over trachoma cases and professional beggars and finished in King Farouk's nightclub wearing garlands of mimosa.

The waiter asked us, "Please not to laugh at the belly dancers", and we were persuaded to leave and returned to swim in the hotel pool. Fortunate it was that both jumped in feet first. The pool was empty!

Port Said and Dewdale received the comedians again the next day. The captain was waiting.

"One of the Goanese crew took ill this morning. He says he's going to die. Die he will because he's counting his beads."

I dismissed this statement as superstitious garbage and went below heedless of "I know these people, clever lad, he's made up his mind!"

Below in the crew's quarters lay a Goanese deckhand peering unseeingly straight ahead, muttering and repetitively counting the beads which lay on his chest. The interpreter informed me that the man was well until that morning and then had suddenly taken to his bunk and announced his impending demise.

"Eet happen often, Doctor," said the informant. "When the time come they go away."

Forty-five minutes later a dejected Surgeon Lieutenant admitted defeat. I could not elicit one abnormal manifestation and covered myself with an insurance policy of a massive dose of sulphonamide into the patient's buttock.

Dewdale sailed in the evening. By morning the patient was dead. He was buried at sea by a patronising Captain. I was delighted not to have to write out a death certificate.

CHAPTER SIXTEEN

Mail, weeks old, had arrived on my cabin desk. Our marriage was arranged and all that was lacking was a precise date. My brother had enclosed a cutting from an Edinburgh paper which referred in a few crisp lines, to an 'incident' in the High Street involving United States and Scottish servicemen. The accompanying letter indicated that my brother, Jim, had been present in the bar when an American officer had used a 'Jock' Officer's swagger stick to solve the age old problem of what was worn under the kilt.

This minor piece of scientific investigation precipitated "The Battle of Edinburgh High Street". The hostelry exploded into internecine strife as Jim witnessed the initial act of provocation and escaped just in time to avoid the mass incarceration of a hundred of the participants.

I felt homesick and sought the selective diversion of the Bridge table until Gibraltar. Having traversed the Mediterranean, the four Bridge friends stepped ashore and, after crossing the border into a somewhat shoddy La Linea in Spain, returned thankfully to lunch at the Rock Hotel. Almost three months had passed since Dewdale crept out of Tandjoeng Priok and there was an awareness of finality—perhaps particularly felt by 'True' who ordered a magnum of vintage champagne. It was a magnificent occasion and we awoke to a gentle Biscay, a slight hangover and agonising thoughts of packing.

Customs came aboard at Portsmouth. The procedure of the wartime farewell was still in force. A handshake and a smile terminated an unusual chapter in the lives of "the card quartet" as we had come to be known.

My possessions preceded me to Scotland as 'luggage in advance' and I had a few niggling regrets regarding the matter of the crate containing my Batavian car—which might have got through Customs anyway. I met someone in the train North who swore his commandeered motor boat would arrive in Glasgow the following day.

When the crates reached Edinburgh my relatives prised them open before I arrived. As the spars were forced apart in the kitchen an army of cockroaches scuttled forth—the women took refuge on chairs and tables as the men subdued the invaders. When I reached home the next day the spoils of war had already been distributed and I was left with the clock from the consulting room in Tandjoeng Priok.

Scotland's austerity was disturbing but the stark simplicity of my disciplined country was relieved by Lesley's presence. She welcomed me with a huge grin as we stood and peered shyly at each other—looking for change—in appearance or in attitude.

"You've made it! With only seven days to spare! Serious business marriage. Thought you might have altered your mind?" My tension had brought back my stammer and I remained inarticulate—but not for long.

The wedding itself had the stark simplicity of rationing. Lesley and I stood in church, trembled together and escaped to Perth for the honeymoon where we had only time to buy a Tay pearl brooch in Cairncross's before a telegram came from Admiralty recalling me to Portsmouth. Angered by this gross intrusion, I obeyed instinctively, said goodbye to the puzzled new bride and was in Portsmouth Barracks next morning.

And why had this happened? Who had called me from foreign service leave to languish, striving to find accommodation in a town flattened by enemy air raids? Ten days passed before I found a room in a boarding house and escaped from barracks.

"Gas ring, use of kitchen and bathroom," said Mrs Turnbull as she named a crippling rent.

I didn't hesitate and telephoned Lesley that night. The young are very brave. The new bride was scheduled to arrive on August Bank Holiday. The new husband met the wrong train. The bride arrived at an empty platform in a state of exhaustion after the chaos of Waterloo Station. Her demented spouse had returned to duty; but the Navy looks after its own and a vigilant Petty Officer, with a car, picked out his quarry and bundled her off to salubrious Southsea.

It was a strange unsettled period in a small room with a single bed, two upright chairs, a card table and a large sideboard. Lesley took all this with an equanimity acquired in seven years of nursing. My medical work had a gnawing monotony and predictability. One night each week I slept in barracks as duty officer—which gave time to worry about the effect of boredom on whatever store of original thought I still possessed. Progressively more disenchanted with the Royal Navy in peace time, I was positively rebellious when my application for a Marriage Allowance was turned down. I requested an interview with the Surgeon Captain who was kindly and paternal.

"How old are you?"

"Twenty-four, sir."

"Then m'boy there's no hope of a Marriage Allowance." You have to be twenty-five. Between ourselves, Illingworth, twenty-four IS too young for marriage."

Can't agree, sir. It's not too young to spend fifteen months in the Atlantic!"

The Lieutenant Commander, R.N. in charge of my department was very sympathetic and encouraged his disillusioned junior.

"The rules can't be bent, but I believe you should stay on in the Service. I've been watching you. You're higher diploma material and I think you should remain with us." Silver's cruelty in Singapore still rankled but this compliment was a great morale-booster—after three years with seldom a pat on the back.

Nevertheless the concept of 'signing-on' made me aware that I must plan ahead.

The Green Room in the Royal Naval Barracks was available to entertain one's lady to dinner. Once a week, in this room, we two newly-weds sat solemnly down together and were served with dinner. We relaxed in the protective atmosphere of the Senior Service—forgetting that we shared a single bed in one room and had travelled to and from this blissful digestive experience by bus—electrically powered and soundless, they were locally dubbed "Silent Death". In this acme of comfort, surrounded by the trappings of success and privilege, we were able to discuss our relationship and attitude to the Service.

Lesley had known H.M.S. Killin in wartime. How would she adapt to the Royal Navy in peacetime? Neither of us was very articulate about it—even after the statutory two sherries. It seemed inevitable that life would be secure in the Service but in the light of past events, deadly dull! Perhaps it was time to proceed to the next less rank-ridden discipline. So I took demobilisation.

The Navy regurgitated something vastly different to the odd human being it had ingested many months earlier. The demob. Outfit contributed nothing.

I was now convinced that life was only a series of uncontrollable happy accidents—one long "happenchance".

PART III

HOSPITAL REGISTRAR

CHAPTER SEVENTEEN

The Dean of the Medical School scarcely recognised his revamped former pupil—now honed by human contact, informed by experience and matured by fear. I was despatched to the Post Graduate Director, Sir Alexander Biggam, who appraised the young doctor in the awful demob. suit.

"What do you want to do my boy? The situation is that you're entitled to a course of some kind and, if you wish it, a six month period of hospital retraining. How do you feel about it, Illingworth?"

I studied the serene face and mischievous eyes of the Director. Here was a man to whom one could talk and this was a keynote encounter.

"I wish to be a surgeon, sir." Sir Alexander smiled gently and turned to his assistant, Dr James Innes.

"My God, another one! Look here Illingworth, all those we've put on our books this week want to be surgeons. We'll make you a physician."

I experienced a brief recall and heard again the 'ping' of the Asdic, the detonations of the 'Squid' and the ear-bursting reports of surface armament. How could a hell-raiser like myself descend to the emasculated messages of a stethoscope? I who had been toughened in war's furnace and drained the chalice of experience, could still hear the bosun's pipe sounding "Wakey, wakey, wakey! Heave ho! Heave ho! Lash up and stow. The sun's burning your eyes out!" Me—a physician? I'd be a joke!

"Is that an order, sir?" The man was reading my mind—blast him!

"Laddie, the war's over. Forget about blood and thunder. You're an old married man of twenty-four. Here's a note. Go and see this fellow. He's new—and English! And we'll enter you for a three month course in Internal Medicine."

The Physician-designate crept out of the office convinced that he had been out-manoeuvred. But perhaps Sir Alexander was right—maybe HE knew something. I began to walk home to save the cost of the tuppenny tram ride.

Home was a furnished basement in the New Town of Edinburgh. The floors were of stone and all the windows were barred to give a convincing illusion of prison life.

In October 1946 I returned to medical school in the first University post-graduate course in Internal Medicine. A great camaraderie was instantly generated. Almost all the lecturers and would-be physicians were ex-servicemen. Sir Alexander's judgement was vindicated. I came to see what an appalling surgeon I would have made. I also had the stimulus of the promise of a job from a Dr. Turner—the new medical chief at the Western General Hospital.

"Turner" was the name written by Sir Alexander on the vital piece of paper he had pushed across his desk—at the interview some days earlier. I investigated Turner before 'phoning him and had learned of his Double First at Cambridge, decorations as a Lieutenant-Colonel in the Desert War and a formidable array of medical qualifications.

Surprised to think of an old council hospital having teaching status, I, as requested, called by appointment on Dr Turner at the Western General Hospital. It wasn't all that simple to find my prospective boss. The porter escorted me to the Chief's office, knocked once and opened the door. The room was empty.

The anxious eyes of the would-be physician took in an electro-cardiograph from which led a tangle of wires. Vision followed the machine's cables to an open window and beyond—where the image transcended credibility. In the yard outside the window stood a racehorse, wired up to the machine, and anxiously supervised by a sporting type in a flat cap. Dr Turner, who seemed all hair, gestures, verbalization and stethoscope, was in a state of great mobility and excitement, moving repeatedly through the window to the machine from the horse and back again.

"Afternoon, sir, I'm Illingworth. I 'phoned you," I said to this incredibly boyish enthusiastic physician—whose ideas overwhelmed even his articulate tongue.

Dick Turner, surrounded by an impenetrable wall of thought, made no acknowledgement of the greeting but darted from the window waving the recording.

"Come on, Illingworth, let's give 'em the good news," he shouted. The open window disgorged two doctors, one of whom, Turner, was so excited that he became a highly vocal blur pirouetting between the horse, the owner, the electrocardiograph and me.

"Splendid recording of benign ectopic beats. All's well with the patient. Here's Dr. Illingworth, he'll tell you all about it. That horse is fit—plus, plus, plus!

I looked at the glass tracing which had been thrust into my hand.

"Benign ectopic beats alright," I echoed. Turner smiled encouragingly and said mischievously,

"There you are. This doctor confirms that all is well—even looking at the recording upside down."

Pupil and master clambered back into the hospital. Cheeks suffused, I faced Dick Turner.

"Yes, sir, it was upside down. I think it was also back to front."

Turner grinned,

"At least you're honest. When in doubt tell the truth! You may come and work with me –but don't think it'll be easy. You'll have to learn from me, teach students, look after rows of patients, do research and pass your post-graduate examinations.

Accustomed to nature in the raw and bush-doctor medicine, I accepted this impossible assignment with the confidence of youth. Besides, Turner had a certain dynamism about him which made the younger man glow at the prospect of toil and trouble. I knew I needed to be stretched anyway.

"Three hundred a year and six months trial. That's the position. You'll have to get either a Membership or a Doctorate if you want an extension. Incidentally I'm looking for others so if you know of anyone suitable send 'em down. "But I don't want 'em unless they'll work a ten-day week."

Feeling that I had spent two hours coping with an uncontrollable force I left the unreal world of the hospital behind me. I felt tired as I sat down on the top deck of the tramcar. With all that energy burning inside him why didn't Turner glow in the dark, melt his spectacles or liquefy the wax in his ears. Pondering on my inadequacy, I was startled by a grunt from beside me. George Thornton, who had been in my graduate year and was now sharing the internal medicine course, was sitting beside me. The tram negotiated the Mound as I produced a crumpled packet of cigarettes.

"Have one of mine, George. I've just got a job. Going back to the Western where I started as a student in 1941—but I'm doing Medicine this time—with a bloke from London. Odd chap! It'll be like living with an electric light bulb."

"Lucky bugger! Any job would do me. You see I'm married. I might even be pregnant!"

George and I alighted at the Royal Infirmary and wandered into a lecture on intestinal parasites. George dozed off—a feat theoretically impossible in the East Medical Theatre's sadistic seats, but woke when the lecturer gave a vivid account of the highly active segments of the pork tapeworms.

"Sounds like this chap Turner at the Western, the one who's just given you a job."

"See here George, he's looking for other assistants. You MIGHT do worse."

On such trivial incidents do careers depend. As the New Year started in a flurry of snow, Thornton and Illingworth became inextricably linked with Turner. Uninformed and incompetent the two novices supported each other. In teaching, research, helping the houseman and studying in the worst winter of the century, we worked impossible hours. Even Dick Turner conceded we were diligent—"plus, plus, plus."

By January 1947 our basement area had filled up with snow. An icy blast relentlessly pursued the cyanosed inhabitants of our stone-flagged home. We shared a single bed—but this was a bonus—proximity kept us warm! A tiny electric fire in the bedroom was equalled in impotence in the sitting-room by a solid fuel fire which devoured coal as it heated the floor of our landlady's flat above. The only way to keep warm was to sit with your feet on the mantelshelf and hope your trousers wouldn't ignite.

Clutching my first pay I slithered across the snow to the front door. My wife was sitting in "the lounge" with her feet up and a smoking briar pipe was sticking out of her mouth.

"Sorry laddie! No money; no cigarettes; no food and a frost-bitten bottom. What have you to report?"

"Only that we're rich. There's twenty-five quid in that envelope. We're dining out after the shopping—and some of the cooking sherry."

We had a steak high-tea in the West End Restaurant and crossed the road to Wilkie's where we bought a fur coat. Almost next door was Gibb's pet shop. A bull terrier pup was sitting in the window looking abjectly pink-eyed. Lesley hesitated only one second and then slipped past the assistant who was trying to lock up the premises.

"My God what have you done?" I enquired, peering at the shivering morsel of life in her hand.

The three of us walked home through the snow. The fur coat was hung up; the dog was fed and Mrs Illingworth vomited.

"Must be that strong 'pusser's' tobacco from the Navy," she ventured, contemplating her two purchases which didn't seem to like each other. The pup eyed the fur coat as if it were a rabbit—at that price it must have been anyway. By morning Lesley had vomited again and the pup had killed the fur coat—stone dead.

"Looks as if a fox had found the hens," muttered Lesley as she surveyed the furry debris of battle and bade her husband farewell. At the hospital George at once diagnosed pregnancy.

"I know about these things, old chap. Matter of fact my own wife has the morning sickness too. Worse, she's eating coke!"

A few nights later Lesley sat up in the single bed.

"I must have raw carrots!" was her passionate plea. For the next month sleep was destroyed at 2 a.m. when her caprices flared.

It's difficult to sleep in a single bed when your soul-mate is crunching carrots and your M.D. examination comes ever closer.

"Straightforward, old boy?" George was enquiring—after the written exam paper.

"You know, David, has it ever occurred to you perhaps that we're brilliant and don't know it? Delayed maturation may be our problem. Shall we try the Union beer?"

Two relieved quasi-physicians sat at the bar of the Students' Union soaking up their ale. George was in rampant form.

"We should show our appreciation to our wives David. Oh let's take them out to "The Aperitif"." I burped in alarm.

"God, that's expensive!"

"Don't be miserly. It's the least you can do. Anyway they're both so nauseated they won't be able to eat much."

I felt my empty wallet and confessed I was, as usual, "skint"; but made a conditional acceptance—provided we asked for children's portions for our wives we could visit "The Ap."

This sophisticated restaurant was not in my world. I'd never been there before whereas George was instantly recognised by the barman. The meal was excellent and all was well until George's Camembert arrived—it was fluid and smelt of Indonesian canal corpses. But George was delighted with it.

"It must suppurate or else it's useless."

I settled for the sweet as our wives vanished to the powder room—to be sick.

One week later came the clinical examination of the M.D.—as immortalised in "The Students' Song Book." I drew a long straw. Suave and handsome, Professor Dunlop showed the aspiring physician only one patient—a pathetic creature with

Motor Neurone Disease. Responding well to Dunlop's gentle approach I did well.

The Dean's Office soon confirmed that the two of us were, as we suspected, brilliant post-graduate students. The successful pair celebrated their examination result once or twice more and prepared for the emotional stresses of childbirth and the Membership examination. In retrospect their sheer impertinence was breathtaking, if understandable. Our "research" had got off the ground; our teaching was honest, if not impeccable, and our care of patients was devoted. So involved were we with the clinical aspect of our appointments that we didn't notice that our strange working hours left no time for textbook study.

Youth disregards disadvantage. The cold got colder; the single bed grew smaller as Lesley enlarged; six feet of snow entombed our New Town refrigerator. The Illingworths pressed on regardless—having no idea of their destination.

The Bull Terrier dog continued to blot his copy book. Lesley and I arrived home and walked into a cloud of feathers from Mrs Adam's cushions. The entire basement was littered with fabric and filling. The trail led upstairs to Mrs Adam's luxury flat. Every cushion, and there were at least a score, had been attacked and maimed.

"It bursts my membranes to think about it," Lesley said, "but Mrs Adam comes back tomorrow." She sat up all night, sewing, to repair the wreckage.

George and I battled on with our research. The patients in the male ward were talked into an investigation about the pressure in their venous systems. A needle of vast diameter was inserted into their veins and connected to a guage. Neither scientist was quite clear why this had to be done. The patients were convinced that it didn't have to be done at all.

"These two buggers take off so much blood they must be partners in a black pudding factory," said one "volunteer".

Confidence was even further reduced when, with the blunt needle failing to enter the vein on one side, we had to resort to that pathetic admission of medical failure.

"And now we'll have to do the other side."

In spite of the patients' cynicism we completed a draft of our first scientific paper a few days before the Membership examination and presented it to Dr Turner. We met him the following morning in his office.

"There it is chaps. I've altered it +++" The boss returned the draft with everything scored out except a few commas and the terminal full stop.

George erupted.

"There's six months work in there, sir. Are you telling us to start again?"

"Fraid so, George. Can't attribute inferior work to this new Unit you know."

Spectacles misting up, I hastened to point out that we had sacrificed study time for nothing. The examination was about to begin and we weren't ready. George picked up the mutilated draft, paused at the door and spoke with the ministerial authority of a son of the manse.

"It's not the first time people have been crucified for doing good work."

The two friends parted outside the Chief's office. I cycled homeward. At the hospital gate a carload of students honked loudly at me and left behind a trail of ribald personal remarks. I pedalled on. It was August 1947.

One day...................Perhaps?

But there was no doubt about the labour when it started. And in no time at all we had a son—called "Lawrence"—after my alter ego, lost at the Flushing beachhead. Fatherhood was great! It was about to be tested in a new location. Stimulated by the M.D. success we moved to a small bungalow near the Western General Hospital.

The 'phone rang and a male voice said "Got a note from you bearing your number. I'm at the railway station, will you come and fetch me."

I thought it might be a hoax.

"Who on earth is that?"

"Don't you know your own father?"

"Well perhaps not as well as I should!" And certainly I can't pick you up. I don't have a car. My bicycle has a back step though." And I liked the image of the Commodore of Cunard White Star Line grimly hanging onto my shoulders as we negotiated Princes Street—on a bicycle! The caller didn't laugh.

No words were wasted.

"I'd like to stay a few days."

The rented bungalow was a vast improvement on our icy basement. The removal had been simple—a baby and two suitcases. But the Membership examination was in a few days time and now we had a guest—my father—whom I vaguely remembered meeting just once in my life.

Bewildered, I answered the doorbell to find a father who, as expected of a wandering mariner, adapted at once, made himself at home and charmed my wife as he explained.

"I wish to remarry and want you to persuade your mother to divorce me. If you succeed I shall settle £3,000 on her. If you fail I shall divorce her in Reno U.S.A. and she'll get nothing. Over to you!"

It was brutally frank. Time was short as I wheeled out my bike and cycled to my mother's flat—which she shared with her sister. The expected happened.

"You mean he's staying in your house! I can't believe he just arrived. So much for loyalty—you deceptive ingrate!" "I'm not giving up my rights. I'm innocent. Go back and tell him so."

Vainly I protested in the withering blast, "Financially I can barely support myself."

And a failed diplomat cycled home. But the 'phone rang as I arrived

"Let me speak to your father." So I led "Dad" to the phone. Twenty minutes later he re-entered the sitting room, having discoloured from pink to cream.

"Your mother doesn't need a 'phone. She could just hang out the window."

So I emptied the gin bottle and added a splash of the Government issue of "orange juice for babies" to the tumbler.

Father went from cream back to pink—as I wondered how the hell I'd got involved in my parents marriage—especially in the shadow of "The Membership". Father groaned.

"She agreed. I felt like a 'snottie' at a court martial! But she agreed!"

In 1948 Valvona and Crolla refilled one's empty sherry bottles for 5/- (25 pence) and an enterprising Lesley sauntered in at Father's moment of triumph and flourished the 25 pence worth at the new man in her life—whom she rather liked. She charged a pair of enamel containers—father had the tumbler—as she said impishly

"I'm drinking to the marriage of my father-in-law who's being divorced by my mother-in-law on the advice of my husband who is their son. Sounds Gilbertian but I hope and pray it works out and that things aren't further complicated by our son, Gordon the third, becoming someone's nephew—or would it be 'uncle'?"

Two days later Father departed for Boston. In a way we were sorry to see him go—his going perhaps hastened by the proximity of "The Membership".

We were to meet only once more. The search for a father was only partly successful. I determined to cling fast to what I had gained—a wonderful wife and a son.

CHAPTER EIGHTEEN

Dick Turner had not failed to notice George's reaction. The following morning we were paraded before the Chief.

"Did I detect a note of rebellion recently, chaps? Don't you know how lucky you are? My God, you might be bank clerks counting money all day. Life may be hard but it's not dull. Face up to the next hurdle, the Membership. If you succeed you're made. But should you fail, you'll have to depend on the mercy of the Post-Graduate Board for an extension of your appointments. Don't let me down! If you do, you might go hungry. In the meantime I've got news for you fellows. I had twins this morning." He reached into the cupboard of his desk and produced a bottle of sherry and three chipped mugs. The trio drank solemnly to the new Turners and, as an afterthought, to the future of the would-be physicians.

The candidates rushed home as soon as possible for a last look at the textbooks. The underground in Medicine had it that only 20% of the candidates succeeded in the examination for Membership of the Royal College of Physicians and that it was really a competitive event. Their very survival depended on the result.

On the clinical side George and David did well, but the written papers were tough going for both. Everything hinged on the "orals". George was asked about his school, his father and his war record, before being nailed on an esoteric medical problem which made him quite speechless.

I was led into one of the College cubicles and faced two expressionless men. The younger one, Dr Batty, began.

"Tell me about the development of the lens of the eye."

The candidate was at least honest.

"Sorry, sir, I don't know."

"Tell me then Illingworth, the percentage of people who are left-handed?"

The other examiner stepped in as my stammer prevented articulation. I didn't know anyway.

A leaden silence ensued during which the candidate struggled for self-control and rational speech. But it was too late. I'd answered nothing!

"Thank you, doctor, that's all."

I bowed and stumbled out to await the outcome of the examiners' meeting the next morning. Things looked black!

The examinees were huddled at one end of the large hall. At the other end stood the secretary who read out the names of the successful doctors in alphabetical order. "Illingworth" located nearer the beginning of the alphabet, knew before George that he had failed. Thornton had to wait rather longer before joining the disconsolate majority who trooped away to their personal oblivion.

Turner shuffled his feet.

"Bad luck, chaps, but at least you've tried. Re-sit and I'll try to get your appointments extended by the Post-Graduate Board."

"Might as well apply for a season ticket," groaned George. "I think we should lay off for a bit."

I agreed that the dice had been loaded against us. The examination had devastated me. I had vomited each morning of its duration. On the third day, in an effort to occupy myself, I had bathed my baby son. So nervous was I that I dropped the child on its head. Lesley forgave me, understanding that her husband was playing for impossible stakes.

So we concentrated on medicine and forcibly forgot about our failures. We trundled from clinic to clinic, burning electricity far into the night as we devoured text-books and articles and neglected our marriages. Happily there came easier times with the arrival of Drs. Warnock and Robson to supplement Turner's staff. Each newcomer had a sense of humour—and a Membership of the College. Not only was the teaching load immediately reduced but they began to help

George and me in the examination gamble. Best of all they defused Turner and made him seem less omnipotent!

Three days of progressive anxiety about his hearing were seriously troubling the Chief. After two disastrous ward rounds, in which he had failed to measure up, he confessed to his four acolytes,

"Chaps, I must tell you that these murmurs which you heard in our patients' hearts are NOT audible to me."

Norrie Robson nodded sympathetically and turned to me

"David, you've done E.N.T. Must be wax in the ears, why don't you syringe them?"

The syringing was not very productive but Dick Turner's hearing recovered dramatically during the next ward round. It was some days before Dr. Robson admitted that he had plugged Turner's stethoscope tubing with cotton wool and had winkled it out during my attack on the Chief's ears. Late the next afternoon Professor Stanley Davidson came down from the University to inspect the medical unit at the Western General Hospital. He brought with him the mandatory gift to commemorate his first official visit—an unwrapped but large box of chocolates. The Professor's right hand man, Dr James Innes, had obtained this rare delicacy which lay in the Chief's room while sherry and talk circulated freely. George and I didn't converse but munched steadily away at the Professor's chocolates. Confectionery was still tightly rationed. What did it matter if there was an occasional tiny flaw in the coating of some of the chocolate? The only deterrent to our indulgence was a proposed visit to The Aperitif Restaurant at the end of the day's work.

We were to collect our wives as soon as we left the hospital and we departed at 6 pm with Professor Davidson. By 7 pm we had settled in our baby-sitters and entered "The Ap." As usual there was a hot noisy crowd through which we struggled to our table—where drinks magically appeared. George's blue eyes crinkled with discomfort.

"Sorry fellow you know what I haven't done? Haven't had time. Must go NOW." Finding a fellow-sufferer in myself, we weaved our way to a packed toilet. There was only room for one at the far end of the white porcelain slab but the pair jammed themselves in over the gutter which had an inclination downwards past six other men busily occupied in relieving themselves.

"Nice of Stanley to come down....." A series of horrified cries and blasphemies stifled all lavatorial conversation. The six other men in line abreast were peering at the gutter in horror.

"Oh my God, look at that! Get the Manager, someone's ill.

Within seconds the two young doctors were being scrutinised by twelve eyes as the other men hastily backed away.

"They're BOTH doing it—look!"

We looked and then looked away. A small wave of brilliant blue colour had coursed from us down the gutter past our startled neighbours. Further assessment revealed that we were both passing what appeared to be ink.

George grasped the situation first.

"It's the old methylene blue trick. I bet James Innes, or somebody, got at the Prof's chocolates."

Latching on I remembered the tiny holes in the confectionery.

"Very sorry, gentlemen, it's a trick." There was a chorus of protest.

"Dam' bad manners! Gave me a hell of a fright! Can't say I'm hungry now! A trick indeed—they're mad! Sister is going swimming this evening!" hissed George.

We now had penicillin—but little else was new. In spite of barbiturates, digitalis and mercurial diuretics people continued to die—in the same old way. Tuberculosis and Syphilis still lurked as traps for the unwary. There were rumours of Cortisone—but many succumbed who would later have been saved. The epidemic of Coronary Artery Disease had not yet started—and everybody smoked. Thoracic surgery had begun; cardiac surgery was still in its infancy. But the future looked good.

Together we chronicled the hospital diseases of 1948—many of which were soon to become curiosities. We recorded and discussed Amyloid disease, tuberculosis of bone and lung, spondylitis, cardiac syphilis and the legacy of tropical disease left by the Second World War. Asthmatics seemed particularly common and tended not to do well. Cases of mental illness, often presenting in physical terms, strained our resources. One is especially memorable.

Olivia, by any standards an attractive girl with an engaging personality, was a nurse who eluded diagnosis. She suffered from episodes of intermittent fever of considerable degree during which she became strikingly blue in colour. After three months admission every possible test had been performed. She had been assessed by a dozen doctors from every speciality and had become a medical "cause celebre" in Edinburgh. Even Professor Davidson admitted defeat. After another two months she was still valiantly facing up to batteries of tests and multiple examinations. As she entered her sixth month in hospital the fever and discolouration became intense. This deterioration coincided with the arrival of a new house physician who had not acquired the conditioned thinking of his seniors. Dr Loudon had the bright idea of having the blood examined for abnormal pigments. With Olivia's permission he cleansed her sapphired earlobe and laid the used swab on the dressing tray. By chance he did something no other doctor had ever done—he looked at the swab. The swab was as blue as the ear. Such is hysteria—an expensive problem!

News came through from the University that George and I had been confirmed in our appointments at £600 a year. George bought a car. Renting a bungalow near the hospital was expensive, so I had my bicycle professionally overhauled. After an uneventful month, during which the Chief reduced the third draft of our paper to a dozen words (and punctuation) we took four weeks unpaid leave to resit the Membership..

We called it 'leave', Dick called it "holidays without pay". Our 'holidays' arranged, I received a succession of news items of which the most significant was that we were flat broke—apart from 5/- in Lesley's Post Office Savings Account.

I looked at my wife and my son and realised just what I was—a disaster! There was no way to cope with the month ahead. I had let the side down completely. Better if the Germans had pushed the torpedo button one half second earlier. My desperation couldn't be concealed from Lesley as we ate a meagre supper. "Is it money again?" We've got 5/- you know." She laughed in my tormented face. "You've dealt with worse situations than this. Let's work it out."

And the problem was simplified—though not solved—as she calculated our liabilities.

"Examination fee £25; Month's rent £15; New suit £25; Food £20; Fags etc £5; other expenses such as your mother £10; Total expenditure £100: total assets—5/-."

"Sounds like Micawber! But I'm O.K.!"

I demurred in vain about the cigarettes and the suit.

"This is no time to conquer an addiction. And as for appearing in that obscene shroud of a demob. suit! You won't get in the door of 9 Queen Street—tradesmens' entrance for you!" Lesley continued and shortly I felt much better about life. But I had missed something.

"Wait a minute. What do you mean you're OK?"

"Well Davie, I didn't mean to tell you yet but it looks like a brother for young Lawrence." I felt strangely happy.

The next week I entered an intellectual cell of study and isolation—emerging only to telephone relations who obviously wouldn't miss £100—lent in a good cause. Their response was appalling and as I prepared myself for desperate measures something happened.

It was spookily appropriate. Fifty years on I still wonder at my return from borrowing fags from George to discover Lesley holding an envelope which she'd opened to find a legal letter and a cheque. A distant cousin had died and left my wife £100—a precise response to an implausible prayer! I began to wonder if my life was to continue as a series of happy accidents and one long "happenchance". So much had occurred, so fortunately, that I looked for some controlling mechanism which was in charge of my destiny. So I went to church! Was I hedging my bets?

It was the examination mixture as before. I vomited each morning; George had tremors. On this occasion it was the candidate in the next examination cubicle who was asked about the development of the lens of the eye. He promptly walked out and was replaced by a doctor, hooked on barbiturates, who had calmed his pre-examination nerves with Sodium Amytal. The first question answered, the candidate then dozed off and slipped from the chair. I looked across in time to see the servitor dragging out the examinee.

"That's two less to reckon with," I thought and began to assert myself as Norrie Robson and Guy Warnock had taught me. The next morning our names were included in the 20% success list. George was speechless and quietly disappeared. As for me, stunned, I asked for confirmation and wandered blindly along Queen Street looking for a telephone kiosk. Each was occupied—until I reached Castle Street. I dialled home and fell apart at the overstretched seams of my emotions. The instant security of success, although ephemeral like all else in medical life, was too much for me.

Why were my cheeks wet? I recalled Sir Alexander's statement.

"It will take two years and when you succeed you can begin." Who was it who wrote, "Life is a procession of endless horizons"—or something?

I walked home, reflecting on how it had happened. I reached home to find Lesley and my son waiting at the front door—those who had made it all possible and worthwhile. I opened my arms and held fast. The Scots aren't supposed to show their feelings—but the emotional floodgates wouldn't close until the dam had emptied.

That took an hour. The forces of natural energy then began to accumulate once more. Now we knew we wouldn't starve. But the challenges would continue—maybe they were even beneficial. Anyway the framework of specialist Medicine had acquired a new disciple—one who would gratefully conform.

Four hours later George's car drove carefully uphill from the Cramond Inn, preceded by an unsteady pedestrian shining his clinical torch to find out where his feet were. I don't know how we got home.

George's milkman found a note in an empty bottle as he did his round a few hours later.

"Please refill this with whisky."

The medical ward round at the Western General Hospital was curiously restrained next morning. George and I worked on, convinced that we'd have to give up booze and parties.

In July 1948 the N.H.S. began and I became a Medical Registrar.

Turner's energy and dedication were perplexing and occasionally irritating. Unforgettable aphorisms flowed from him.

"When in doubt tell the truth." "I don't mind discussing it but we both know I'm correct." "An order is not a basis for debate." "This is the not the Army. Do it NOW!" "Cyanosed patients usually wear purple bed-jackets." "You don't need to feel the position of this apex beat—you can see it!" "I don't understand. What's the truth? Give me a summary of the facts—soon+++." And on a more personal basis, "For this experiment we need a human volunteer—that's you David, you've got good veins!"

I was despatched to the medical periphery to help work up the less glamorous hospitals. At the Eastern General I found Dr French—the archetypal physician—for whom I went to work. Ted was a doctor's doctor; a unique teacher and an original thinker. The size of his mind matched his physique. His diaphragm was so powerful that he could belch The National Anthem. He also tolerated people—such as me—and infected these lesser creatures with his enthusiasms. Within hours of joining him I was lost in the ebb and flow of the eosinophil cells of the blood. We began to count these cells twenty-four hours a day, at hourly intervals. This entailed staying up all night studying volunteer patients.

At 1.55 a.m. I moved from the microscope to the laboratory door, carrying my "blood tray". The door was closed and the handle rotated impotently in my hand. Although imprisoned, I was equal to the situation and lifted the telephone.

"Dr French, please, in B. Block. Ted, it's David, my next blood count is due at 2 a.m. and the door lock's bust. What's that? Why not unlock the door? It isn't locked! Alright, Ted. I'm not locked in; I just can't get out. Go out the window? Hell, of course, Ted! Sorry."

I jumped up on the laboratory bench and opened the window as the 'phone rang.

"David, it's Ted. You're on the second floor! I'll get a ladder."

At 1.58 a.m. Ted's skull was visible as he stood on the top rung of the ladder. He was still six feet short of the window.

"If you hang onto the window ledge you can just do it—running up and down to the ward. But I'm damned if I can see how you'll carry your equipment. I'm coming round by the stairs."

Ted's massive frame made the door shiver as he hit it with his shoulder—but the broken lock held fast. Night Sister appeared and gabbled hysterically through the door at the trapped Illingworth.

"Dr French is all padded up with cushions now—and says he's going to run straight through the door."

"Geronimo!" shouted Ted. "Stand back!" Suddenly the laboratory was full of human protoplasm—most of it was Ted, with a bowler hat, who looked like an American footballer. Most of his six feet five was covered with protective cushions as he stood amongst the wreckage.

At 2.05 a.m. the blood test was completed and the eosinophils were being counted. Whatever happened to the results?

It was a happy year on a frontier of hospital medicine. Robson had arrived from the Western and had initiated chemotherapy. The male ward seemed full of young men with lethal testicular tumours. None survived but there were those who, at a cost, got extra time.

Ted French, in physique and intellect, was a giant. A born teacher, with a gift for stimulating thought in others,nothing passed him by without assessment. "Why" was his mantra. He resented the docile acceptance of others' beliefs. He and his wife, Yvonne, had the unique distinction of contracting "mumps" shortly after the birth of their youngest son. At their home I found, in bed, a turnip faced mother and father—their new baby lying between them—with an even greater enlargement of his salivary glands. Photography was prohibited.

While Ted became a court of last medical resort as his reputation grew in the diagnosis of the undiagnosable, he made time to feed, with enduring phrases, young immature minds. Service in India was reflected in:- "I thought I was abused because I was un-shoed, and then I met a man who had no feet." And, "I didn't know that I lived in a primitive society until the missionaries came."

Dick Turner still visited the "peripheral hospitals"—often irritating those who did the work. Yet he was treated with that amused tolerance often accorded to intelligent eccentrics.

Ted used to say, "He's a damn nuisance—but at least he's different and he certainly isn't dull."

I was ambivalent. I had learned much from this strange medical guru but felt I had been exploited. But the legends remain. How he had ordered five tons of manure and then forgotten to collect it until an irate lorry driver dropped it into his basement area. How he developed visual problems after visiting the optician until I suggested he clean the lenses of his spectacles—which he couldn't do as no lens had been fitted. How, sitting his bath, one evening, the floor gave way and he descended rapidly into the porch of the Turner residence. No it wasn't tedious! But my hospital life was unsure and unpredictable—although the arrival of consultant cardiologist, Mike Matthews, brought a welcome normality. He, John Strong and John Macleod each possessed an aura of kindness and level-headed intellect and I unashamedly absorbed their wisdom and knowledge. The debt is acknowledged.

Ted's reputation as the man for insoluble problems was challenged by the Matthews' dog.

"Oscar, poor chap, keeps passing out on me."

Shaved and wired up to an E.C.G.—which he hated—the tracing showed a profound state of Digitalis intoxication!

"Who's poisoning that dog and why?" queried Ted. But he admitted defeat as a criminologist. We had failed Oscar!

A month later Oscar was found in Mike's bed of garden foxgloves—happily munching himself into Digitalis poisoning as he saved our reputations.

But all this wasn't my concept of a normal medical world. Surely medicine is about people as well as disease, and wellness rather than illness. Here I was, locked up in a hospital—a sort of medical monastery in which I was sheltered from the realities of life. Financially secure, even my disciplined mind was becoming steadily more disenchanted with the hospital hierarchy—its distortions and clinical disconuities.

Dick Turner, a splendid teacher to whom I am forever indebted, provoked and maintained for those four years of training, an inability to make me comfortable in his presence. But Dick had nothing to do with my sudden enlightenment. The scales fell from my eyes when I realised that the patients were more interesting and much more important than their pathology.

I had become a displaced person entrammelled in the maze of scientific medicine and multiple tests with discordant titles and mystical acronyms. I was losing the gentle artistry of Medicine and was in need of the great undiscovered simplicities of the medical frontiers.

Sandy Donald, the last of that invaluable breed, the Medical Superintendent, was impressively blunt,

"The fragmentation of Medicine into many specialties has produced a restriction in knowledge and judgment which only the family doctor has so far escaped." This startling statement was well received by Ted.

"We must beware of "The Humpty Dumpty Syndrome" in which Medicine breaks up into small ineffectual factions."

I was left with a strange sense of bewilderment mixed with unfulfilled destiny. Had I been practising at the wrong side of the medical spectrum? At the wrong end of Joseph Addison's bridge? I should try to promote health rather than do salvage work in hospital. It sounded pretentious but it would be satisfying to repair a few apertures in Joseph Addison's metaphorical bridge.

The compass needle was plainly pointing—where was the next happy accident?

PART IV

FAMILY DOCTOR

CHAPTER NINETEEN

And so in the summer of 1950 I was twenty-eight years old—and, after seven years in medical practice, was still struggling to find my next horizon. One of my in-laws had discovered a furnished terraced house for us at a rent of only £12 a month. This stroke of luck helped enormously and, with examinations behind me, I was now a second-year Hospital Registrar. Much influenced by French and Robson who had indoctrinated me with the necessity of looking at the person behind the disease, I found myself listening more and more to the patients. Their clinical pathology was interesting but the people themselves engrossed me.

With increasing frequency I sat on beds in the wards to learn about patients' lives and hopes, their successes, fears and failures. Some of the conversations were far removed from the speciality of Medicine but I excused myself by recalling one of the great maxims of the profession. "You must listen to the patient for he is telling you the diagnosis."

Confidence and trust developed in these relationships. The patients' discharge from hospital generated at times a feeling akin to loss. Hardly ever did I discover their future progress. I was reading only part of a novel. Having become involved in a human story, I seemed fated seldom to learn its outcome. Later I was to refer to the "emotional isolation" and the "sensory deprivation" of hospital doctors—in sorrow rather than captiously. Many years afterwards, however, my defences were shattered by a young post-graduate who said at the end of her training period, "I still don't know whether your patients need you or you need your patients. Some of us want to be wanted."

But in 1950 I was too involved to examine motive or philosophy. I only knew that, in hospital, the air was a little rarefied and that I could never feel fulfilled because my skills were with people rather than with their diseases.

Therefore, when a local General Practitioner telephoned to ask help with an occasional evening consulting session, I eagerly accepted. The "doctor's parlour" with its atmosphere of intimacy and permanency made an immediate appeal to the human being behind the scientific sophistication.

I had found the type of medical relationship I was seeking. In the weeks that followed I would frequently step out of my white coat and make my way, by tramcar, into another world of medicine. Was I climbing over a wall?

Ted said "You're twenty-eight and now in your eighth year since graduation; you've got a lot of experience and one or two successes behind you. On the debit side you're too young for a consultant post and you have a family to support. Problem is how do you earn more?"

I recalled that I had had two job offers from overseas but really wanted to settle down and make a stable home here—a security I had never experienced myself. It was a bad week. No horizon was visible.

And then the 'phone rang. The caller was Dr. Robert Morton, a general practitioner with a fine record, who had formed a city practice with Dr Lamont—a much respected and long-established family doctor.

"Lamont and I would like to see you tonight. We're interviewing people who might be suitable as a third partner."

I had often met Morton and liked him. Lamont was an entirely different personality. Feet firmly clamped to the ground he had no time for discussion—unless it might help his patient. He met clinical life head on. When the N.H.S. began in July 1948 he promised his patients the standards of personal continuous service which he had provided in the days of private practice. This was an unwitting deception—but he couldn't compromise and accept a lowering of standards. So he tolerated young hard-working partners who purveyed a mechanical time-orientated medicine—which may have satisfied the masses who couldn't make comparisons—but which occasionally provoked guilt feelings in doctors given to self-criticism.

"What's your private income doctor?" was the question which gave me an insight into Lamont's approach to medical practice. The reply "zero", had quite an effect on the senior partner.

"Surely you don't expect to make a profit out of the National Health Service. You're not in medicine for the money, are you?"

For the first time I saw the conflict with which British doctors constantly struggle and the threat of a double standard of medical practice. Perhaps I'd be safer behind the walls of a hospital. At least my conscience wouldn't bother me.

But a puzzled Illingworth joined what Robert Morton called—"This utilitarian system"—and in a way I felt comfortable because I had found a niche from which I would not forever have to clamber uphill to some academic Calvary.

"Three surgeries and twenty home visits a day; every third Sunday is free" was Lamont's shibboleth, and, in spite of some glaring deficiencies, this odd trio were able to furnish twenty years of first rate service to their community.

There was little sense of time or of any other responsibility. Your wife reared your children—whom you saw on the school delivery run and perhaps at bedtime when you heard their prayers. This apart, your life was the practice; the practice was your life. But there were forty-two sacred days each year, which were YOUR holidays. A few days in the spring and autumn; a month in the summer, when a bizarre but absorbing life style reverted to normal; when every day was lived; when each family moment was precious.

After three months' probation I was offered a partnership with a salary of "not less than a thousand pounds a year". It was wonderful to have the fear of financial failure removed. I could now look ahead. I had a job with a future. Could I buy a car to replace the one lent to me by the practice? Could I go further and buy a house?

The bank manager proved surprisingly accommodating about the car. Buying the house was a different matter. Robert Morton intervened—choosing his words well for reasons to become obvious, "The Farquhars have a nice house at the Braids. They're an old couple and want to sell. They've bought a wee place further down the hill. I've told them you'll buy their present house. I gaped at my partner. They expect you at 8 o'clock. Let's get on with the work."

I slipped out of the practice house before surgery ended and drove a new car to the Farquhar's house. It was a charming dwelling with old furniture and that indefinable olfactory tang of elderly occupants. Mrs Farquhar was clearly in charge and hustled the young G.P. round the premises.

"It's yours if you want it, doctor. You know the price and we'll let you have the furniture cheap. What have you got so far?"

We possessed a card table, a rug and a set of "liar dice."! Mr Farquhar was instructed by his spouse to draw up a list of articles and prices.

I drove home to a wife far advanced in her third pregnancy—and very ill with acute labyrinthitis. I looked at my wife's tired face and thought only that I must get that house. I telephoned H.M.S. Killin's midshipman, Ian Stewart, who had entered the Faculty of Law, to find out how you bought a house. What it is to have friends! Within two minutes I knew that all I had to do was put down £500! I woke up Lesley who had dozed off in a chair.

"We only need £500 and we're there!" Lesley grimaced. "Might as well be five million."

But her husband had the bit between his teeth and I fired off a salvo of telephone requests to likely relations. Some of them were people of substance—but all were "fully invested" and immune to cajoling, threats and promises of high interest rates. Twelve hours later the list of relatives was exhausted—as was the supplicant.

The Illingworths peered blearily at each other. "Hate to tell you, I'm going to vomit again." Lesley said and disappeared.

I went along to hold her head over the loo. We sat together on the lavatory floor as the water spiralled round the toilet bowl. Lesley's mouth opened after she wiped her face and the nystagmic eyes.

"It's the water, Davie!" I reassured her—thinking she'd forgotten that it always goes clockwide. She retched again as the room danced round her.

"You mean your membranes have ruptured? That's the last straw!"

"No, you great gowk. There's that wee man across the water. Your father!"

My parents had of course divorced, but my father was now remarried and settled in California. Reaching for the telephone, acutely aware that I had only met the man twice, and after an agony of waiting, I heard my father—crisp and controlled—although dragged out of his bed. The voice boomed halfway across the globe with a commanding officer's authority and decisiveness.

"Is £500 enough, old chap?" It was quite unreal.

The cheque arrived three days later and, as I wrote an emotional acknowledgement, it seemed tactless to inform Grandpa that we wouldn't have thought about him if Lesley hadn't vomited into the toilet bowl. But this odd piece of lateral thinking produced our first real home. It also seemed to induce Lesley's third labour. A month later—after five years of marriage, vicissitude and uncertainty, the five Illingworths entered their new home.

The house faced west and, high about the city, gave us a series of splendid sunsets. The garden was small and easily managed. The substantial garage had an inspection pit. The stove ensured constant hot water. There was even a refrigerator to keep the baby's feeds sterile.

The two parents in their eyrie on the crest of Edinburgh never lost their feelings of wonder—and gratitude.

The practice of medicine continued.

CHAPTER TWENTY

"Three surgery sessions a day and twenty house calls," droned Lamont yet again. I sighed as, not for the first time, the corollary followed.

"And you do your own Midwifery."

Saturdays were working days but, on Sundays, only one doctor took new calls. The others might do "repeats" but were otherwise incommunicado. It was a great scheme if no one was ill or on holiday—as happened half of each year. Not all the registered patients of the Group Practice had learned how to use the services. It became clear that 10% of the patients made up 90% of the work and that 1% provided 100% of the irritation.

And yet there was so much real need which was demonstrated in the revelation of chronic sickness by a vast number of old people who had suffered in dignified silence. The advent of the National Health Service opened the floodgates of concealed morbidity. Waves of long term social and medical problems simply submerged the General Practitioners. Those doctors who survived the initial onslaught were either strong, stubborn, stupid or indifferent.

Lamont, Morton and Illingworth stuck it out—agreeing that, in the fullness of time, the practice must become totally orientated towards the National Health Service.

Predictably, a small number of Scots refused to join "The State Scheme". Some of those non-conformists were known as "the sixpenny patients" because they were proud old people, in straitened circumstances, who solemnly presented the visiting doctor with a sixpence as he left the house. The inflexible state scheme did not allow these independent creatures the free medication which came with a National Health Service consultation—even though they had paid their National

Insurance! The pharmacist's fee for dispensing the prescriptions of these private patients was usually much in excess of the doctor's sixpenny fee. It made a nonsense of government morality.

Conversely, a tiny minority who had joined the state scheme expected an unchanged type of care—a domestic visit for a cut finger or a boil; a midnight house call to view a cold sore or an ingrowing toenail! Manifestly it was all about training your patients in how to use the available services. The National Health Service had come too rapidly on an unprepared populace—but I knew that I had found my professional niche. My personal affairs might be disastrous but the young are averse to self-examination. Lesley and David clung together. We drew strength from each other and inspiration from our own brand of family life.

In all this we were sustained by Lesley's mother—a remarkable lady whose unobtrusive nature concealed her excellence. Her substance and constancy made the Illingworths domestically secure, while I was supported by the great anodyne—work. And in my still embryonic practice there were so many who were much worse off than I was.

The General Practice of Medicine, in its range and diversity, was totally absorbing. One never knew what was coming, and, with my empathy, each day I shared fifty peoples' lives. We had taken on the care of the Edinburgh theatres and I often stood in the wings for snapshots of the performances of Olivier, Mills, Richardson and others. And I began an Occupational Health Service for the Northern Hospitals Group. This cocktail of experience enriched my knowledge and abilities as I ranged from Olivier's glamour to "Ah've pit baith feet into the same leg of my knickers, doctor, and ah cannae move!"

I felt that my medical training had let me down somewhere and, totally helpless, consulted the secretary.

On my first night on call in our new home the 'phone rang at 5 a.m. A charming Edinburgh voice spoke—"This is Mrs Chalmers, doctor. I'm 'phoning to say your breakfast is ready."

The wealthy Mrs Chalmers had taken to the bottle after being widowed. She had lost her sense of time and had telephoned "the doctor" for two years at precisely five o'clock each morning. No-one ever responded to the invitation but I used to look at my infants and regret all these wasted calories which had been promised.

For some perverse reason the obstetrical factor always intruded on free Sundays or on nights off-duty. Lamont and Morton frequently exhorted me to deliver as many babies as possible—preferably at home. This was the way to build up a practice and it also earned money for the partnership—they told ME!

My first home delivery was one of eighteen calls on Christmas Day, 1950. It was a first for both mother and doctor. The midwife arrived at 7 p.m. exuding assurance which I didn't share. At 7 a.m. next day the central figure had not yet put in an appearance. I had departed and returned thrice on other nocturnal visits. Each participant had consumed a gallon or so of tea and confidences had been freely exchanged. The midwife who was a dedicated advocate of breast feeding forecast a delivery before dawn. Pressed to explain her dogmatic statement she pointed out that the moon was full. I wasn't aware that this mattered.

The father of the unborn child was a quiet dedicated soldier—but ultimately he overcame his reserve—drew the doctor to one side and confessed.

"I couldn't stand the breast feeding, doctor. It's asking too much of my self-control."

The soldier looked pitifully embarrassed.

"Everyone knows you never touch a woman who's pregnant or breast feeding. If you add it up I'll have been a virgin almost a year and half you know."

I struggled to explain and reassure and had just set the record straight when the head crowned. Dawn broke and the full moon vanished. The midwife looked complacently across the perineum at the doctor.

"A full moon and NO stitches."

Now I felt strangely complete. I knew I could survive in the front line. In the next year I delivered 50 babies at home!

I had become the first contact, the last, and the way through the intervening maze of medical circuits. On this frontier of medicine patients remained people—not hospital problems or cases. One practised the art of coarse medicine amidst the great undiscovered simplicities, striving for an attitude of conscious ignorance, intellectual honesty and freedom from all emotional bias. This triple amalgam epitomises the General Practice of Medicine.

Yet there were frequent reminders of my own insignificance. Mrs Skene, aged 80, lived alone, severely handicapped by osteoarthritic hips. She struggled around pushing and leaning on a tea-trolley—although all her courage and ingenuity could not control her angina pectoris. Each fortnight I visited her and a close relationship developed. As the social services had not yet developed, friends and neighbours filled the caring gap. Like many Scots, Mrs Skene spoke little of herself, but, after a year she suddenly volunteered.

"Dr Illingworth, you're so like my Bobby."

Knowing better than to intrude on Mrs Skene's privacy, I said I was very pleased about my resemblance to the mysterious Bobby. Six months later, after recalling the similarity many times, she added, "Especially when you smile."

My inquisitive nature could no longer be quelled. I asked if there was a photograph of Bobby. Mrs Skene went to her little escritoire. "Bobby" was an enormous tomcat!

But that afternoon George Fowler nearly spoiled the joke. His wife telephoned during afternoon surgery to say that George was "desperately ill". There being only this abbreviated, vague but urgent message, I drove rapidly to the house and walked in through the open door—shouting the usual greeting. – "It's the doctor."

The silence which received me ended suddenly as I entered the kitchen and the door was slammed behind me. George Fowler stood in the escape route clutching a large carving knife.

Clearly mentally disturbed, he spoke in a curious flat staccato tone.

"I have my orders. You are to die."

I felt strangely unready.

"Who told you this, George?"

"Who else but the Lord? He instructed me that you are worthless and vile. How can you argue with Him?"

Although I knew the Lord was absolutely correct, I racked my agonised brain for an excuse. At all costs I must be conciliatory. If I upset George now, I was dead. And where the hell was George's wife?

I heard my tremulous cracked voice. "It's not for me to argue against your orders, George and I accept the decision, of course. I do know you are a fair man, however, and every condemned man has the right to one last request. I just want to say my good-byes to my wife and family."

"God and I agree," Fowler replied and I walked gingerly into the hall and picked up the 'phone.

Having dialled the police I explained to an astonished but alert desk sergeant that George Fowler, at a certain address, had been ordered by God to kill me with a knife; that I had accepted the death sentence but had asked to bid farewell to my relations.

Having made what seemed positively my last public appearance, I returned to the kitchen with my pocket scissors up my sleeve; thanked Fowler for his understanding and thoughtful interpretation of his religious instructions and asked if I might pray.

The last request was sincere and the answer was immediate. Two brawny policemen pinioned Fowler from behind.

Acute paranoid schizophrenia must not interrupt the practice of medicine. I returned to the consulting room and effected the transition, that afternoon, from near homicide to bunions—without too much effort. Six months later the Fowlers emigrated to Australia. I still wonder how they got on. Somatic illness was quickly and easily dealt with—thanks to an excellent training. For emotional and social upset, especially mental illness, I was totally unprepared.

Perhaps more psychological knowledge would have handicapped me further in my attempts to provide total primary care through successful juggling of physical and emotional needs.

Indisputably it was the problems of mind, temperament and attitude which made the working day too short. Patients viewed psychiatrists and mental hospitals with fear and suspicion. To enter an institution for mental illness was, it appeared, a tacit admission of character failure and moral weakness. Henceforward, the patient was stigmatised—as with a mediaeval branding iron. Among the general public an attitude of hopelessness prevailed and psychiatric problems were obscured by fatuous euphemisms. The relatives (and doctors) spoke of "psychological institutes: breakdowns: overwork and the strains of the 'time of life'"—any time was apposite it seemed. Mental hospitals were a combination of secure places—where injury was improbable—and penal settlements. Many doctors believed that a punitive element, or at least, firm discipline, would speed recovery through helping the patient to —"pull himself together".

Mental upset took up so much medical time—and rightly so—there was a need to be met. The only medicines were barbiturates—and the therapeutic dose was dangerously close to overdose. But, given a serious attempt at self-damage, drugs were preferable to coal gas from the oven. Many who sought an escape route through the household gas of these early days were, if rescued, permanently brain-damaged.

The financial pressures of John Cunningham, the local tailor, simply overwhelmed him. Now in his fifties, the small personal business could no longer compete with the mushrooming growth of cut-price clothing shops. Always professional and immaculate in appearance he epitomised the reserved Scotsman. Perhaps I was too immature to appreciate that the sudden exhibition of various bodily symptoms might be a distress signal. To Cunningham, loss of dignity was worse than death—and the creditors were pressing. Had he known that coal gas produces vomiting the outcome might have been different.

Mrs Cunningham returned from her shopping, couldn't open the front door and smelt gas.

Doctor and police arrived simultaneously, broke down the door and pulled the pathetic vomit-fouled tailor from his oven.

He survived ten years more—as a human vegetable.

"Life comes in lumps." Lamont groaned in response to yet another urgent message from Kate Brown, the Secretary.

"It's Miss Abernethy in a dreadful state. She's just back from school and says her sister's dead—in the gas oven."

In response to the request, the new boy in his new car hurtled through the rush hour traffic. I attracted police attention at once and a sleek saloon began to pursue me. The one thing not to do was to stop and argue, so I hung my stethoscope out of the driver's window. The police had probably seen this trick before and tucked in behind me for verification purposes.

They hadn't long to wait. The doctor and two policemen burst into the kitchen where the distraught sister was slumped over the table. The other lady's legs protruded from the oven. As the men pulled out the body we realised that death had occurred hours before. Our hands were smeared with the inevitable vomit of the coal gas victim. I thought the policemen took it well.

Mr Colquhoun's whooping cough had left a legacy of Bronchiectasis. His residual lung cavities were full of pus. The odour of his breath had a dreadful stench and his visits produced an incompatible reaction in other people. If he coughed the waiting room was virtually emptied as he was left in isolation by the open window. One could tell of his presence as one entered the front door of the surgery. And he was such a nice middle aged man. We could do little except hope for a pertussis vaccine for our babies. Thoughts of "Clochemerle" struggled with our helplessness and the prospect that only those in genuine need would remain waiting to be seen by the doctor. And oh the clubbing of Colquhoun's fingers—indicating his chronic pulmonary sepsis. He was happy to be a source of learning to our students—indeed, even, a piece of medical history to be extirpated by the pertussis vaccine—yet to come.

CHAPTER TWENTY-ONE

The unpredictable nature of the work was part of its fascination. One could never see what lay ahead as, with Lamont and Morton, we faced up to the vagaries of primary medical care. We worked in isolation drawing support from each other and the secretary, Mrs Brown, who although young, had seen everything. Nursing support was distant and impersonal and the laboratory services were for hospital patients only—the doctor provided his own technical investigations.

Urine analysis involved boiling urine in test tubes and anything within ten feet was liable to be soiled or scalded—so the wallpaper was yellow in colour. Analysing in bulk was preferable for detecting sugar and, after surgery, a blend of up to a dozen samples of urine was concocted from the motley array of containers. I had a theory that the volume of urine donated reflected the patient's personality.

With the help of Benedict's Solution this nightly torment became tolerable. Unfortunately, if a positive result were found, all the samples had to be tested individually to identify the abnormal one—which usually had no name on it!

Patients visiting the consulting rooms had their names entered on a list. If they expressed a wish to see a particular doctor this was also recorded. Appointments were unheard of and the patients were called in turn from a packed waiting room. This arena also had a social function. There was much interchange of tittle-tattle, symptoms—and infection. Saturday evening was a popular time to visit the doctor—especially if you were male and could visit the pub on the way home.

The doctor would open the waiting-room door, call out the next name on the list and usher the patient into his consulting room. If no-one responded to the call it was assumed the patient had become disenchanted and departed for home—or the pub.

At the close of one three-hour session old Mr Skelton, a kenspeckle figure in the community, was found sitting peacefully still in a corner of the room he had entered hours earlier. I had called his name at least twice—forgetting that Skelton was deaf. Contritely I walked up to the patient and apologised. Mr Skelton looked directly at me and said nothing. He had died at least an hour earlier. But not alone! Poor Skelton had left this world from a crowded waiting room. Just as he had lived his unobtrusive precise life so he gave it up in the same fashion—without disturbing the thirty others sitting near him.

The ambulance crew were, as always, most helpful and tactful under cover of darkness. No-one ever spoke of it again although Morton's wry humour overcame his reticence the following morning.

"Hell of a fine advertisement for the new partner. Patient walks in, dies unnoticed and gets carried out! Are you sure he was dead?"

This last thrust was a consequence of a stramash at the Crematorium when Morton had to restore his young partner. The practice 'phone had rung at coffee break when the home visits were being allocated.

"Edinburgh Crematorium on the line Dr. I'm phoning about one of your patients who's arrived here."

"Not surprised about that; I've been fighting a high mortality rate recently." The crematorium secretary interrupted "But this patient's still alive!"

I felt my face change colour as I turned to Morton—"Robert old chap. I've done something awful. Somebody I certified as dead has revived at the Crematorium."

And the farce intensified.

"Mrs Harrison, the secretary there, is a patient—with a terrible sense of humour. Disregard! Before you have a stroke! But ask her what she's done about it. She knows you're fairly new here."

So I did as I was told by my senior partner and got this odd response.

"This middle aged woman walked in on me and said she wanted to be cremated! She's a Mrs Temple—and a patient of yours. I explained as best I could—'No death certificate—no cremation.' So I sent her straight up to you for a death certificate. I thought I'd better warn you."

A thunderous hammering on the front door produced instant silence.

And there was Mrs Temple. She peered ferociously at Mrs Brown and me.

"A'm here fur to be cremated. Gie's the forms—now!"

Mrs Brown was looking at me.

"Doesn't it need TWO doctors for a cremation certificate?" she asked.

Mrs Temple didn't know this fact but was persuaded as I drove her home. So convincing was I that the poor lady let a second doctor visit her at home that evening. She was safely tucked away, under certificate, in psychiatric care before nightfall and was discharged, well, a month later.

My medical training had prepared me well. But I was singularly unready, for the coarse outside world in which I had to employ these skills. The environment was too hostile for the practice of the educated art of Medicine. It was hard to survive amid the alien social pressures.

Opposite my medical school at 2 a.m. in thick snow the weakness and irony of my situation were being emphasised yet again. The voice on the 'phone had curtly said.

"Taggart—facing the Medical arch. Door's open."

A bag in each hand, I looked wryly across at the great University which had trained me. What could my clinical teachers have done to prepare me? Puzzle find the patient. God it was cold! I'd forgotten my gloves. The tenement's door was visible through the blizzard and I went in. The only light was my pencil torch. On the second level I found another open door with a further pool of darkness beyond.

Crossing the threshold I paused in the hall with its acrid smell of damp, sweat and urine. A candle spluttered in the bedroom. The electric light switch was functionless but it was just possible to see that the windows were frozen up inside. The room I had entered contained a bed—nothing else. Taggart lay on a filthy mattress—wrapped in a soiled blanket as a pathetic defence against the cold.

"Remember me, doctor? Mrs Taggart liked you."

The voice was barely audible but brought back memories of a wonderful lady who had died of breast cancer some months earlier. Her amiable but dependent husband had simply disintegrated when left on his own. Now here he was again—but clearly not for long.

"It's cold, doc," muttered the grubby old man, "and there's this pain over my chest." In went the heroin and the suffering magically ceased.

In deep shock from his coronary thrombosis, the blood pressure was unrecordable. I bolted down the stairs to the nearest telephone box and, teeth chattering, called the local hospital. As I returned to the flat through the snow I wondered if Taggart were still alive to accept the offer of hospital admission. A comatose hypothermic patient smiled unseeingly up at me in the torchlight.

There was no chair to sit on. The bed was not inviting as part of the note-writing process. I scribbled my latter of referral standing up in the dark and signed my name as the ambulance stopped outside. All the participants left the house together. The doors remained open. There was nothing to steal.

Later in the morning I visited the ward to learn from the houseman that Mr Taggart had just died. The hospital doctor complained that he hadn't been assisted by an "appalling" letter of referral. Enraged, I was moved to educate the younger man about the realities of medical life in the community. I was looked at with disbelief—as a man justifying his inadequate medical conduct. A sad and disillusioned Illingworth drove to morning surgery.

One day we must bridge this yawning gap of cognition and experience which divides the profession of Medicine.

The balance of nature was maintained during these first formative years. Any guilt feelings over Mr Taggart's death were rapidly counterpoised by the cheerful lovable Mrs Lambie's obstetrics.

The Royal College gave a Members' Dinner. This was a remarkable occurrence as, hitherto, the Members had had neither rights nor privileges. On this occasion we were invited to contribute a significant sum—"TOWARDS the cost of the Dinner."

I couldn't resist it—being convinced that my examination fees had virtually bought the College anyway. I went with my old friend "The Professor" and even chauffeured him to the dinner where most of the Members sought to quench with good wine their burning conviction that they had given more than they had received. At the sweet course I noticed that the Member on the left of Professor J. D. Robertson was unconscious. When "The Queen" was proposed he disappeared from view and as I drank the toast to "The Imperial Forces" I realised I was standing on something. The Professor also reacted and we met under the table over the comatose body between us. The hasty discussion under the tablecloth was terminated by MacLeod, the College Officer who joined the ad hoc committee as the cigars were being circulated.

"It's all right gentlemen, we'll get him out of here—nae bother!"

MacLeod, in complete control, spirited away the unconscious doctor with a cardsharper's legerdemain. The proceedings finished at midnight but there remained a group of about eight doctors who had previously known—and regretted—the pleasure of an after dinner singsong. This octet foregathered in a flat in Edinburgh's New Town where, complete with guitar and piano, the hours passed unheeded. At 4 a.m. the Professor said he was hungry and I having sung myself dry, drove him home to a professorial boiled egg and toast.

At 5 a.m. I prepared for bed. At 5.30 a.m. the telephone came alive.

"District Midwife, Dr. Illingworth. Mrs Lambie is fully dilated."

Full of instant coffee I headed for the town centre in my pyjamas and my evening dress jacket—with medals. Mrs Lambie was progressing fast and, as the foremost shoulder of the baby followed the head, the intravenous ergometrine went in; the newest Lambie emerged with commendable speed.

All was well as, reeking of alcohol, I straightened up and looked at an alarming number of female neighbours and friends who had arrived. Mrs Lambie clutched her baby, smiled serenely at the doctor and quivered gleefully as she glimpsed the audience.

"You should be charged half-a-crown for watching this trick. In fact it's worth much more. Look how carefully Dr Illingworth has dressed himself. What a lot of trouble he's gone to!"

The accoucheur realised he was wearing the jacket of "tails", complete with decorations. So I twirled for the audience. "Sorry I hadn't time to get the trousers on. Now Mrs Lambie give us an encore! Give us the afterbirth!"

An hour later the crowd was beginning to lose interest. One or two drifted away. The midwife kept looking at the doctor who gave a tentative pull on the umbilical cord. Said Mrs Lambie, totally relaxed, "Do that again and I'll flush the bloody thing out. I am not a W.C.!"

But it wasn't so funny when the midwife squeezed the uterus. That was painful. Nothing happened.

"Manual removal," she queried. "It's now almost two hours. She'd better go into hospital."

"Not on your nelly!" said the voice from the bed. "I'm doing this at home. Just wash your hands doctor and pay no attention to the midwife."

"It really is a hospital job, Mrs Lambie" said a hesitant doctor. "And you'll need chloroform." The midwife looked apprehensively at the tail-coated comedian in pyjama trousers.

"Please do it for ME doctor," came from the rather worried lady on the bed.

"O.K. Chloroform, manual removal then more ergometrine. Let's get it all ready."

A few minutes later I began to drop chloroform onto the lint pad on Mrs Lambie's face. Word got around fast and as Mrs Lambie dozed off there was scarcely any standing room.

My scrubbed hand passed through the narrow canal of the neck of the womb into the more spacious comfort of the uterine chamber itself. And there was the afterbirth waiting to greet me. We shook hands—but the placenta wavered not at all.

"God it's stuck! I'll have to peel it off," thought the accoucheur—now stripped to the waist.

Gently, over about ten minutes, the ungloved fingers prised away at a placenta almost as tenacious as a limpet on a rock. Finally the placenta was free in my hand—a hand which, holding the afterbirth, made too large a fist to withdraw through the tight entrance to the uterus.

"Pull it out, doctor," said the agitated midwife.

"Can't. It's the catch-monkey situation."

The midwife, who had been in the Services, immediately understood the problem and explained it to the other women.

"The doctor knows how to catch monkeys. You get a large vessel with a narrow neck and put the bait inside. Along comes the monkey, sticks his paw in for the bait and can't get his fist out—unless he opens his hand. But they never let go and they remain in position until rescue comes and they're captured."

I gently stretched the recalcitrant muscle fibres which entrapped my hand and, after an interminable time, I held the trophy on high. It was like scoring the winning try at Murrayfield.

To the sweet music of respectful applause the hero shot in more ergometrine as the midwife removed the anaesthetic pad and wrapped up the unsociable placenta in newspaper. We all tacitly thanked God for coal fires as the now useless organ was consigned to the flames.

"Hope this new-fangled central heating doesn't catch on. 'Twill be the end of domiciliary midwifery," said the midwife. "Won't be able to burn the placentas then. That was a great job you did, Dr. Illingworth. Must admit I was scared. But then you've obviously done a lot of obstetrics." I put on the tail coat and medals, congratulated everybody and modestly held my peace.

This escapade added greatly to my reputation and practice. I took on the role of the local obstetrician though, as Morton, my partner, often said, he wouldn't trust me to deliver the morning papers—let alone a baby.

Obstetrics never really appealed to me although in my first year I delivered 50 babies at home. My confinements would occur during the night or on my rare free week-ends; and I hated the hanging about, although the high spots of G.P. were undoubtedly the successful home deliveries. The enjoyment was obviously greater in retrospect but the experience shared by the family and the doctor made an enduring emotional bond.

It was impossible not to be aware of the relaxed atmosphere of domiciliary midwifery; of a patient tranquil in her own home; of a woman liable to infection—but yet immune because she was living in harmony with the familiar bacteria of her own environment.

And the rich coarse humour of home obstetrics went unfettered.

"Doctor my stitches are hurting."

"Oh I'm sorry. Show me where it hurts."

"Well actually, doctor, I CAN'T. It's my husband who's complaining." The arrival of the interior spring mattress counterbalanced the damage done by the loss of the open fire—in which afterbirths were ritually burned. No longer did one find one's patient folded up like the filling in a horsehair mattress sandwich.

The 20 watt bulb vaguely indicated a woman in labour in a Gorgie single room. A lean girl, the old mattress had doubled over her at either side. She lay in a hollow at the bottom of a valley. Her husband had gone out—no place for a man. He had left a roaring fire but where the hell was the midwife? The head was crowning in the light of the torch, but the perineal tissue was stretched too thin. How do you do an episiotomy in the dark when the part you want to get at is in the depths of a chasm? Torch in one hand, scissors in the other and a quick snip was the answer.

"Thank God that's done. I'm sorry dear I've cut your mattress cover too. Oops, there's the baby. Where do you keep your string dear? Where's that bloody midwife? Oh there you are, Sister! I've tied the cord but she needs a few sutures. Damn, the batteries have failed in my torch! How can I get the sutures in? I can't even SEE her bottom? Could you strike a match? Thank heaven, that's two in. One more should do it. What do you mean you can't move, dear? Oh that's easily put right, your mattress cover has caught up in my stitch. That's the trouble with these old mattresses, Sister, the patient becomes inaccessible in a crevasse!!"

I spent the next ten days in a state of septic anticipation. Nothing happened. Lamont heard the story without any surprise—adding his favourite maxims "Life comes in lumps" and "A hospital has an alien biological environment."

Within the week came the third miracle of obstetrics. Mrs Borelli was the wife of the Italian Consul and arrived in Scotland five months pregnant. A charming and brave lady she had survived the ordeal of the official initiation parties, hosting not only her guests but also a pork tapeworm. The segments of this parasite were, as always, highly active and muscular. They could emerge at any moment and dance around the hostess's feet as she carried out her social duties. She had withstood this trial with credit—but, lying on my couch she broke down.

"I have two theengs in me." Then she explained about her two lodgers to a startled doctor. When I gathered that she wanted her double delivery at home I nearly had a stroke. After she departed I 'phoned the midwife. I was going to enjoy this telephone call!

"Sister, I have an Italian lady who is harbouring two passengers. One's a pork tapeworm and the other's a baby."

The midwife, with a vivid recent recollection of a bemedalled doctor demonstrating how to catch monkeys, was equal to the occasion.

"Which one do we deliver first? What are the chances of the baby pushing out its buddy when labour starts?"

So we met at the house one evening.

The encounter was brief but well laced with jokes—all in the poorest possible taste—spoken in the psuedo Scozia Italiano language. The midwife's comments were most helpful.

"You see Missus Borelli, we gotta be careful. If we made a da worm morte, y'ken, we may dolere il bambino." And then to me— "I'm so glad I served in the Italian Campaign. She may deliver both her problems at the same labour? What a wonderful case for the 'Nursing Mirror'!"

Mrs Borelli understood the scenario at once. The midwife was delighted with herself as a linguist, recalling her service in a Field Hospital in Italy—which was rather irrelevant in the present circumstances! Quite convinced that the baby and parasite would appear simultaneously she claimed she wanted "The Scotsman" to dignify the tapeworm's arrival and produced a birth announcement which ended "........a boy (Roberto) and a pork tapeworm (Taenia).

Three months later she proved correct about the sex of the baby but she was disappointed by the coy behaviour of the parasite. "Mussolini" —it had even acquired a surname and folk lore of its own—refused to part from its owner.

Thus it was that six weeks later, a tense, expectant group met to negotiate the formal extradition of "Mussolini".

After twenty-four hours total starvation Mrs Borelli bravely swilled a ghastly witches' brew concocted by the local chemist—who wanted to come along to take photographs of the parasite. An eight hour vigil followed before my phone rang during morning surgery.

"Il Duce arrivo." Those three terse words from the midwife and veteran of the Italian Campaign were enough to cause a total evacuation by the staff of the practice house. The horde rushed into the bedroom where the midwife had assumed command.

"Right! All you men outside! "Mussolini" is mine!" We were sustained by a running commentary.

"God what a whopper! It goes on forever. Bet it's a record. Dr Illingworth has a tape measure. Look we've got the head. What sex is it?!

The sporting midwife tried to get bets on "Mussolini's" measurements as soon as the door was opened, but "Mussolini" wasn't beautiful and nauseated some of his audience.

"Got to measure him though," said the midwife. I thoughtfully gave her the tape measure. She promptly went off "Mussolini".

"Can't touch the bloody thing. You do it, doctor" "Doctor" didn't like his job but couldn't back down. I then realised that with furniture, fittings and folk in the house I couldn't measure the new arrival. Morton's inventive brain was equal to the problem and he carried the bedpan to the top of the communal staircase of the luxury flats.

"I'll take his head and you run down the stairs." "Mussolini" stretched the full distance without any tension. The two scientists measured the worm in all its magnificence.

"Thirty feet of best Italian protein," said Morton crouching over the evacuee. Just then we realised that our activities were being watched, with fascinated reluctance, by a policeman.

"I came up gentlemen because there's one car parked in the middle of the road and another up on the pavement. But now that I'm here would you please explain yourselves?" His startled gaze wavered from the audience to "Mussolini" and then to Morton and me.

"You're not going to believe this officer."

"No, sir, I don't think I am. I don't think I want to anyway."

"It's like this, officer, we're measuring a giant tapeworm."

"Why, sir?"

Mrs Borelli timed her appearance to perfection.

"Because thees ees my worm. 'e is call "Mussolini" and I mus' know 'ow beeg 'e is." The policeman swallowed.

"I see ma'am. Very interesting I'm sure. I don't think I shall report this—if the cars are moved now."

So the parasite—after three months of speculation, vanished from sight down the loo. The midwife's sense of humour didn't falter.

"It's like saying farewell to an old friend. I became quite attached to "Mussolini" ——but not QUITE so firmly as Mrs Borelli did.

CHAPTER TWENTY-TWO

The three partners prospered slowly but drove fast. Petrol was still rationed and the roads were uncongested. The practice sprawled over most of Edinburgh—but even patients on the north side of the city were easily accessible.

Waldo Channon, the internationally famous violinist, resided in the New Town. Seldom ill, he and his wife were best known to the partners through their dinner parties. Evening dress was mandatory and a strict protocol was observed. After the liqueurs Waldo would be persuaded by Mrs Channon and the guests to play for them in his studio. It was a lovely old house—perhaps a little infirm. Waldo shunned contact with material things. Drains and gutters were almost as uninspiring as "this wretched jazz stuff they dribble out on the wireless."

The ten guests and the Illingworths sat enthralled as Waldo played Bruch's violin concerto. He had reached an almost orgastic crescendo of resonance when, with an almighty crash, the entire ceiling fell down.

Time stood still briefly as we all froze rigid inside a ghostly garb of plaster dust. Waldo rose to the occasion. His voice came firmly and proudly through the murk and grime of centuries.

"At last dear friends, I've done it. I've brought down the house!"

All the injuries were minor and Waldo steadfastly refused the offer of a sedative.

"Dear lad, don't fret, I might have broken my violin."

Next morning he was fully restored and reliving his unique dinner party. "Maybe I should retire, doctor, having reached the ceiling of my ambition." He laughed again at his joke, coughed and lit another cigarette. "Dammit I must have consumption, I even bring up a little blood."

I stiffened at the significance of Waldo's chance remark, and nagged the shirt off the musician. It was a depressing examination—revealing an intractable condition. Waldo, that unforgettable character, died two months later.

Other patients were equally memorable if less pleasant. The "heavy breathing syndrome" was becoming a problem. Such telephone calls were not obscene but always occurred between 2 and 3 a.m. No word was spoken. The only sound was of sighing and gasping. It happened consistently each morning. I used to create a diversion, lay down the receiver near the toilet and flush the W.C. repeatedly. Robert was more earthy and offered the caller an explanation which I once overheard as he addressed "a dwarfed and emotionally stunted pervert." But his bluff was called. He had to replace the receiver because he was on duty. As soon as he did so the procedure began all over again.

Morton was becoming not a little strained by the "phantom yearner." His golf was suffering and the caller was not influenced by reason, by abuse, by sympathy or by understanding. Dr Lamont's immunity from these nuisance calls suggested that the perpetrator knew the duty rota and therefore must be a heavy user of practice facilities.

"Female, unmarried and neurotic," Robert reasoned "and this one knows so much about us she must attend regularly." After Kate Brown had provided a list of possibles we waited.

One of Robert's regulars was a sad woman of forty. The only child of older parents, she had become a school teacher. Robert was gentle and tolerant with her—saying that she deserved some sympathy because she had dedicated her life to her parents. He reckoned that she was entitled to a few symptoms—to compensate for years of such exploitation. However, her latest complaint, of "something coming down", was a departure. Dr Morton, rightly wary, sent the patient behind the screens to prepare for examination and called in the indispensable Mrs Brown to chaperone him.

Robert found the examination difficult. There was something in the way—too hard for a tampon—he would have to go above the obstruction and hook the object down. He accomplished the delivery—of a champagne cork—and asked the obvious question. The reply came with reluctance.

"Since my parents died I've been going out a bit and I know I drank too much last Friday. I was at this party and I felt a bit lonely I suppose. I don't have any real friends and I know I passed out."

And then she sighed. It was as if she had pressed a light switch—to reveal herself as "The phantom yearner".

Robert Morton tried to explain the anguish she had caused us. "We are puzzled and weary but we still want to help."

"Help me?" the woman replied as she climbed off the examination couch. "Men can't help me. You're all the same; you're all sex mad. I don't like men anyway. Even my father used to pester me. Dr Lamont's different though." She brushed past Kate and Robert who looked ruefully at the cork as he placed it on the tray.

"Not even a GOOD champagne Kate—but put her down for a home visit by Dr Lamont, because she's not bad, she's mad. I liked the bit about Dr Lamont being different. Is that a compliment or an insult?"

She transferred to a woman doctor whom she never consulted!

I was on call the night of that revelation. There was no heavy breathing to upset me but the problem I got instead was tangible and clear.

"Help me, doctor, ma man's aff his heid and I'm no' gaun hame alone." Having ascertained where 'hame' was, I found myself standing in a dank tenement stair. In my hand was a torch and behind me was a tremulous wee lady. We climbed two flights then entered the inner corridor of the flat. There was something creepily familiar about it all and I muttered to the woman who had telephoned.

"Get the police."

She scuttled off. It was TOO quiet. I switched off the torch and waited in the blackness, listening. Someone else was breathing in the enclosed space. The harsh sound was getting closer. Finally my nerve broke and I pressed the torch button to reveal in the beam of light a very small man with a very large and shiny knife.

"Never waste time in argument," Turner used to say and I turned and bolted down the stairs. In the torchlight I could see the steps and by the time I reached the street I was at least ten feet ahead of my pursuer and gained further advantage by strategically dropping the medical bag. Regretting every cigarette I had ever smoked I sprinted round the block—unashamedly shouting for help and protesting my innocence. I took a quick glance behind. There were now three sprinters involved and the last one seemed enormous.

"My God there are two of them now," I groaned. "If I don't reach a main road I'm dead. And I'm getting very tired." I looked round again in time to see that the third man was part of that marvellous institution— "The Bobby on the Beat." His crash tackle was in the finest tradition of the Police Force and its rugby team. The aggressor was laid out cold.

"I think the police are wonderful," said the doctor.

But, in accordance with Lamont's dictum that life comes in lumps, the violence continued. The practice was temporarily enveloped in a dark cloud of dependent depressives and experienced a wave of suicides. Sometimes there had been warning manifestations to alert the doctor which, in retrospect, should have been identified.

Colonel Conrad had retained his trusty '45 revolver and a store of depressing memories. Uncharacteristically he visited me several times in a few months to complain of minor discomforts—which were, with hindsight, the physical expression of mental distress. Sadly I missed the significance. In the small hours he dressed himself immaculately in uniform and decorations; secured the bathroom door, filled the bath with hot water, cut his wrists and pulled the gun's trigger with its muzzle in his mouth.

I worried about my failure to intervene and about guns in general. I even surrendered my own weapon to the police. But this was no help when a few weeks later, Arthur Williamson, the gentlest of men, locked himself in the bathroom and refused to come out. As Mrs Williamson 'phoned me that Saturday morning I heard the detonation of the 12 bore shotgun over the 'phone. The mess was indescribable when, five minutes later, I broke down the bathroom door.

Williamson, small and delicately made had fired both barrels into his chest. His distraught widow repeatedly wailed the inevitable question—to which there was no answer.

"Why?"

I was getting quite used to the white stains of dried tears on my shoulders as I shared Mrs Williamson's bewilderment and suffering. I was angered by my inability to comfort, but more disturbed by my lack of recognition of warning signs. Surely there was some indication of an impending act of self injury. But I was learning to look below the surface especially at the critical first contact. Why? Why did the patient really come? If only there was more time.

Morton would have none of it.

"If the means is there it will be used—impulsively and on slight provocation. That's why the suicide rate is so high in doctors. Anyway, our lives may be in other people's hands but our deaths are our own concern." In no way did this thought help the searing indignity of such tragedies.

The Scots go to great lengths to preserve the prestige of the departed—though perhaps not with the fervour of their American cousins. My father, now remarried after the divorce which I had arranged for him, swore that he had attended a farewell cocktail party to a dead millionaire in San Francisco. During the occasion the new widow drew him on one side behind a screen at the far end of the room. There, in his favourite armchair, sat his old friend, deceased, but impeccably dressed; in his buttonhole the traditional pink carnation which he always affected; by his elegantly angled hand a large Dry Martini.

Thinking of the American way of death I handed Mr Cluny's death certificate to the sobbing widow. She had already slipped out to get her hair done and spent a small fortune on a widow's wardrobe. A highly perfumed lady, I recognised the bouquet of her "Tweed". The sense of smell is such a primitive evocative thing that I stared at Mrs Cluny—oblivious to everything but the olfactory memories going on in me. Was it Cairo? I pulled myself together.

"I'll call on you tomorrow, my dear. Your husband died as he lived—gracefully and with dignity." This was a standard utterance to aid the grief reaction. It was useful therapeutics—not an ingratiating mouthing.

On my return, respecting the Scottish protocol, I followed Mrs Cluny into the dining room. There were flowers everywhere and in the centre of the room an elaborate coffin lay open. I had experienced this ritual before and approached the coffin raking through my standard list of banal phrases for something appropriate to say.

Mrs Cluny beamed with pride as we looked at her deceased husband. I took the only way out. I bowed my head in respect.

"He's like the archangel Gabriel and I knew you'd find it difficult after the long years together" declared the widow as she embraced me.

"You're all heart!"

A kindly hand led me to the front door. I was given a tissue to dry my eyes and somehow got into the car to recover. Mr Cluny, in death, had shocked his G.P. Skilfully made up, Cluny lay in his coffin wearing his best blue suit, a stiff white collar and his regimental tie. On his abdomen lay his bowler hat; a white carnation adorned his lapel; at his right hand was placed a silver topped cane; at the left, his favourite putter.

Mr Cluny was fully prepared for his introduction into the Royal Celestial Golf Club.

The failures of the junior partner were often of a social nature. Regardless of birth and experience the wonderfully expressive words of the Scots tongue were sometimes enigmatic. I hadn't initially grasped the fact that when you take a family onto your National Health list you also become answerable for their pets. The children judged their doctor not so much on his performance with appendicitis or otitis media but on how he squared up to a languorous tortoise or a bird with tar on its wings.

"While you're here, doctor" (a phrase which makes all G.P.s catch their breaths) "this spara' I found canna fly. It's goat tar on its fithers."

Ether is marvellous for contaminated birds. It acts as a solvent as well as an anaesthetic. My reputation as an ornithologist soared and I wasn't sure whether to feel offended or flattered when a swan appeared at Holy Corner at rush hour and I was at once, anonymously, informed. I arrived to find all traffic stopped as drivers stared in incredulity at this enormous bird—loose on the town.

The doctor, on foot, tried to establish a relationship and tracked the swan down Colinton Road. My efforts halted the local traffic of suburbia. Motorists believed in their unbelief and the immediate area rigidly clotted with cars. Becoming even more convinced of the inadequacy of medical training, I encountered an equally disenchanted policeman who, thinking the swan was my pet, conjured up "The Cruelty to Animals People". Within minutes the bemused swan was in a van heading for Blackford Pond—blissfully unconcerned that he had brought the southern half of Edinburgh to a standstill.

Robert was delighted by the episode.

"I always felt you were better with animals than with human beings."

"Maybe Morton's right." His comment came back to mind at 1 a.m. on February 28th as Mr Nelson was gradually pulling through his cardiac crisis after two hours of oxygen, intravenous drug cocktails and sheer fortitude. Mrs Nelson received me in her lounge. The doctor felt really fulfilled.

"We've been lucky. He's infinitely improved and he should now do fairly well." I basked smugly in the warm rays of success and admiration. I disregarded a large wasp which kept circling my head. Dammit it was still winter and miracle workers ignore trivialities like insects!

Hovering at ceiling level above the happy medico the wasp went into a dive bombing manoeuvre and shot straight down my starch-collared neck—one should be properly dressed even in nocturnal emergencies. Yet the ghastly animal was crawling about between my should blades. Mrs Nelson spoke—hesitantly, "Dr Illingworth, I've just seen something unbelievable—a huge wasp has flown down your neck."

"I know, Mrs Nelson" the nonchalance was obviously forced. "But it will be alright."

"No, doctor, I can't agree. At this time of the year I imagine they're quite venomous and you'll be stung—because it's out of season. You only see wasps in the summertime."

The wretched creature crept ineluctably downwards. There was no barrier to its determined progress—as everyone wore braces on their trousers in 1954. I could feel its dedicated progress to my nether regions and spoke up in a controlled falsetto.

"Mrs Nelson please take that magazine and hit me hard on the bottom. That'll kill it." The lady demurred.

"If I do you'll have a very painful behind. There's only one thing to do, doctor. Strip!"

Fortunately, my mother had always warned me about the importance of regular changes of underwear in case I was knocked down in the street. The testing of such advice at 3.30 a.m. on a winter's morning because a wasp was strolling across her son's buttocks, she would never believe.

Neither did my partners!

Chiefie in Killin used to have a saying which he used if he thought I was threatened by what he called "Caledonian gloom". He seemed to think that Scots were especially prone to episodic depression. Perhaps he was correct. He used to decree,

"If you're down, lash out!"

So, after this series of minor perturbations, I lashed out and bought a new bowler hat, cocking it over one eye to visit a wee soul with measles. I laid down the hat and sat on Lynn's bed to confirm the diagnosis, demonstrate the rash and show the classical buccal spots to my student. I was unready for the additional entertainment in the shape of Lynn's Boxer puppy. Sham-gabbit, like all its breed, the dog picked up the "bowler" by its brim. The underslung lower jaw at once tilted the hat over the animal's face and a frantic sightless Boxer, wearing a bowler hat, took off round the house pursued by the two medicos. The rim, perforated by the dog's teeth made the hat useless and when the local vet popped out a lumbar disc, a hatless doctor reached the house on the hill. It was built in 1715 and I had to crouch to enter the front door. I was ushered into an empty lounge as vast as a rugby pitch. At each end there was a coal fire. It was a cold day and I held out my hands to the warmth as I waited.

"Good morning," said a voice behind me. I replied in kind as I turned round to greet the speaker. No-one was there. Puzzled, I stared around the large room and finally focused on a cage out of which peered an ancient parrot. Extroverted to the point of exhibitionism this unique bird burst into song.

"It's a long way to pack up your troubles so don't forget to write." warbled the parrot. I had never before interviewed such a creature and made a trivial response.

"Pretty Polly."

The parrot squawked in disgust and silenced the doctor with an Anglo-Saxon expletive. There was a second's fraught silence and then it screamed.

"Fifi!"

A large poodle burst through the door.

"Going walkies," carolled the bird. "Get your lead." Fifi vanished and reappeared a moment later carrying her lead and leaping about in glee.

"Aw shut up!" said the heartless parrot.

While the prolapsed disc which I found made the visit worthwhile I was fascinated by the parrot. My interest was reinforced by proof that the parrot, born in 1850, possessed numerous trophies for articulation.

Fourteen years had passed since graduation in 1943. The art of coarse medicine erased all thoughts of mortgages, bills, minor personal symptoms and family peccadilloes. The inadequacy of my training continually worried me especially where ears, noses, throats, teeth and eyes were concerned—while mental illness was a disgraceful confusion where I understood few questions and fewer answers. Happily I preserved my attitude as a perpetual student and was delighted to find other family doctors who shared my bewilderments.

We began to meet regularly to try to solve the insoluble. My contemporaries helped me; the seeds which were planted have germinated. Sadly my panel of ancient icons—Galen and Hippocrates especially—failed me repeatedly.

"Doctor, I'm a good Catholic girl but I can't keep my hands off myself. What do I do? I'm going crazy with guilt. Don't send me back to the priest. He says it's a sin and I must control myself."

"You know, it's a phase many people go through and the important thing is not to feel you're odd. One grows out of it."

"I do hope it's soon, Dr Illingworth, because I'm now thirty-two! And, while I'm here doctor, there's another thing, I'm breaking up my best friend's marriage."

"I see; you've fallen in love with her husband?"

"No, doctor, it's NOT the husband!"

"That's not medicine. Is it my job to cope with sex problems?" I would ask. And Robert Morton would look up.

"Where else can they go lad? You should be flattered people approach you at all. They must be desperate. Tell us your answers."

The three partners decided to form a discussion group for clinical problems which were too involved for their twice daily practice meetings. Once a month we spent a discussion evening together. This notable advance greatly pleased me. I was gratified by the novel concept of doctors outside hospital educating and encouraging each other through an intensive study of their patients. The solutions which we reached, even if later shown to be flawed, did have the comforting authority of multiple opinion.

How encouraging it was to hear other doctors admit that they didn't know—and to hear tales so unlikely that they rivalled—or outshone one's own experience.

Mrs Brown's voice had that urgent edge.

"There's a wee girl phoning you. She's called 'Dewar' and she's in a fair state." On the extension I could hear the asthmatic wheeze—gasping,

"I can't breathe."

Jumping from the car, I ran straight into the Dewar's lovely home and climbed the staircase uttering the familiar password.

"It's the doctor. I'm coming up." There was a grunt from behind the door and I threw it open—and then rather wished I hadn't.

Professor Dewar was in bed fully occupied with the 'au pair' girl.

I quietly withdrew, contemplating protocol, when I heard the sound of severe asthma from the adjoining bedroom. There I found her—Deborah Dewar, aged nine years, who had telephoned the doctor in desperation as her father drained himself—emotionally and physically. My own first reaction was,

"Perhaps I'm not as bad a parent as I think."

Twenty minutes later Deborah had stabilised.

"Mummy's out and Daddy's having a rest. I'll be alright now."

I marvelled at her maturity and gained even more insight when, as I slipped away, I found, still closed, the door of the adjoining bedroom. What was it Professor Dunlop had said?

"Every illness has a psychological factor!" What a pity Prof. Dunlop was sheltered by hospital walls from the realities of human behaviour. He might have been an even greater influence for good had he known what really went on in the community.

Dr Grieve was similarly deprived from community contact. This was a waste of talent. Grieve was a doctor for the people. He was also a superb scientist, a gracious man of 60 years, full of social urbanity. There is no medical job which allows you to combine ALL your mental endowments and he had opted for science—where he was effortlessly competent. But I lamented that circumstances had compelled Grieve to bury talents in academic ground—talents which other people, had sharing been practicable, could have used to their great advantage.

In ten years Dr Grieve had never sought medical help and now here he was ACTUALLY IN BED! The alarm bells sounded. "Good of you to come so quickly David. I've had stomach pain for an hour." He was still fully dressed under the bedclothes and very apologetic—but if Grieve was complaining there was something serious going on—and I cut all the usual corners.

The fingers indicated the centre of the bared abdomen and I could see, just above the navel, a swelling about the size of a small orange—and, the "orange" was pulsating in time with the scientist's heartbeat.

I headed past Mrs Grieve for the emergency call which explained both to her and the ambulance service that we had a vascular emergency on hand. On my return, the pain was more severe and the swelling clearly larger. I rebounded to the 'phone and the hospital.

"Undoubtedly we have a ruptured abdominal aortic aneurysm. It's our own Dr Grieve and the arterial wall is giving way." The duty surgeon responded superbly.

"If you're certain we'll clear a surgical theatre now. When will Dr Grieve arrive? In five minutes? O.K.!"

The ambulance men walked through the open door, lifted Grieve onto their stretcher and took off again for the Royal Infirmary in one swift movement. I was in hot pursuit. Jumping all the traffic lights the two vehicles skidded to a halt outside the emergency department. The trolley, Grieve, the surgeon and his team raced for the theatre as we all anxiously contemplated what had become a melon in Dr Grieve's abdomen. We passed into the theatre and I, now superfluous to complement, dropped out and tried to get my breath back. Grieve waved his thanks.

Less than five minutes later the surgeon reappeared and slowly came up to me. I knew the worst at once.

"Will you tell Mrs Grieve?"

And that was the worst bit.

CHAPTER TWENTY-THREE

I was a lucky doctor. I was appointed to care for the staff of the Northern Hospital Group and given five beds in Edinburgh's Western General Hospital under the clinical care of Sister Barbara Macleod. The Occupational Health Service, which was run by Sister Jenny Spence, was a remarkable success. Thanks to these two splendid women I pursued a unique career as a family doctor with hospital admitting rights. The years in this ideal position were to prove the happiest of my life.

"Nullum sine auctoramento est" was one of "Sandy Mac's" special phrases in my school Latin class. "There is no evil without its compensation." I remembered the significance of this 1937 emanation—attributed to Cicero—as, twenty five years on, I looked at the patient with a feeling that nothing had really altered.

The war had seen plastic surgery bound forward as ruined faces and limbs had been restored and remade. Peacetime brought continuing public pressure of artistic—not of martial—origin. The patients' search for perfection had begun. The public had never heard of Professor Purkinje but certainly acceded to his ultimate ambition to create a human paragon.

Irrespective of such wonderful philosophies, Shona was an unprepossessing eighteen year old student nurse from the Hebrides. Between her eyes was a large barren area where normally would have been sited the bridge of her nose. As I vaccinated the shy creature I strained tact and sympathy to reach her.

"That's it, nurse. You're now immune from smallpox; have you any other problems you'd care to speak about?"

"No, no, doctor," replied the beautiful highland voice. "What difficulties could there be in Edinburgh. It's a lovely place."

Early next week I was looking at a successful vaccination site and concentrating hard on my choice of words.

"Shona, there's another wee matter." Home Sister Dykes tactfully disappeared. "Is it possible that your nose is a little too broad for your face?" God, I was making an awful mess of this. The girl replied.

"In the Hebrides we don't often see doctors and I've got used to my nose."

Shona and I lost each other in a cloud of embarrassment.

"Never mind, you did your best" said Home Sister. "Shona could look much better. Let me try a 'heart-to-heart' with her."

A week later Shona reappeared having, at great expense, telephoned her mother.

"Mum says she's thought it about it too but as the nearest doctor is some miles away by boat it never seemed reasonable to trouble him. Home Sister says I could be quite pretty." She blushed.

The following week Shona was facing a concerned plastic surgeon who wrote me a homily on the concealed needs still being revealed by the National Health Service. One week later she was admitted—reappearing at the Western's Nurses' Home with her nose in plaster, a bruised face and a stitch or two in the area used to provide the required structural support.

The operator, like all plastic surgeons, had an artist's eye. Sketching her profile he had given her a choice of surgical modifications. The removal of the plaster revealed that the ugly duckling had become a swan—albeit rather a battered one. Home Sister Dykes and I allowed our astonishment to overcome our tact as our eyes riveted on the fairy tale which had come to life. Jeannie Dykes' rich Glasgow voice vibrated sympathetically.

"Doctor, are you thinking what I'm thinking? And if you are, what's going to happen to her? She's been transformed. Maybe I should take her under my wing—she's resident in the Home."

But six months later even the phlegmatic Jean Dykes was in a turmoil.

"The bees are round the honey pot! And WHO made the honey? Have you seen Shona recently? She's changed emotionally as well as physically."

I was looking at the heart-shaped face, wide-set oriental eyes and chiselled features of a poised young woman—the product of some remote rock in the Atlantic—and a surgical miracle.

"Your parents won't recognise you, Shona."

The nurse smiled.

"To be honest they're not as pleased as I am. They think I'm different in every way—and I am! Main thing is that I'm happy!" Confidently serene she slipped out of the consulting room as Sister Dykes materialised—wearing an enquiring look.

"Why can 't we get anything completely correct? We've been too successful."

I again thought of Edward Albert's dwarfish footman running at the stirrup of good intention.

Six month's later Shona "flatted out" of the Nurses' Home—as she was entitled to do.

The Poisons Unit pulled no punches eight weeks later. "Aspirin overdose and we don't think Shona will make it—but she keeps on muttering your name."

I visited Shona repeatedly over the next two days to the exclusion of routine medical matters. She survived and on day three I was ushered into the small side ward of the Royal Infirmary—totally unprepared for her hostility.

"It's all your fault, Dr Illingworth. If you'd left my nose alone perhaps I'd never have had this awful affair. I've been wicked and I've let my parents down. I can't tell them or you what I've been doing. But YOU started it!"

I tried to cope with this outburst. Shona was alive—only that mattered. For half an hour I counselled her as intensively and intimately as I could. I WAS accountable. I must find the words! But I failed and left—sadder and wiser.

Four years later Shona visited her old hospital. She came with her husband and baby. Dykes and I had got it right after all. Home Sister rubbed her own nose and grimaced cheekily at me after Shona left.

"One of the new entrants is a fushionless wee thing. She's bright—really—but her harelip has been badly repaired in the past. Should we talk her into the beauty treatment?"

"Perhaps, Sister, but after YOUR face lift."

"Let's have your hair transplant first doctor," came the reply.

The search for beauty was becoming relentless. Ears were pinned back. Noses were shortened, jaws were lengthened and, on psychological grounds, some of this work was justifiable.

The practice felt less certain about mammary glands. With patients I insisted on using the word "bosom" which irritated Lamont.

"I hate euphemisms. They're not 'bosoms', they're breasts." Morton snorted. I've got another name for them! In Africa we had an anatomical classification of such appendages—into 'boopers', 'droopers' and super-droopers'. David's present clinical problem is with 'super-droopers'—which should be pared down. Quite seriously some sort of 'boob' job may be permissible. Lamont was scandalised. "Boob job indeed! You're not doctors. You're beauticians! I'm the senior so I set the standards. I have more experience than the two of you put together.

The silence was intolerable. I excused myself and made for my car.

The partnership was now only a legal document—a strained and troubled relationship for which the future would be short.

But somehow the lay staff held the machinery together for a time. A medical practice wasn't only about doctors and their peculiarities; it was about the people they served; it was about the dedicated women who organized it.

Mrs Baillie did the typing and shorthand. She was also a mine of information—of the law, the ministry and English literature. And what she didn't know she would find out. In these days the doctors dictated and Mrs Baillie recorded in shorthand what was said—correcting and polishing later as necessary. She was inscrutable and her professional pride never permitted any form of self-expression—unless on request.

I succeeded in breaking this composure only once. It was over the affair of a slender wee soul, Mrs Robertson, who was a dedicated sun-worshipper—which was sad because she was almost devoid of breast tissue. Perhaps understandably her poor mammary development had obsessed and depressed her—to the extent that, as indicated, it had also stressed the fabric of the medical partnership. "Breasts are breasts, NOT bosoms!"

The National Health Service couldn't help her. So letters winged to-and-fro until Mrs Baillie found the name of a private plastic surgeon down south. She became deeply involved.

"A boob man and a good one. I've studied his background."

Having passed judgement she set the wheels in motion. It was a private job. Here again Dr. Lamont was upset—especially when the surgeon wrote to say that he had on offer four inserts—small, average, large and extra-large. After seeing Mrs Robertson the average size was advised—because she was so slim. In view of the distance involved he would leave the follow up to me.

One month later Mrs Robertson and husband re-appeared at the surgery. They vanished behind the screens and I guessed from the stifled exchanges that there was a surprise in store.

As she pulled back the screens she turned her bare upper half round to the doctor.

"There! What do you think? Aren't they magnificent."

Mr Robertson gave one of the pair of mammary coconuts a tentative prod and said she ought to go topless for evermore. I was more concerned about the effect of gravity and the defiance of the laws of physics. Mrs Robertson's super-structure seemed disproportionately large for the rest of her frail anatomy. Nevertheless it was an impressive result, which remedied a severe personality problem.

It was the follow-up letter to the English consultant, which disrupted Mrs Baillie's composure. She remained bravely disciplined until the closing paragraph.

"She called on me yesterday complaining of insomnia. Mrs Robertson explained that she had forgotten to mention to you that she has always slept face down. Her new chest now makes sleep difficult—but a mild hypnotic may help her to adjust."

"Do you think we should comfort him with the quotation about the dwarfish footman?" Mrs Baillie quipped.

The surgeon acknowledged the letter at once. He particularly wanted to reassure Mrs Robertson that she was not at risk "at high altitudes".

"I have just been at a convention in Washington and one of the papers was rather worrying. Apparently some implants react badly to low atmospheric pressures. Could you please inform your patient that her implants are secure? She may hear of the "exploding air hostess" syndrome through the media."

Mrs Baillie got the last word when she saw the letter, "Well, there's now no chance of a bust-up, I suppose."

By the 1960s there were three Illingworths at Watson's College and the entire financial edifice was finely balanced. The bank manager was cordial but strained as Lesley juggled her sums.

Worry turned to anger at the discovery of Dr Lamont's failure to claim certain professional fees. His reply that I should not expect to profit from other's misfortunes made matters worse. I pointed out that being cushioned by a private income had made him lose touch with the real world and that he should resign from the practice.

The next week brought the school fees, a polite but pressing letter from the bank and a statement of intent from the building society to increase their rate of interest by 2%.

So the house was sold. The debts were settled and, I transferred my overdraft to another bank. The removal van arrived and departed with the precipitate of 13 years of marriage.

The old Austin, loaded to the gunwales, drove down the drive for the last time. Festooned with luggage and household goods it headed north and west through 250 miles of pouring rain. The annual holiday had coincided with the removal and some weeks earlier we had rented a remote Highland croft looking out over Rhum and Eigg. Twelve hours and one puncture later we reached a narrow track treacherous with pot holes and deep mud. A voice full of highland gloom addressed the occupants of the travelling pantechnicon.

"Stoap the veetchicle here! Get ye oout and walk. Here's the key."

The five Illingworths fell out of the car into a sort of morass. Through the murk we could see a small building which our new friend indicated.

"Ye look fair furfluthered. Ah'll help ye!" But the family, sturdily independent, courteously declined and slithered forward through the quagmire to their holiday home. Everything was soaked and we had mud up to our knees by the time we reached the front door—each with a dripping burden. On the left was a kitchen with a huge stove, a single bed, a table and some chairs. A tiny bedroom lay straight ahead and a larger bedroom for the children was on the right.

So we reached Acharacle.

Somehow we got the stove alight, pumped up some water and dried the sheets by the time darkness fell. We also found a small door leading to a bathroom which functioned—provided we put our backs into water pumping. We sat in the candlelight clutching syrup sandwiches and mugs of cocoa. We had successfully made the first adjustment to the simple life. Tomorrow was another day and all would be well.

Morning brought a confusion of neighbourly advice.

"Morrison the grocer in Salen is ten miles awa'. There's anither shop nearer but the stuff's nae guid. Ye can hae eggs but dinna' ask for chickens. Butcher comes to road end on Tuesday but he can be affa' slow and it might be Thursday."

What time does the butcher come?"

"Dinna ken—but your neb'll tell ye. His meat fair stinks! Ye'll can get a pail o' milk a mile awa' but it's no' clean. See yon burn? The Campbells live on this side and the MacDonalds on the ither. They're Catholics but old Mrs MacDonald has a fine coo. She'll gie you guid milk but mind—you must get a hud o' the coo afore she'll milk it.

She did milk it after my pathetic efforts had provoked a suggestion that if I simply held on she would get the cow to jump up and down.

Aided by this rich lore we measured up to our environment and the simple necessities of survival healed the wounds of mortgages and overdrafts. For a month the rain poured down and the midges ate their fill as we splashed around Ardnamurchan. Never did we have worse conditions—or a better holiday. Nature in the raw is therapeutic!

My mother welcomed us back to Edinburgh and sheltered us as we looked round for a new home. We were starting again and had to get it right this time. We did—and found a house of "forever and ever" type.

We started once more. The patients didn't wish to be excluded and, when we moved in, a variety of trophies arrived—each to be acknowledged and treasured as a hallmark of security. One of my maternity cases even pushed her baby round in her pram. Lying across the baby was a beautiful spiced ham. Lesley, as usual, struck the right note.

"In an uncertain world it's so important to belong. You are obviously part of the community in which you work. The evidence is all around you and I'm happy to share you."

Her Aberdonian shyness then overcame her—but the point had been made. The people who matter in life are the permanent ones—be they the parish minister, doctor, blacksmith, policeman, postman or lawyer. Even the village idiot is part of the tapestry of local life.

My patients continued to educate me—improving my vocabulary of standard English by adding picturesque pieces of dialect. Lesley's origins in Buchan made her a valuable interpreter. How sad if we continue towards uniformity of expression!

"I think my wee quines' got something smittle, doctor."

"No, no, your little girl's got measles"

"Then it is smittle, doctor"

"Your child's got measles"

"But measles is smittle"

"Is that the local name for it."

"Flech, doctor, dinna be so perjink. 'Smittle' means 'infectious!'"

When Lesley heard this account she simply said, "Basically, I suppose it's your parentage. Of course your father was English." This joke was used to explain every possible sin in "the black book"—which, as all Scots know, is kept by 'Auld Nick'.

The old standards were fading fast. Orthodoxy was out. Females were liberated and equal to men. They went on "the pill", sought sterilisation and devalued the catastrophe of abortion. The general ethos was destructive rather than creative and I had trouble in adjusting my service to the patients' new attitudes. And I constantly struggled to adapt to the ever-changing vernacular. As one girl put it, "the pill" prevented her consort getting off the train at Haymarket station—where there was a brief railway stop just before the Edinburgh terminus.

"There's a long tunnel between," observed the G.P. as the liberated girl vanished with her prescription for the contraceptive.

How was I to know that "getting off at Haymarket" is the local expression for coitus interruptus!

Inevitably the group practice failed at first to reach agreement on the contraceptive pill. Which was worse, an unwanted child, a termination of pregnancy or the doctor's provision of a possible incentive to promiscuity?

It was the same difficult type of sensitive moral problem as helping the dying over the last hurdle. The stimulus of pain and distress prolongs life. Should one prolong the dying by allowing the patient to suffer or quietly induce comfort and relaxation—and thereby shorten a life no longer worth having? And people wished for some sort of legislation!

The doctors made their own decisions and they didn't speak about it although they might have a conversation (without many words) with their nurse colleagues.

"You can carry it further", Morton said, "If you fill up the dying with blood, steroids, antibiotics and stimulants you may win them another day or two. But if you talk to your patient; speak to the relatives; then look into your own heart you'll find the answer. If you cannot, then get out of General Practice—because you are not emotionally equipped for it. Get thee back into the hospital or the laboratory—and stay there!"

Full of these great philosophies I brought in the next patient—a woman of 40 with generalised bruising. She was also a depressive of brittle mood whose rheumatic heart disease had left a volatile disturbance of hearth rhythm.

"I don't expect you to believe this, doctor, but I was stretching up to the top of an old fashioned wardrobe to get a parcel. The wardrobe door was open and when I pulled the parcel down the entire thing fell on me. I was trapped inside the wardrobe for two hours until mother came home with the shopping." The image of this austere school teacher encaged by an old wardrobe made my choice of words rather unsuitable.

"Poor soul, you needn't have come round here like this you could have telephoned me." The school teacher scorned the sympathetic approach and the suggested home visit.

"What on earth makes you think we have telephones in our wardrobes?" I tried to explain but the next day she changed her doctor.

Perched on a step ladder as I painted the kitchen mantelpiece I was beaten to the front door by Lesley's brother, George, who was directing the decoration. Lesley, bruised and frightened, gasped her way to safety.

"Attacked—handbag stolen." George dialled the police as I examined my wife whose successful attempts at self-control exacerbated my anger. Perhaps it was as well that Lesley was hopelessly laden with shopping and couldn't defend herself in the dark as her handbag was snatched.

Half an hour later, after several sweeps round the neighbouring blocks the trail was cold. Only George was resolute. He would patrol the area on foot, he insisted.

And within a few minutes someone broke cover from the driveway of a large neighbouring mansion and glanced back to see a large figure behind him. He began to walk more quickly. Brother-in-law George heard money chinking in a jacket pocked and increased speed. So did his prey—who finally took to his heels. The police sitting in the panda car were impressed by what was obviously a pursuit and halted the quarry—now terrorised by a large man clearly intent on mayhem.

And there in his pocket was the evidence—Lesley's personal belongings. The fugitive bolted into the security of the police car before the threatened dismemberment occurred. By midnight he was secure in a cell in the High Street headquarters and had freely admitted his guilt.

With my anger unrelieved by physical action, I was sleepless and the telephone call from the inspector of police was answered at once.

"Dr Illingworth, that man who attacked your wife has just told us that he is a diabetic and is not at all well." "Then call his doctor, Inspector, and I hope he's in as much trouble as my wife!"

"Well that's why I'm phoning you, doctor, he's YOUR N.H.S. patient." I choked.

"By God Inspector, I'd love to come—but I'd probably kill him. Let's not strain my professional oath. Don't tempt me."

The patient got a visit to the Royal Infirmary then sixty days in "The Queen's Edinburgh Hydropathic." I wrote to the prisoner to advise a change of doctor.

The grey and yellow kitchen was a sensational success.

For once the influenza—the factor which separates the men from the boys in general practice, came in May. Robert at 10 p.m. was trying to complete his last home visit. He wasn't on call but the epidemic was in its third week and all the doctors were whacked. Dr Morton sat down behind the patient and started to examine the back of her chest. He lay back on her pillows as he examined her with the stethoscope. About ten minutes later the patient, still with thermometer in position, realised that something was wrong. She looked round. Her beloved doctor had nodded off.

"Poor dedicated exhausted man," she thought. In spite of her fever she rose from her bed and wrapped Robert up in blankets.

All hell broke loose at midnight. Robert was reported missing and there was a general practice alert. Mrs Brown studied the housecall book and pointed out that no-one could know where Robert was. One only knew he hadn't reached home. Anyway it was now 1 a.m. and they could do no more than drive slowly round the practice area. The police and hospitals knew nothing. There was no sign of Robert's car and to promote further enquiry might be damaging. There would be a simple answer–surely.

About 5 a.m. Dr Morton was awakened with a few words and a cup of tea.

"We're both much better, aren't we doctor?"

Later that day the G.P. said—yet again.

"That's my story and I'm sticking to it.

Wisely I refrained from comment as I was myself pretty vulnerable.

An old lady down the road had sent for the doctor—convinced that she had bronchitis. The doctor was not allowed to come in, however. I rang the bell, the letter box opened and I was refused entry. I peered through the letter box, saw the fevered face of the recluse and heard a chesty cough and a request for treatment. "Please let me in. I must examine you if I'm to help you."

"You're not coming in doctor, but you can pass your instruments through the letter box."

The concept of such an examination made my mind reel but I passed the chest piece of the stethoscope through the aperture and heard the bronchitic sounds as the patient held the diaphragm in position on her chest.

"Look, dear, an examination through your letter box is ridiculously inadequate but I'll prescribe—only on the understanding, however, that if you don't improve in two days you'll let me or nurse come in. Who's going to get the medicine for you, anyway?"

The letter box closed with the prescription and no more was heard until a year later when the postman alerted the neighbours to the pile of mail in the box. The neighbours 'phoned the doctor who, with the local policeman, broke down the door. Icy blackness met us. There was neither light nor heat and there were shutters on each window. The house had that scent of the end-products of metabolism which produces instant anorexia. We found the bedroom and, in the bed, a peaceful-looking corpse. Beside her on a filthy table lay a lawyer's letter which gave a point of instant reference. The entire flat was uncarpeted and the public rooms contained old tea chests full of prune stones which had eroded through the containers and were aggressively attached to the floor boards.

I went back to cover up the deceased's face with my handkerchief and as I did so I kicked something metallic under the bed. I pulled out not a chamber pot but an ancient biscuit tin packed with treasury notes. After asking the officer to confirm the find we left. I 'phoned the lawyer.

One hour later the solicitor rang to say he had been to the house with his clerk.

"Guess what we found? Another tin of notes. I'm going back shortly with the banker. He'll be in touch with you about your discovery." The banker called the next day to collect my hoard.

"Now we've got four biscuits tins. I found two more. There's several thousand pounds in all.

I remain optimistic about biscuit tins.

The streets of Edinburgh were deserted at Sunday lunch time as I responded immediately to the message, "My husband has chest pain." I headed towards the centre of the city through a prime residential area. The spectacle which made me stamp on the brakes was unreal. In the centre of the road stood an elderly barefoot lady wearing only a nightgown. I addressed the apparition.

"Can I help?"

"How kind. I'm afraid I'm lost. I just stepped out for a breath of air." It seemed an unlikely story but I didn't like to question it.

"Where do you live?" I'll take you home." The lady clambered into the car and gave an address on the other side of Edinburgh. Ten minutes later we pulled up at a gate with the lady saying excitedly.

"Yes, here we are. Thank you so much, my son is inside." I thought it only kind to ring the door bell first. Sure enough a middle-aged man appeared.

"I'm a doctor. I've got your mother in my car. I found her about three miles away." This news clearly shocked the other man.

"Good Lord, she went on holiday to Orkney last week!" The lady in the nightgown slipped past us through the open door.

"Home at last," she murmured as she entered the house.

I was brusque—time was passing.

"Sorry. Must go at once—possible heart attack." And I ran down the path and began to turn the car. I glimpsed the man running from the house and as I accelerated away there was a hammering at the driver's window.

"Stop! That's not MY mother."

Wearily I pulled up and got out.

"Then who on earth is the old girl in the nightie?" By this time the hubbub had lured the neighbours from their Sunday afternoon pastimes to the scene of the action. The uninvited guest, now completely at home, looked steadily at the invading crowd.

"How good of you to call! Get them some tea, Willie."

"I'm not 'Willie', I'm Jimmy—and I'm NOT your son. There's something wrong."

One of the neighbours said tremulously.

"Excuse me, I think I know this lady. She's Mrs Macdougall who lived here about twenty years ago. Her husband died and Willie, her son, emigrated to Australia. She's been in a nursing home for a long time. Who brought her here?" Several pairs of eyes looked accusingly at the doctor.

"Well, I did. I found her wandering in the street near my home and she said she lived here—she says she's Willie's mother."

"I'm not Willie, I'm Jimmy—and she's NOT my mother" said the harassed man. "You brought her, now please take her away again."

The neighbours nodded their agreement. I offered my arm to the central figure in the face. Regally she arose.

"We're going now. We don't like your company." The lady in the nightie and the G.P. walked stiffly to the car—the doctor now fully aware that he had been deceived by senile dementia. We drove off with as much dignity as possible—but I was worried.

One possible coronary awaited me and I had one demented lady in a nightie in my car. And in the salubrious suburb where it all began I reached the street of odd encounter to find it swarming with nurses and orderlies. I stopped the car beside a worried figure in uniform.

"Is this the lost sheep? She's had a nice drive." Before any discussion ensued she was winkled out of the car and I drove furiously to the man with the suspected heart attack.

"Never fear, the doctor's here," I shouted in characteristic fashion and I and the medical bag crashed through the Tanners' front door. "Where's the patient?. He was disarmingly honest and confessed.

"I feel so guilty, and I didn't want my wife who telephoned you to know, but I was at the office party last night and was introduced to "White Ladies." You know, Gin, Cointreau and Lemon, and I had so many I've burned the lining off my inside. I'm so sorry about the false alarm."

I was much relieved. The coronary epidemic had started and I had already learned the value of instant treatment. I sat down and sighed. Mrs Tanner, who taught music to supplement their income gave me some tea while her daughter, Heather, made further amends by putting her new hamster, Robert the Bruce, into my hand. The hamster promptly bit the doctor and vanished inside the grand piano. Ten days later I interrupted my round to enquire—mainly about Robert the Bruce. Heather informed me that he had never reappeared and that her dad had said Robert the Bruce must have died after biting the doctor.

CHAPTER TWENTY-FOUR

Miss Gulliver's opening gambit that she really didn't know where to begin boded ill for my schedule as I murmured reassuringly—with sinking heart.

"Start at the beginning. You won't surprise ME, you know."

The middle-aged lady flushed..

"Well, doctor, it's like this. I'm thinking of marriage."

I contrived to make my gasp into a cough.

"Can you tell me if I am physically able for it?" The bung suddenly came out of the barrel of words.

"No! " No I've put that badly. I know I'm sturdy. I really want to know if I'm alright as a WOMAN—although I'm sure that my fiancé"—she smiled proudly as she used the expression, "is a man of the world!"

"But lots of ladies have no experience," said I. "It's a diminishing proportion, however, and liberation doesn't always bring happiness."

"You're being very unselfish and considerate in coming here and I know it wasn't easy for you. You'd be amazed how few women come for this sort of "check-up"—although it's something I encourage. The pre-marital equivalent for men is a total failure, incidentally. Men won't accept."

Two days later Miss Gulliver, suitably screened, prepared and comforted by Sister lay on the examination couch. Inexplicably her dentures were clasped in her hand. I wondered for a moment if I'd got it all wrong until Sister explained.

"Doctor's just going to have a wee look down below. We often do these check-ups on ladies. He won't hurt you." I inspected the sepulchre.

"I'm going to touch you lightly—there will be no discomfort however." And, as the gloved fingers made gentle contact, the entire lower part of Miss Gulliver went into spasm. Marriage wasn't going to be easy for the sweethearts!

Worse was to follow. There was absolutely no way into the sanctuary.

"Well done Miss Gulliver! You're perfectly formed but I think it would make married life more comfortable if we smoothed the path for your husband to be." Miss Gulliver nodded understandingly—rightly convinced that she had already achieved a great deal.

"What we need, my dear, is a gynaecologist—a woman—who will make you even better prepared." I was beginning to feel like a mechanic working on a racing car.

Magically transformed under light anaesthesia into a woman of physical readiness Miss Gulliver stopped off on the way back from the hospital to thank the doctor and give him a bottle of Bruichladdich. How could she possibly know about the merits of Bruichladdich?

A month after the marriage Miss Gulliver reappeared. She looked awful—even allowing for the fact that her other new discovery, mascara, had lost its way as the tears coursed down.

"It was all for nothing, doctor. My husband has been impotent—for years—he tells me. I've been so silly." I felt curiously guilty.

"But you haven't! You've been very brave and understanding."

Such measured verbal treatment for reactive depression occupied the new few weeks.

It was a very happy marriage nevertheless.

I was listening to the distraught wife of a minister. "I've been charged with shoplifting and I don't know what to do."

I'd heard it all before and, not unreasonably, groaned. "Oh for an acute appendix, a good old pneumonia or a violent middle ear infection—anything immediately accessible." But here, yet once more, was the time-consuming intangible consultation for which I had not been trained and which the National Health Service had never envisaged. Again I bemoaned the fates which made my patients and myself age synchronously—and the older the patient the less the excitement and the worse the problem. I thrived on drama and yet, because I recognised that this was a medical problem of equal importance to the sparkling clinical pathology which was the happy lot of younger doctors, I listened carefully.

"For two cakes of soap and a jar of face cream I've destroyed a career. I walked out without paying—I admit it—but I didn't intend to steal. You've known me for years doctor. Do you think I'm a thief?"

The benefits of knowing your patients were again apparent. This minister's wife was a wealthy rigid only child who had married late—for security rather than excitement. She had not anticipated the enormous social pressures of her position in the community and the by-now familiar pattern of reactive depression had developed—with its sequence of explanation, encouragement and anti-depressant drugs. I was pleased that I had used medicines—as in her notes I read,

"She would rather be a medicated zombie than an agitated depressive."

She spoke again as I turned over her medical record.

"I'll kill myself. God would understand. And being a trained nurse I have the ability to be discreet about it."

I suddenly felt very protective and eager for action and intervention on behalf of this determined woman.

"Things will be sorted out. I promise you I'll take it up now. I'll 'phone you. But if you kill yourself in the meantime you'll feel awfully silly!" A faint smile flickered round her wan face as the lady of the manse departed and I reached for the telephone. I spoke to the Procurator Fiscal and gave him the facts.

"The police should charge the doctor who gave this ill woman her medication." The lawyer moaned in response.

"You doctors and your bloody drugs! But I accept that this is genuine and I'll talk to the police. I don't imagine your patient will hear any more."

The good news was relayed at once but, now half an hour late, the rest of the consulting session was mainly apology, pressure and anxious time-keeping.

Yet once again submerged in emotional problems! This is the fate of senior partners in a group practice, and the following evening I was trying to help a woman with chronic diarrhoea. She had been investigated in hospital with normal results. Finally she disclosed that she dosed herself with laxatives to control the social pressures contrived by her extrovert husband. I had (not for the first time) been treating the wrong person—and wrote to her husband.

I was getting really unsettled about the future of what they now called "Primary Medical Care."

New Year's Day was something of a turning point. By tradition one of Scotland's days for self examination, I peered inside my Celtic soul and felt dismayed. I had become used to a life of successive hurdles—each of which dismayed me. But an existence without challenge and discipline was worse than a complacent acceptance of security. It was all very confusing.

I would have to discover another horizon and I decided to make an appointment to talk to Professor Dunlop about how it should be attained. Sir Derrick was as suave, charming and handsome as he had been twenty years earlier. I stammered, as I often did when tense.

"I didn't think you'd see me, sir. You won't remember me and it's all rather silly in the cold light of day. The truth is I want to do something original. I had a friend once who used to worry about whether or not he had an original mind.; I now find myself asking the same question. I want to write a thesis." Derrick smiled reassuringly as he stood up. His suit was, as always, perfectly cut. In his quiet cultured, lisping voice and from a great height the professor addressed the nervous G.P.

"Silly fellow, Illingworth, I know all about you from several sources of information. You're a good family doctor and therefore the equal of three specialists. Your record's not bad—I examined you in the M.D. I know you did well. If you want to be stretched, continue to put your back into that excellent practice and write your thesis. It's a tall order and an unusual combination but it can be done. I believe General Practice will need more academic people. What have you looked at so far?"

"Anticoagulants and alimentary bleeding, sir."

"Dear lad, the former is not suitable for a family doctor and the latter sounds rather disgusting." He wrinkled his elegant nose. "However, you'd have access to an unlimited number of subjects." Derrick laughed. "There might even be a fringe benefit in the shape of tons of fertiliser if you assess diagnostic tests in gut problems. I believe they are now calling it 'recycling'. But how terribly coarse of me. Please forgive me."

I had always admired Dunlop. He was the most inspiring teacher I had ever had and now I felt a surge of enthusiasm.

"If you think it possible I'll try it," I said firmly.

Derrick smiled again.

"Perhaps I've just encouraged the seedling of an idea. That's a good teacher's duty. I hope I survive to see you complete the task. It won't be easy for you. Now go away and think about it."

A euphoric Illingworth, with high ideals, drove to his afternoon surgery. Mrs Brown showed me my appointments list. All the names were female and I hadn't a student to act as buffer. I started with Sheila—she had exhausted Lamont and Morton before being passed on to me. She couldn't therefore go any further down the chain of command and we were stuck with each other because she wouldn't see the assistant! The difficulty was that, while there was a physical problem—she had hypertension, which the doctor could control—I couldn't control Sheila!

In her early forties she dressed provocatively and the effect was not unattractive. I always left my door a tiny bit ajar and Mrs Brown rang the extension to give me a fictitious telephone message every few minutes. The game was always the same.

"Miss Reilly, you're three weeks early. I know you have constant access but you may be keeping others away."

"Oh doctor, I really haven't been so well. I've had some chest pain and I KNOW my pressure is up!" By this time the blouse was off and the doctor felt compelled to listen to the heart as the patient looked straight into his face.

"I wish you'd call me 'Sheila'. Is my perfume too strong for you?"

I wanted to tell her she made the room smell like a Batavian brothel—but thought I'd be misunderstood.

"No, Miss Reilly, the heart sounds are good and the blood pressure is satisfactory. Please come back in a month." The 'phone would then ring again.

"Certainly! I'll leave at once Mrs Brown. How shocking!" I shouted to Mrs Brown at the switchboard.

Miss Reilly remained motionless in the chair as I rampaged round the room collecting irrelevant equipment. The patient was impervious. She'd seen it all before.

"Do you think it's my nerves doctor? I've had some harrowing experiences. Last night my best friend's husband seized me and kissed me passionately. What shall I do? I'm so unlucky with men. When I was a Wren I was sexually assaulted by a padre in a cruiser and, after I became a Catholic, a priest misbehaved in church."

The doctors used to dread this sexuality by proxy. While the syndrome of "verbal intercourse" was well recognised, Sheila was especially persistent.

"I don't think you believe me doctor. Perhaps you think men don't find me attractive." And then the final unanswerable question would come,

"Do YOU regard me as attractive?"

At this point I would walk to the door and open it. The hall outside was always busy. On would go the blouse and if Sheila Reilly didn't budge the ploy was to walk out and leave her. In an overcrowded building there was nowhere for me to go except the toilet. After some minutes, Kate Brown would bash at the lavatory door.

"You can come out now."

Sheila was one of several women who regarded male doctors as love objects and couldn't come to terms with medical sexlessness. In their role of patient they unwittingly enshrined themselves in a garment of inaccessibility and relinquished their own sexuality. No amount of provocation produces any medical response. Doctors are neuter and reserve their hormones strictly for home consumption.

The years were beginning to telescope together. No longer were poor children sewn up in their underclothing for the winter. The last of the rustling ladies—parcelled up against the cold in underwear of brown paper and string—had gone as the welfare state spread its supportive net even wider. Even he of the bronchiectasis—whose lung cavities contained such foul pus that he could empty the waiting room in ten minutes—had gone. Medicine and Surgery marched ineluctably forward making a nonsense of prognosis.

Mrs Blackford's narrow heart valve had confined her to bed for two years. An heroic surgeon operated on her when she was 80, gave her a new valve and eight wonderful years of life—during which she even played a little golf. She remained on anticoagulants and had an occasional tiny cerebral attack in which she invariably heard Dr Illingworth singing "Amazing Grace". Mrs Blackford said it was a small price to pay! In those early years of heart surgery, artificial valves made an audible noise. Neither she nor Jock, her husband, had good hearing—so that they both wondered, during the dinner party, about the behaviour of the guests celebrating her recovery.

During the main course conversation languished and finally ceased. The six guests sat silent as the Blackfords tried to distract them. Finally one guest said in an uncertain voice,

"I may be imagining it but I keep hearing this strange faint sound." The other five guests sighed with relief.

"Yes, there's somebody knitting in this room—but I can't see them." They all listened even more intently before rounding on their hostess.

"Mrs Blackford, you're clicking!" The hostess dismissed the idea as nonsense but the evening ended early.

My explanation provided miles of conversational mileage.

"I may have to put up with noisy machinery and spells of Dr Illingworth singing Amazing Grace, but it's been worthwhile. Incidentally what do I do if I stop ticking?"

"That's easy! We'll just wind you up again."

Mrs Blackford clicked another eight years.

Alcohol was becoming an increasing problem amongst liberated women. The woman alcoholic was despised; the male was tolerated and his conduct was often rationalised. Women were, in general, less able to cope with the problem of addiction. Be it cigarettes, alcohol or drugs the female was less accessible to advice than the male.

As for drugs, by the mix-sixties three "heroin families" had been identified in the practice—young people living together sharing drugs, needles and hand-outs from their parents. Our first hepatitis victim from needle sharing was admitted to hospital—where she remained for a few days before she discharged herself—after Sister found her "main-lining" in the ward. Three months later she was dead. There was now a new problem in our midst and nobody knew how to cope with it.

Mrs Harper's addiction had, at least, a faint undertone of humour. She used to become dreadfully and luridly drunk. Alcohol transformed a shy personality into a foul-mouthed, aggressive and licentious woman. Her husband, a successful business man, simply threw in his hand when, for the second time, the "special unit" of the hospital failed to cope with her problem. However, she, through her doctor, had carte-blanche as regards admission to the unit for the treatment of alcoholism. Mr Harper's message for me was only that his wife was unwell and would I call that afternoon. I drove into the short drive leading to the Harpers' graceful residence. One of the lounge windows was shattered—but I entered the hall anyway, calling out who I was. The silence was absolute and lounge door was closed. I opened it. A silver cigarette box whizzed past my head followed by a crystal decanter which was less well aimed—but came with a clear verbal message about my parents' indiscretions. Mrs Harper, supported by the mantelpiece, lurched forward clutching a small garden folk. Not a small woman even when sober, she seemed to have grown in every dimension. I went with her as she attacked and she made a neat arc over a collapsing doctor as I went down on the floor.

I promptly sat on Mrs Harper and waited for her husband. Ten minutes later I was still perched on the lady's bust. Mrs Harper's mood was becoming increasingly affectionate. It soon became clear that I would have to go it alone as the patient's hands became increasingly purposeful.

"Mrs Harper I like you too. You really are a great girl. Tell you what, you get a bottle and we'll go for a drive."

"O.K." she slurred. "But only after we've drunk to it." We drank. The neighbours of genteel Colinton then saw a large lady being disentangled from her G.P. and put into his car. Once seated she put the bottle to her mouth and stuck her legs out of the car window. In between swallows she shouted out verse after verse of "Eskimo Nell", waved her legs to the audience, covered the doctor with lipstick and attempted to remove my trousers. It was summer and the driver was much too harassed to drive rapidly. I could only hope that the people might believe we were doing it for charity. No reputation could survive this dissolute display. Ten minutes later we reached the psychiatric hospital. Mrs Harper's blasts on the car horn ensured a reception committee to contend with her immediate admission. Dishevelled and daubed with lipstick I reached the security of home.

Bleeding from the gut is certainly not among the more glamorous aspects of medicine. Samples of the end-products of digestion arrived steadily; the back kitchen was transformed into a laboratory and the librarian of the College inundated me with references for study. I worked consistently from 11 p.m. to 2 a.m. and Lesley found me a secretary who was familiar with thesis work and displayed the results well. And my large family were a fringe benefit for my research.

"Your patients are a liberal lot," sniffed Lesley as another dozen large containers arrived. The instructions for the patients were typed and distributed to those under assessment. A SMALL sample was requested—but the Scots are really a generous race and perhaps they felt flattered that the doctor took such an interest in their innards.

"Professor Dunlop was correct," continued Lesley. "Wasn't he the one who made the joke about an endless supply of fertiliser? Maybe we could make a living as compost manufacturers."

"Fergie Buckets"—no-one knew his real name—used to come round to sift through the refuse bins for choice pickings. Occasionally Lesley made him a sandwich and placed it, carefully wrapped and labelled on top of the household garbage. An impressive, dignified man in spite of his humble activities, he and I used to talk if we met over the Illingworth's bucket. Fergie, on this particular day, was standing looking into the garbage as I pulled up at home to use the 'phone.

"Yon's no' funny, sir. It's no' a nice thing t' dae!"

At once I realised that the charwoman had found the specimen containers in the laboratory and had tidied them into the garbage. Fergie never returned. Clearly people who didn't use indoor sanitation were not worthy of inclusion on his round. Lesley felt humiliated.

"This dam' thesis has taken up three years of our lives. Even Fergie doesn't want to know us any more."

However, the thesis was completed and was sustained (with commendation) twenty years after my first graduation.

Dr Lamont's response to the news surprised me.

"Do you intend to continue to look for mountains to scale? Are you pathologically ambitious? Science and general practice are incompatible so don't include me or my patients in any high falutin' research."

The cognitive gulf between us was widened further by a letter from the Nuffield Foundation suggesting an interview in London and a possible research grant to expand my interest in cancer diagnosis.

The Selection Committee of the Nuffield Foundation probed hard at the aspirant Illingworth who had armed himself with flowing replies to certain questions which, I anticipated, must be asked of me. The problem lay in making the memorised script sound spontaneous.

"What is your scientific background, doctor?" was the first question.

"Not a very solid one perhaps but I know that I work and live in the greatest laboratory of all—the general practice of medicine. I'm therefore surrounded by a wealth of learning—little of which has been assayed." I could hear myself speaking and thought...........

"Lousy actor! Hellish lines."

"How then, in general terms, would you approach your theme. 'Cancer Diagnosis and Detection'!"

"With—um—strict discipline—a triple amalgam of behaviour perhaps. May I quote from my recent paper on method in research?—'Imagination with restraint, doubt with receptivity, incisiveness with sufferance' Research is only organized curiosity."

This time the well-rehearsed words came out much more robustly and seemed less contrived.

I knew I was off to a good start and my unaffected sincerity then took over. The panel must have sensed that they had before them someone deeply disturbed by the quality of cancer detection in his own country. Remorse begets reform; action is the product of dissatisfaction; I was weary of the tragic procession of those with advanced disease who sought me out—too late. I wanted desperately to discover malignant disease while it was still accessible to treatment—and preferably before it manifested itself in clinical terms. Conviction and realism emanated from a diffident being outlining his programme of work. I believed totally in my project—and it must have shown.

Two days later came the offer of a Travelling Fellowship of six months duration. Additionally, a locum tenens was to be provided for my patients. There were two conditions in the award: my wife had to accompany me and I must return to work in the United Kingdom. Neither requirement presented any problem. There was much communication between us and North America before the travel agents were finally briefed on the itinerary. Lesley's mother moved in to look after the three children and the dog—quietly and unobtrusively.

CHAPTER TWENTY-FIVE

In 1966, in a June mist, the liner left Southampton. The temperature was 55 F.

Lesley and I were the only British passengers travelling first class and we were glad we weren't paying the bill. There was a vast chatter of Americans who seemed to study us closely at mealtimes. On the second day Albert Rosman of Baltimore came over, introduced himself, and solved the reason for his approach.

"It's all this knife and fork stuff. The way you English eat tickles me to death. Mind if I sit down and watch?" I thanked God I wasn't eating spaghetti as Albert pulled up a chair.

"What's that ma'am, you're NOT English? You're Scotch! Well that's even better. Tell you what, if you translate nineteen and a half guineas into dollars I'll give you lessons on our coinage. Our system is much better." Albert became a close and valued friend during our voyage.

Mrs Abram personified the rich American widow. Wealthy, bejewelled and extroverted she spent most of the year cruising about the world. Grossly obese—she admitted with great good humour that she'd never known what it is to be hungry and she was charmed to meet two Scaatch people!'

"Gee. I love Scaatland and I adore your bagpipes. They're delicious! On my last visit we ate them with cream sauce."

The Illingworths conducted an ocular conversation without words before Lesley recaptured her social composure.

"There must have been a helluva noise, Mrs Abram. Perhaps you're talking about 'tripe'!" I choked on the olive in my dry Martini as our American friends laughed loudly (if not discerningly) as I visualised this barbaric act of sacrilege—or cannibalism!

The five day crossing of the Atlantic was, as it should be, a carefree period of suspended time and a retrospective non-event.

Mrs Pat Allan, Head of the Foreign Desk of the American Cancer Society, had been standing on the New York quayside in a temperature of 90 for almost four hours. She remained immaculately unruffled as officialdom took its course with the ship's passengers. We were eventually disgorged to droop in the insufferable humidity. I immediately had an abreaction. My days in Tandjoeng Priok came vividly to mind as I felt the damp patches appear on my jacket between the shoulder blades. Pat Allan was doing a sheepdog act rounding up porters, luggage and transport. Within ten minutes we were on our way to her apartment where we showered and changed before walking to the Café Arnold on Central Park.

There was a queue for the Boston shuttle at La Guardia airport. The Americans are not good in queues—"lines" as they call them. There exists none of the British discipline with its docile uncomplaining acceptance of the need to behave fairly and take your turn in an orderly manner.

The stampede was a classical example of the survival of the fittest. Lesley was assisted by a charming man who sheltered her in the rush to board the Caravelle aircraft. Although the soul of courtesy he had clearly been drinking.

"Call me 'Phil'. I know the ropes," he said—his breath heavy with bourbon whiskey. On the plane he sat beside the two travellers and unburdened himself of a great pressure of words. He seemed desperately lonely—talking sadly but fiercely about his isolation—oblivious to the lightning which flashed round the aircraft. Lesley and I looked significantly at one another and when Phil vanished briefly Lesley said,

"What a pathetic mannie; nice but 'affa fou'!"

"We're going straight to our hotel in Boston", I said to Phil. "It's been a long day for us. So we'll say goodbye and thanks."

Our new friend caught up with us again at the baggage carousel.

"Come with me. The bar's just over there." And Phil marched us off. After half an hour and two drinks I was really worried as we hurried over to the baggage area. There was nothing and nobody there.

Twenty minutes passed before we recovered our lost property—one bag of which had been rifled. Thoroughly upset we marched to the cab rank, instructed the driver and climbed in. The cab drove off but we were not alone. Phil, as loquacious as ever, was huddled in a corner. At the Copley Square Hotel I paid the fare, waved to Phil and walked with Lesley into the lobby. The cab drove off—without the American! At the reception desk he was becoming rather maudlin.

"Just can't bear to leave my new friends. I'll come with you to your room."

This intrusion upset me and I said so!

We reached our room in a mad rush.

"That'll teach you not to speak to strange men. Lock the door! I'll make sure he's not under the bed by now."

This strange beginning of our American trip was followed by a sleepless night. The room had no air conditioning and the heat and humidity made life most uncomfortable.

So we filled the bath with cold water and took it in turns to soak in it, wishing we had the courage to order ice from the night porter.

But we were learning fast and next morning there was an argument at the hotel desk which culminated in the arrival of Dr. Sam Boyer, with whom I had frequently been in contact by letter.

"You can't live in a dump like this," exclaimed Sam. "I'll put you in a place you'll like—at the same price." He was as good as his word.

Later that day I reported to Dr Raker at the Massachusetts General Hospital and we were enveloped in the warmth and generosity of American hospitality. The tour had begun and nothing and neither of us would ever be the same again.

I was to have six months of intensive education in all aspects of malignant disease. Weeks of study without clinical responsibility: without disturbed nights and without financial worries. It was a uniquely wonderful opportunity. My American colleagues couldn't do enough for us and the Illingworths incurred a debt which they could never settle.

It was pathetically ironic that the only sadness of the tour came from my own medical practice. Lamont's letter was waiting at our contact address in Boston.

"We are concerned that this trip is causing you to overdraw your account with the partnership and I have proposed that you move onto half-salary." Our monetary arrangements for my devoted mother-in-law and family were now in ruins and wherever we travelled we were pursued by the obstructive shadow of the eldest partner who had now obtrusively emerged as an excellent doctor, a good man but an impossible partner—who was equipped only to work alone in an atmosphere of medical stalemate. He hadn't even had the courage to talk to me. Written words can be the refuge of the emotionally destitute.

But our travels had started and at their end I would consider the partner who had forfeited my respect.

Massachusetts General Hospital was a revelation and between its intellectual support and that of the American Cancer Society, on each of my fourteen days attachment, I learned something, contributed perhaps a little, and dictated to Lesley each evening a summary of the day's proceedings. At week-ends we toured New England, feeling so much at home, that our departure for New York's Plaza Hotel was something of a wrench.

New York was a spiced half-cooked omelette—but a unique excitement. I was attached to Memorial Sloan Kettering Hospital and walked there each day, exposed to the prodigious spitting, hawking and sniffing of other sidewalk users. Nor could I protect myself from the perils of disgorged chewing gum and tobacco—while discarded toothpicks littered the sidewalks like the broken arrows and lances of mediaeval battlefields.

Dr Schwartz, Chief of Surgery at Memorial, accepted me as one of his team and surprised me during my attachment by asking my opinion—with a certain deference. I would be introduced as "the expert from Glasgow, England." Attempts to clarify the confusion with my distant cousin, Sir Charles, failed—but I don't think I sullied my cousin's name. However we crossed scalpels when I realised that surgeons dictated individual radiotherapy treatment—indeed all anti-tumour therapy.

My displeasure was greater at the practice of radical removal of the pelvis for widespread malignant states of female organs. Little was left form the waist down. An American colleague told me that the patients were known as "Schwartz's Busts"! Surely death is preferable.

Buffalo was our next stop. The attachment was with Roswell Park Hospital and I was privileged to work with the Grahams—man and wife—whose contribution to uterine cancer diagnosis has never been adequately recognised. I was now aware of my remarkable opportunities—contemplation without action: thought without responsibility—in a nation of extremes, antitheses and paradoxes. Random disparate experiences—medical, social, spiritual, secular, solid and liquid were on offer and we had to make use of this wonderful change of ethos.

In Chicago I was received by two eminent doctors—Stuart Roberts and Owen Wangensteen who took us to their hearts and gave me a personal intensive course in Oncology. I shall never know for sure why they bothered, but the day before we departed for Minneapolis Dr Wagensteen took me to "Grand Rounds"—where about two hundred doctors deliberated on difficult problems. A young man with gastric cancer was presented first and as the discussion proceeded the Chairman said "We are honoured today by the presence of Sir Charles Illingworth—a famous surgeon from Glasgow, England.

Simpleton that I am, I was thinking that it was remarkable that we were both present when I realised that the Chairman was looking at me! He continued. "Tell me Sir Charles, when doing a total gastrectomy do you always take the spleen." In complete bewilderment –

"And where would I take the spleen?" I replied.

After a moment's silence there was loud applause as it appeared that the Scottish doctor was gently condemning splenectomy in these circumstances.

"Well said" quoth Dr Wangesteen. Fortunately Sir Charles never knew of his diplomatic expression of opinion.

I was fortunate to have in Lesley a meticulous recorder of my observations and someone who would discuss and simplify the bewildering influences of a new ethos.

In Toronto's Princess Margaret Hospital I garnered much information in tumour diagnosis but it was in Minneapolis, with Dr. Gilbertson, that I really got lucky and found an attitude to cancer precisely similar to my own. Diagnosis inferred interpretation of established symptomatic disease. Detection meant discovery of disease before it declared itself. This immaculate ideal might never be wholly practicable but must be pursued especially in the high risk groups—which were identifiable.

And I carried this banner across Canada and the U.S.A. and even began to put out ideas about cancer PREVENTION—which were regarded with polite astonishment. Preventive work had no prestige, no glamour, little status and almost no financial support. Nevertheless the quest for early disease must inevitably become a search for the disease prone and mature further into matters of behaviour and inheritance.

My talks were well attended. I made least impact on the medical students and this was understandable when one considers that the medical course is almost entirely about disease. Health is scarcely mentioned and may even produce mild antagonism when compared with the drama and fascination of sinister illness.

How does one promote health in a society conditioned to disease and focus on wellness not illness?

Seattle was enchanting aesthetically and academically. We lived peacefully on the campus in the Edmund Meaney Hotel as I followed a gentle but well planned course of tumour study—supervised by Lloyd Nyhus. Vancouver, our previous stop, had given us so much Scottish hospitality that we appreciated the slower social life.

And so to San Francisco where I was to address the General Hospital on alimentary cancer. Admiral Silliphant introduced me to a large audience. My lecture was illustrated by slides and I repeatedly turned clockwise from lectern to screen—forgetful of the cable which led from the wall to my neck microphone.

The final applause was stilled when the speaker—bound like an Egyptian mummy—fell off the podium. A few weeks later I was informed that the hospital had never had a more memorable lecture. The generous cheque accompanying the letter made me change my mind about major appearances.

In North America the best medical care was wonderful—clearly ahead of that in Great Britain. However it was tainted by the venal element in it and I couldn't come to terms with a situation in which the wealthy could buy better health care. But excellent medicine was not only practised in the centres of excellence patronised by the rich, I encountered good doctors in small clinics—in Harlem, in Houston and out in the boondocks—where sheer geographical size militated against good care. There were many admirable doctors labouring on the periphery—and with the poor and lowly. There were others!

Charles Katz was a practitioner working near a city centre who had a thriving practice almost as large as his ego,

"They like me Dave because I give 'em what they want. They all get 'shots'. My patients EXPECT to feel better when they leave me. They do. The amphetamine shot comes first. That gives 'em a lift at once. Then I put in Vitamin B.12 for their blood followed by an injection of mixed vitamins in case of dietary deficiency."

Excusing myself I hastily exited through the waiting room which carried a huge sign on one wall. "If you're waiting why not visit Dr Katz's anti-staphylococcal laundromat opposite?"

I was beguiled by the idea of importing the Katz principles into my sedate Edinburgh practice. Then I realised Katz had followed me.

"You don't like my approach Scottie I see—but 'needs must' my friend. I'm having trouble with my third wife and a little business like mine helps me to survive. Priorities y'know. Come along to the country club and meet her tonight. I'll pick the two of you up at eight."

Cheryl Katz was a striking beauty in her thirties whose appearance didn't accord with her claim to have a Ph.D. She insisted that I should dance with her. Charlie Katz' s problem wife was rather high—not with amphetamine but with alcohol.

It was not so much a dance as a massage.

Lesley and I changed partners and danced out the exit—without giving a backward look.

Sometimes I felt that we must be in a Hollywood film. As the plane circled over Sky Harbor (Phoenix airport) Lesley broke her thoughtful silence.

"It's three months since we left home I've had a long holiday and I'm brooding over my mother, the children and the dog. You can cope without me and this must be the last stop in our adventure."

At the airport the temperature was 117 F as four of us—George Thornton and his wife awaited us—clung stickily together. Eighteen years had passed since the days of agonized uncertainty in the Western General. George had matured into an eminent gastroenterologist with a lifestyle to match.

We spent the first day reminiscing round the pool—with me much in the water. Periodically George would float out to me a small raft bearing a Dry Martini.

The Hollywood illusion was increased next day as we drove via Jerome to Sedona and continued on to the Grand Canyon, the Painted Desert and the Navajo Trail. It was breathtaking, and after seeing various Indian ruins we took off for Mexico in one of George's cars. Tucson, our first stop, was a fascinating town through which we drove to Nogales and the border. Mexico was primitive and alarmingly commercial. Everybody was trying to sell us something—cheap booze, a watch without works—or worse. Re-crossing the border into the U.S.A. was a curiously comforting experience.

Lesley's departure for Scotland had been arranged. Wistfully she made her final entries in her diary—at which I sneaked a brief look.

The ghetto pathology of Harlem vied in memory with the delicacies of 'Jimmy's Harborside' in Boston. The knifing of the duty casualty officer in South Boston—where husbands delivered their wives of their babies, contrasted with the luxury of our New York hotel. She described a country whose conflicting extremes somehow contrived to survive together in a sort of tolerant hostility. Its medical disparities were best epitomised in Pat Allan's advice to my wife –

"If you're going to be sick at the week-end do it on the golf course. That's where the doctors are."

I stood on the terrace at Phoenix airport—"Sky Harbor"—watching Lesley's plane head East and homeward. I shivered—conscious somehow that I had surrendered a protective garment as well as a companion. I had to conquer a brief recurrence of forgotten vulnerability but returned to start work—the cure for all that ails one.

George had laid on an intensive programme. I spent that evening with Dr Dean Everett—a family doctor with roots deep in Arizona. Much to my delight he recalled his grandmother's account of the repulse of raiding Apaches and the legends of Superstition Mountain and of the Lost Dutchman Mine—with its hoard of gold. My childhood images crystallized by the side of the pool and I was far away from cancer diagnosis when "Trix", the dog, fragmented my glamorous visions by vomiting on my foot.

The three doctors returned from fighting in Indian country to the realisation that Trix's abdomen was distended.

After a phone call and a dry martini the medicos and Trix were on track to Dr Falkenheim—the veterinarian who confirmed our diagnoses of obstruction and took an X ray. After Dr Falkenheim fished out the X ray from the tank a tangible silence fell. "I hope I'm not alone but I see a large frog in Trix's abdomen." said the vet. This obstruction, all four limbs fully extended, was displayed, clearly outlined in the dog's gut. Dr. Falkenheim looked questioningly at George.

"That's not a frog with bones. It's solid through and through. It's a rubber frog. How in God's name did it get there? Trix is a little animal." George laughed.

"Good God, it's 'Fred the Frog'! It's Trix's toy—called after Fred of our favourite restaurant in Edinburgh. David and I knew the real Fred twenty years ago."

Dr Falkenheim flinched.

"I've got to convince myself that this is really happening. I'm just about to deliver a dog of a frog, by Caesarean Section."

One hour later the anaesthetised dog slept—on the front seat of George's car. The frog rested also—in my pocket.

So ended Friday and we began the weekend at Sun Devil Stadium for the football game. But my heart was in Kennedy International Airport in New York where I knew Lesley must be about to board for the U.K. George dug me in the ribs as we left the stadium.

"Dr Turner wouldn't like to see you looking soulful like this. What's the position? Write a summary. Do you remember the chap who got acute heart failure from eating too many salted peanuts at a party? Tell me about the development of the lens of the eye. Oh hell! Sing 'The Irish Tinker'. We're on our way to the Haywards."

Harry Hayward was a ridiculously successful expatriate English anaesthetist who lived in magnificent style. His patio was vast and partly roofed. Tropical plants, palms, creepers, waterfalls and pools provided an illusion of life in a jungle clearing in which, ectopically, a fully equipped bar had been constructed.

"David dear fellow, you're driving and this is YOUR party—because your wife is on her way home. So be a good chap and run the bar. There's everything you'll need—three jugs, one of Scotch, one of water, and one of vodka—all labelled," declared Harry. George grinned at me.

"Haven't had a night like this since we passed the Membership."

"Scotch and water all round waiter!" I did my stuff, running round with a tray of glasses, a pitcher labelled 'Scotch' and one labelled 'water'. George, true Scot that he was, threw all the ice at imaginary alligators in one of the pools. There were twenty people present who, with George's insistence and my administrations—drank a toast to "Bonnie Scotland". The bartender dashed round again and completed his tour just in time to hear George declaim (in his richest Scottish tongue) to the dumfounded Americans,

"To the Jacobite cause; to the King across the water; this glass will give no lesser toast!" Even for George Thornton this was a particularly good effort and he underwrote his superb performance by draining the glass before smashing it in the huge reproduction fireplace. The entire company was caught up in the drama, thinking this was Scottish protocol, and followed suit. Harry Hayward abstained, looked at his wife, his guests and the wreckage in the fireplace. He finally selected the bartender.

"You and your friend have just broken this party up—literally. What in God's name is happening? Good grief—the guests are all smashed too—on two whiskies!" Hayward and I looked at the guests who seemed to be merging into their primeval jungle surroundings. George and his wife were dancing a Highland Fling, the other guests were sitting down—apart from one cooling off under a waterfall.

"Must be the drink," said I. Let's be scientific. I'll have Scotch and water too—no ice of course and see what happens." I sipped the mixture which George had made the other guests gulp down twice—a large scotch with a lot of water to replace fluid from perspiration. We sniffed the pitcher of water from which I had poured so generously. The shortest party in Arizona's history ended as the truth dawned on Harry Hayward.

"Good God," he said, "I put the vodka into the bloody water jug!"

Disregarding the penalties of bartending, I soldiered on alone until I was approached by a friend of George's wife. Claudia

Vincent was forty-ish. Constant exposure to the sun and cigarettes were transforming her skin into a parchment of yellowing mosaics—reminiscent of irregular stained cracked paving. The wiry and still shapely body was encased in a tight black and silver lamé suit. The silver boots and platinum hair underwrote the impression of a female creature from another planet.

"My marriage to a well-known actor is almost ended, Dave. What say we team up?"

This was the direct approach. I was speechless until George intervened and gently let slip that he was treating me for V.D. I heard no more.

For two weeks I shared George's large and varied clinical commitment. Twice weekly he had a sigmoidoscopy session in St Joseph's Hospital. R.A.F. service had introduced a military precision into this clinic. At exactly 8 a.m. we walked into the small diagnostic theatre which contained five men in an attitude of prayer but with their faces buried in pillows and their rear ends angled upwards—pointing towards the aisle down which George proceeded—with Sister offering a fresh instrument for each patient. 25 minutes later we had reached the end of "sigmoid alley". Efficient it was, graceful it was not. The spectacle of five bottoms inclined towards the ceiling—at $25 a time remains etched in my mind.

After another week of garnering and refining a free flow of opinion and experience from my American colleagues I felt I had drained dry the local well of information and, with the facts carefully recorded, I parted rather sadly from the Thorntons and boarded the plane for Houston. The plane landed at dusk. The weight of the suitcase nearly dislocated my arms as I struggled to the nearest taxi.

"A reasonable hotel, please, close to the M.D. Anderson Hospital." There was a laconic 'O.K.' from the driver.

My nose told me there was something wrong with the Burton Hotel in downtown Houston where the cab driver had left me. It had a stale odour of bygone pleasure. The lift spilt out me and the porter on the fourth floor. In each direction the narrow corridor and silent numbered doors suggested an arrival in a house of correction. The porter opened the door of the room, put down the luggage and pocketed the dollar all in one swift movement. He hesitated at the door.

"You alone?" he drawled, rolling his eyes. I knew what was coming.

"'Fraid so" I replied. "But I'm not worried." The hotel porter importunately continued.

"Anything you want, and I mean ANYTHING, you just tell me and you get it, O.K.?" I gravely thanked him and closed the door.

I sat down at the small desk.

"God, this place is terrible" I wrote to Lesley. "It has a tang of unpleasant things—but my problem is probably loneliness. Tomorrow morning I'll be at the hospital. I think I'll change hotels." I looked at the stains on the carpet, briefly inhaled the sour odour in the bathroom and examined the bed for bugs. I had just reassured myself that all was well when there was a loud knock at the door. When I opened it there was a highly perfumed lady up against me.

"I'm here, Joe. Isn't this real cosy?"

"Sorry ma'am you must have the wrong room. I'm not 'Joe'."

"Do I worry? Are you sure you're not 'Joe'?" said the hustler and started across the threshold. I took her firmly by the elbow and pushed her away as I slammed the door. A most unladylike word echoed down the corridor. I completed my letter, double-locked the bedroom door and was repeatedly wakened by nocturnal excursions in the corridor.

Next morning at 8 a.m. I was in a cab heading for the sanctuary of the M.D. Anderson hospital and Dr Clifton Howe, Chief of Medicine—who didn't waste any words.

"I can't understand how you discovered the Burton Hotel. You were lucky to get out in one piece. How could you be so simple? Surely you know our homicide statistics are alarming. WE'LL get you accommodation and at your next stop don't trust the cab driver. You're on your own you know. Aw forget it! How's your golf? We'll play on Sunday."

For two weeks I beavered in the hospital. I was pelted with information and facts as I wallowed in my sybaritic lifestyle.

When I realised that I was intensely enjoying all that the Americans offered so generously and naturally I took a shoehorn to myself and sent a telegram to my next medical contact at Kansas City. The reply was terse and immediate.

"Will be at airport."

I noticed the drop in temperature as I dawdled through the barrier. I was suddenly seized by the shoulders.

"Welcome to Kansas City, sir. Great to see you again! Car's over here," said the rich Scottish voice of Professor Cowan. I was bundled into a limousine and driven off at speed in my usual state of mild confusion.

We're heading for my home, Professor Illingworth, and you'll be our guest for as long as you care to stay. Haven't seen you for almost twenty five years—I was your student in Glasgow in 1942. But you've worn well. Fact is I wouldn't have recognised you as my old surgical chief—except for that typically British hat you're wearing." I couldn't get in a word through the barrage of Glasgow dialect.

The car arrived at the gates of Lake Pleasant estate where a security man looked into the limousine and recognised Cowan. The torch was flashed in my face. Cowan gasped out in his native jargon.

"See here son. I've really cocked it up. It's a ruddy mixter-maxter. The Dean says to me, "There's this Scotch visiting Professor arriving—'David Illingworth'—and I jaloused it must be my former Chief in Glasgow. So I sent you a wire to Houston. Meetin' the plane. I couldna find auld Illingworth then I saw this funny looking bugger in the fantoosh hat. In the dim light and allowing for quarter of a century I convinced myself I had the right man. Now I've had a wee keek at you and heard you speak I know I've got the wrong man. Who the hell are you?"

I explained myself.

"And I've been trying to tell you for the last fifteen minutes!"

As we stopped at Cowan's residence my self-imposed host was still trying to control himself.

"Aye it's no' a but-and-ben in the Salt Market I see" said I as we crossed the threshold in the luxury of Cowan's house. The spurious guest looked on as the bemused host embraced his wife.

"This Dr Illingworth's a bloody impostor but, as I kidnapped him at the airport, he'd better stay. He speaks the language but I'm fetching the Medical Directory—now!"

"No need" said the graceful Mrs Cowan. "He and I were at medical school together in Edinburgh. I'd know him anywhere even though he's lost his hair."

I remained at Lake Pleasant.

Over the third malt, George Cowan, fixed me with a determined look.

"You're a crafty bugger but you'll not be wanting to sit on your bum while you're here. I'm the Chief of Radiotherapy so we've a lot to do. You'll work with me and you'll help with my teaching. I've a spare set of golf clubs and a boat on the lake so you won't weary. We start work tomorrow—I get up at five o'clock. I'll call you."

A rather muddled Illingworth finally reached bed at midnight—only to be hauled out at 2 a.m.

"Guess who I've got on the 'phone?" said Cowan. "Your wife!"

In 1966 it seemed impossible to be talking to Lesley from the middle of the United States of America. I was overwhelmed. But we didn't get beyond the family, the dog and the weather. Unprepared for this unparalleled act of kindness I vowed to do better next time. I tried to thank Dr Cowan whose face was beaming with pleasure.

"Aw, haud yir wheesht!" growled my host.

It was the Kansas City attachment which displayed the difference between American and British medicine. I recorded several incidents which troubled me—fully aware, however, that an American doctor might have equally adverse reactions to

British medicine. I was sorry to criticise those who had treated me so generously and openly, but I was no spy because I spoke freely about my disagreements and the final report on my tour was widely distributed in North America. It received little recognition and even less approval—which was perhaps understandable—I had seen more of the U.S.A. and its medical care than had most American doctors.

The disillusionment began on the first day when we admitted for corrective surgery two patients whose common bile duct had been, in error, carefully ligated and divided by a rural surgeon performing a routine gall bladder removal. Cowan was unhappy with peripheral American surgery and struggled to establish his specialty among a confusion of what he called "friendly-corner radiotherapists"—usually surgeons, who, in hopelessly wrong circumstances showered a few magic x-rays on their patients.

But things were changing in 1966 and Professor Cowan, was asked on the second day of my attachment, to see a man from the boondocks. The request came from a laryngologist and George Cowan and I easily visualised a tumour of the vocal chords.

"Eminently treatable," said Cowan. "Admit him now—this State is so goddam enormous that we can't treat him on an out-patient basis—and send him down for his first radiotherapy treatment tomorrow morning. We'll cure him."

But late the next afternoon the patient had not appeared. Cowan was puzzled

"Be a pal, David," he said in his melodic Glasgow accent. "Go up to the ward and remind the intern about yon laryngeal tumour."

I complied and sought out the laryngologist—who was patently embarrassed.

"We decided to operate—after we explained to the patient that surgery would eradicate the problem."

"A total laryngectomy?! I asked.

"Yes, Scottie—but although he's lost his voice, he'll recover. Anyway the senior resident has had little experience of total laryngectomies—and he did it under my supervision. It's O.K.!"

I had no words.

But the next day I was invited to the Rehabilitation Unit in Kansas City and found therein a sickening number of young people—crippled or depersonalised—by highway accidents. And the standard was incomparably good! One more I viewed America as the supreme disparity and not least in matters medical.

Red Indians fascinated me. One of my Canadian friends claimed that the Americans were still trying to atone for their past infamies by providing a good medical service for the indigenous citizens. And it was a good service! But I couldn't fail to appreciate the irony of the situation in which the original inhabitants of the continent had been allocated "the bad lands" by the government. The "bad lands" contained valuable deposits of oil and minerals—and some Indians—those who avoided addiction to alcohol—had become exceedingly wealthy. Whisky was a menace and their comatose bodies on Kamloops sidewalks became a permanent memory.

Cowan gave me a treasure chest of experience and opinion in Kansas City. It wasn't entirely a professional training. His favourite pub was "The Bigger Jigger". Half of the pub was in Kansas and half in Missouri. The state line ran right through the middle of the bar and the two states had different licensing hours. When time was up in one state the patrons walked to the other end of the bar counter for their next drink.

The scrupulously planned tour moved on to Columbia, Missouri. The University was creating a Department of Family Medicine and was anxious to have my contribution. It was a privilege to be involved at the beginning of the project. On the day I left I was offered a job. The terms of the appointment were remarkably generous.

Richmond, Virginia was notable only because of the insight I gained into American social conflicts. I spent days with Dr Stuart Nottingham who could trace his inheritance back to the MAYFLOWER—and even earlier. An excellent physician he declared that he was also a seer, poet and visionary who had a great empathy with Edgar Allan Poe! The resemblance to

Professor Dunlop was startling—not only physically—his teaching exhibited the hypnotic overtures of a form of dramatic art. He also introduced me to Mint Juleps.

"Looking at you I can't tell whether you're asleep or searching for the next smart thing you're going to say" was his comment within a few minutes of our meeting. "I realise you've seen a lot of the U.S. of A.—but this is different. This is the South!"

Perhaps I smiled patronisingly.

"I know of the problems but it's a hundred years ago."

"It's still them and us" grunted Dr. Nottingham. "We shall never forget what the Union soldiers did."

I questioned my American friend's sincerity and even suggested that he might be playing a role for a visitor's entertainment. Nottingham was furious and dragged me along to one of the main battlefields of the American Civil War.

"You're like all casual visitors. You don't trouble to examine our varied and hybrid interfaces. You believe that everything is just like the Hollywood movies. You will return home oblivious of the undercurrents in our country. If I told you that our finest Virginian orthopaedic surgeon is a Negro—but hasn't a single coloured patient—you wouldn't understand. The greatest intolerances in our country are between the various levels of coloured society!"

I muttered a few nothings about time and adjustment but Nottingham had the bit between his splendid American teeth.

"Another fact you'll overlook is that the woman is always boss in a Negro society. While there's plenty of work for female Negroes, their husbands are often unemployed or unemployable. The men remain at home to do the housework so the women become increasingly in command of the family as their men lose their self-respect and become more and more effeminate. This inadequacy of the male Negro may be compensated for by violence. The commonest cause of death in Negro women from 15 to 60 years is homicide."

I was horrified by this peroration—something far removed from my travelling fellowship theme. Yet was it? Medicine is about human behaviour as well as disease.

"You want something for your notebook? O.K.! David. We have three endemic American diseases—excessive eating, excessive drinking and excessive talking! Now these are the real problems." So I wrote it down—of course.

Johns-Hopkins, Baltimore on St Andrew's night was a memorable experience. The Baltimore Pipe Band played all night long, three teenagers died when their car ploughed into the front of my hotel and the barman dropped down dead shortly after I went to bed—I was so tired that I slept through the fire alarm—much to the manager's consternation next morning.

"My God, we forgot about you," he said.

Next evening Albert Rosman sent his Cadillac to the hotel and entertained me to dinner. It was superb—although the haemorrhagic nature of the steak reddened my shirt front.

Philadelphia, where American Medicine really began, with not a little Scottish help, was next on the itinerary and still listening and learning, I proceeded through Washington to New York. After six months the grand circular tour was ended. Festooned with luggage, I stepped on board the QUEEN MARY for five days of luxury in an emotional vacuum.

My chief contact at Memorial Hospital in New York came to see me off in the Queen Mary.

"I shall remember you—NOT by your contribution but by the fact that, like all Brits, you don't talk—you sing! And in your case you communicate with your hands at the same time!"

As usual, I wrote it down and, when we met again fifteen years later I produced my diary to stimulate an argument amongst what had become senior physicians. I had a gift for stirring things up—which probably originated from my own insecurity.

The voyage home was an eating marathon.

It was two days before the compulsive diarist reawoke in me and I began to turn the pages of my volume of clinical notes—surprised and rather proud that I had garnered so much information. I was less convinced about the merit of my own contribution through the notes of my prepared lectures were well thumbed.

And now the task was to clarify these records and to apply my new wisdom.

I drifted off into a sea of experience.

There would be a price to pay.

CHAPTER TWENTY-SIX

There wasn't, of course, any escape from the consequences of the Nuffield Fellowship. I had made the grand tour and now must share it with anybody—on request. My first duty, naturally, was to my patients but reports, seminars, lectures, committees, hospital meetings and other clinical involvements were to fill the next twelve months of off-duty time.

"The art of coarse medicine" which so aptly describes general practice obviously took priority. The fruits of personal success were to be tasted, only rarely, in leisure periods.

One of the first acts of reparation for my long absence in North America was an open lecture at the University. I intended to make it a light-hearted sharing of a series of experiences—personal and medical. The title chosen by me—'An Eclectic in the U.S.A.' seemed apposite and reasonably appealing. It was widely publicised and the auditorium was crowded.

At the end of the lecture one of my friends, who was a general physician, approached, looking rather puzzled.

"Maybe you too wondered why there was a sprinkling of Neurosurgeons and Neurologists. Although the chairman introduced your spiel as 'An Eclectic in the U.S.A.' the poster in our department entitled it—'An Epileptic in the U.S.A.' No wonder you got such a good turn out—and a mixed reception. But they all listened."

A year later the Nuffield Foundation accepted my dissertation. It was all over—or was it? I was not the same person.

The stethoscope followed its preordained route across Mrs Buchan's lungs. It was difficult to hear the breath sounds as her chest kept heaving about. I was in a hurry and gently chided the lady with 'flu.

"Please try to keep still. Now, through the mouth—breathe in and out." It was useless. Mrs Buchan was beyond my control.

"It's the first time I've been examined by a doctor with a budgie on his head. Look in the mirror." I extricated myself from the various occupants of the bed and faced a ridiculous spectacle. Looking at me was a dejected doctor with a bird clinging determinedly to what was left of his hair.

I resumed my place on the bed along with the two children, the Labrador and the Great Dane. Mrs Buchan continued to talk and laugh. There was only one way to quieten her—I stuck a thermometer in her mouth. Just then the bedspring on my side slipped off its frame. A yawning crevasse opened up into which Mrs Buchan rolled. A chain reaction was set off. The dogs followed the patient down, then came the children and the last to reach floor level was the doctor. Even Mr Buchan, a notable eccentric, was taken aback by the appalling noise of furniture giving way, dogs barking and children crying.

"Good thing these are sturdy houses. You might all have gone through the floor." As the Buchans lived in the top flat of a tenement block this didn't bear thinking about. I brushed myself down, scribbled out a prescription and departed with undignified haste only to be called back for the budgie to be released from my head. At my next stop I remembered I had left the thermometer in Mrs Buchan's mouth.

The Buchans were accident prone and they didn't train or properly exercise their dogs. Neither the children nor the dogs cared for the doctor and I resented the indiscipline which, in the same week, permitted one child to drink paraffin and the other to consume a bottle of iron tablets.

I read the riot act in their kitchen which had four doors opening off it. As I departed I got the wrong one and made a dramatic exit straight into their coal cellar.

Covered with coal dust I emerged to hear Mrs Buchan's comforting observation,

"At least ye've no' goat the bird this time!"

The pattern of my personal practice had now radically changed. No more obstetrics and, rarely, paediatrics. Now I dealt with chronic illness—particularly in older people. This was no bad thing because I had the care of most of the malignant disease in our group practice. Anyway I liked older people and respected their wisdom.

When Miss Burrows died, after twenty years of dedicated and constant attention at the home of her sister, Agnes, there was a real crisis. Agnes had lost contact with her friends and the outside world during her sister's long battle with Rheumatoid Arthritis.

"What do I do now?" asked Agnes. "I've hardly met anyone for twenty years. I can cook and I can knit, but that's all."

"Well, money isn't a problem. I suggest you concentrate on knitting."

"But doctor," Agnes replied, "I don't need any knitted garments."

"Ah but I do," I responded in a moment of inspiration. "I love woollen socks. So do my partners."

The first pair of socks arrived a few days later. They were of ideal construction for an ostrich on a cold day. The feet were three inches long and the legs almost covered the knees.

Until a proper balance was struck the socks made excellent covers for golf clubs and then, after a few tactful hints, dawned the day when the perfect sock came off the pins.

For fifteen years one pair of woollen socks emerged each week from the Burrows production line. Mrs Brown said, "If you were a centipede you'd still have enough socks for five years."

As it was, bazaars, sales of work and fêtes all thrived on Miss Burrows' socks. One reliable source reported:-

"Not only did Dr Illingworth prescribe socks for her cold feet—he actually provided them himself." And Agnes was happy to be useful again.

The practice had been training young graduates for many years. Each served a year. For the first six months their activities were carefully monitored. Thereafter they were given responsibility but with constant back-up. Most of those trainees were very gifted people. Others were skilled but couldn't tolerate the stamina-sapping pressures of general practice. A few should never have been allowed to venture outside the protective carapace of the hospital or the laboratory. One of those could never deal with a patient in less than three-quarters of an hour; another had no confidence whatsoever in his own judgement and sought a second opinion on every patient.

One trainee, Dr Pope, was however a great entertainer as well as a good family doctor. During his first night on duty he received a 2 a.m. call to a nurse with possible appendicitis. His own car was being serviced so, wearing only pyjamas, he climbed into the car he had hired to look for a street he had never heard of. He had only a vague idea where it might be and he drove slowly round the possible area. After some time he realised he was near the District Nurses' Home and to his joy he saw a night nurse stop her car and walk towards the door of the Home. He jumped out of his own car and ran barefooted towards her shouting,

"Nurse!"

The nurse looked round and saw this apparition bearing down on her. She took to her heels and just beat Pope to the front door of the Home. He hammered on the closed door as she dialled the police.

"Let me in Nurse! Open the door!" he yelled. Suddenly he was not alone; there were three policemen around him.

"May we ask what you're doing, sir?"

"Well I'm trying to get that stupid nurse out here."

"Why?"

"Because I'm a doctor." The policemen looked at the shoeless young man in pyjamas.

"Oh yes, we often hear that claim. Can you prove it?" Dr Pope reached unsuccessfully for his wallet which he'd left at home. He rallied.

"I know—my name is on the back of my wristwatch."

"But you're not wearing a watch, are you? What's your car registration number?"

Pope rattled that off and the voice of the law sombrely said,

"Which is your car?" Pope pointed out the hired car, which had an entirely different registration.

"That's the car I hired for the night anyway." His voice faded away.

"I see, sir. That's your hired car—the one that's moving of its own accord down the road?"

The car, which he'd left in haste without applying the hand brake, was running slowly down the camber of the road.

It ran into the police car. There was an ominous metallic sound.

The poor doctor, ageing visibly, suddenly remembered the message slip in his pyjama jacket pocket. He flourished it.

"There's the name and address. Take me there and I'll prove it. In any case there's a medical bag in my car—I'd forgotten about that."

One police car guided John Pope—who had a police officer as a passenger. The other tailed him.

The nurse, clutching her abdomen, opened the door. Three policemen and a young fellow in pyjamas stood outside.

"Please go away," she said, "I'm ill. The doctor's coming."

The barefoot doctor sorted out the confusion which he had so innocently created. The nurse, one of my Western girls, had her appendix removed during the night—and just in time—while the barefoot Dr John Pope became an excellent family doctor in accord with the French quotation that the doctor's duty is to entertain the patient while nature cures the disease.

Due to an old rugby injury my knee intermittently locked. It first happened during a formal dinner in the Royal College when, as the padre finished grace, there was an audible clunk. The knee was jammed, painfully and fully bent. I leant towards Lesley.

"You'd hear it. My knee's locked."

"Well you'd better get out and have it put right before the shrimp cocktail," replied Lesley.

I, who was at the table farthest from the door, rose and hopped the ninety feet to the exit—where I fell down—just outside the hall. Two consultants had followed my unstately progress and proceeded to roll up my trouser leg. The senior one, Prof. John Bruce, took hold of my leg.

"It's the last ten degrees which matter." He then lent his vast weight on the knee joint. The other surgeon, Charles Falconer, held the victim's nose and mouth so that no agonised squeal would disrupt the proceedings. With my knee wrapped in Mrs Falconer's scarf, I limped back to the dinner.

"God, what a painful experience. There must be an easier way."

I was to discover it the next holiday week-end when, in a small hotel which had a smaller bathroom, not "en suite". The knee locked again—in the bath. I let out the water and crawled over the side of the bath using one good leg and two good arms ("en suite" was then only a foreign expression) and I had to proceed 20 yards to our hotel bedroom. Opening the bathroom door I crawled, like an injured crab, into the corridor—"Skirl-naked" as Lesley later said, and proceeded laboriously down three carpeted steps. Behind me a door opened.

"Oh my God!" a female voice said. The door slammed shut. Five minutes later I had manipulated myself to the bedroom door. I knocked—I couldn't reach the handle. After several "come-ins" and yelps for assistance I was admitted. Lesley stared at her disabled husband and pulled me to safety.

"Please straighten it," I pleaded. Lesley tried but produced only groans of protest. She studied the man with the immobile right knee.

"Suppose you turn on your face? I can't stand the full frontal effect!"

I did so and at once felt more comfortable. Face down I bent the knee up further as if swimming the breast stroke. The pain vanished. As I completed a full and guarded breast stroke kick I felt the cartilage slowly withdraw from the joint space. The cure was immediate. Better still, I was able to pass on this stratagem to similarly affected patients, so much so that the practice adopted it as "Illingworth's manoeuvre".

In 1968 my personal guru, Richard Turner, re-appeared. Dr John Macleod had originated and supervised an initiative where family doctors were appointed, part-time, to assist consultant physicians. I eagerly accepted and became a general practitioner in Dr Turner's unit in the Western General Hospital—a teaching hospital! It was an ideal arrangement for the hospital, the doctors and, in particular, for the patients. I saw myself as a bridge between the hospital and the outside world—hoping to provide and improve the service to both extremities.

For once in my life I felt completely fulfilled. There was inevitably, some shadow in my personal brightness. My elder brother had developed Hodgkin's Disease and, during my American travels, I had been intensively educated in chemotherapy. I returned to Edinburgh with a treasure chest of ideas for his treatment. My American friends claimed a cure rate of 80%. With my brother's permission I searched for any oncologist—or at least someone who would help me treat Jim with chemotherapy.

I searched in vain—while the poor chap steadily deteriorated on radiotherapy—as I received constant rebuffals from consultants. "G.P.s don't give chemotherapy. Anyway I don't have any information and you may kill him. Oncologists? There's no such person in Edinburgh."

"But I know about it! We're ten years behind the Americans!" I replied.

"Now you're being rude!"

And so my brother died leaving a wife and two little girls.

It was a delight to return to the Western after almost twenty years of the medicine of first encounter; to move from improvisation to sophistication and from the initial harsh impacts of the frontiers of illness to the more detached and scientific study of a processed filtrate of the human spectrum of clinical pathology. I could act as a unifying force—I even had admitting rights.

Everything had changed—except Dr Turner—whose appearance was exactly the same as it was in 1946. He was still a visual and verbal blur and the clock turned back as I methodically plodded on while Dick Turner buzzed around the unit—waspish but never cruel. To his staff and to his patients he was "the compleat physician". His aphorisms, slogans and tics of speech had extended in range. While the old ones had been retained, new updated expressions had been added.

"Don't try to baffle me with science. I'm a clinician." "Life is all about genes and habits—nothing else matters!" "Give me the facts not spurious figures." "You young fellows always need laboratory support—which is usually bogus." And, to the patients "Your choice is quite simple—survival or cigarettes."

We were disturbed by the youth of the patients in the Coronary Care Unit. We realised that we were caught up in an epidemic of a disease which was comparatively rare when first we met. Turner summed it up with apostolic evangelism.

"You and I have seen this situation arise during our lifetime. Therefore, the cause must exist in the patients' surroundings. That being the case, the condition is potentially preventable and it's doctors like you, David, who work with people's environments, who can stop them dying prematurely from heart attack—and stroke."

We decided to work on a programme for survival in which we would define and eliminate the factors which put people at risk of arterial disease affecting the heart or brain. It was a tall order and wherever we turned we met apathy and opposition. Only the nursing profession and the clinical chemists supported us. Our other colleagues wanted statistical proofs rather than good ideas. The patients, real or potential, were unwilling to alter their ingrained lifestyles and were impervious to Darwinian-type arguments that evolution had not had time to prepare their bodies for the habits of their instant affluence. The great motivator and persuader was the occurrence of a heart attack. When that happened the brick wall created by an artificial unphysiological civilisation was easily breached by the doctor's missionary zeal. A "new" code of conduct based on the simple lives of their ancestors was then presented, not only as desirable, but as the only probable road to continued survival.

I was pleased to be reminded that one goes on learning all one's medical life. It was an ideal time to be attached to a Cardiology Unit. I used this knowledge and was able to intervene when a "coronary" occurred—at Murrayfield, in the theatre or at church when the minister humorously wondered how Dr Illingworth so regularly found a patient before the collection was taken.

For two years Dick Turner encouraged me to study the environments of patients in the Coronary Care Unit. They shared causal factors it seemed. So many had been subjected to stress; so many had moved from a humble background to a sophisticated and indulgent environment quite foreign to their origins—worsened by improper diet, physical lethargy and cigarettes. So many had a family history of arterial disease where we focussed on cholesterol and tryglyceride levels. We published.

It was a happy time of complete involvement. But I had dispersed myself in so many different ways that I kept failing to meet my own standards. The amoeba had divided too many times and had lost its vigour.

At the end of the second year of my attachment to Dr Turner the partners made their views quite plain.

"It's too much!" said Robert "You seem to be away from the practice more and more."

There was no option and, after two years, it was probably wise to resign. Although I did so, sadly, I had learned a great deal. Perhaps I had contributed something. The volume and the youth of the damaged human beings in the Coronary Care Unit continued to haunt me—just as it troubled Turner whose words echoed on in my mind.

"Salvage work" That's all we do. The future lies in preventive cardiology. Our own puny efforts have been stifled by the 'iron lung' mentality. Think of these thousands of iron lung machines lying rusting and useless—rightly rendered obsolete by someone who set out to PREVENT poliomyelitis instead of treating its ravages. We should be thinking the same way in our field. Let's try to create arterial health instead of being entirely defensive." My partners were dismayed.

"Idealistic twaddle," Morton said, lighting another cigarette. "You can't go around meddling with peoples' lives. How will you find time to treat the sick if you go about telling them to do this but not to do that. Bloody interference!"

It was another hectic week-end in the silly season which began at midnight on Friday when I delivered, at home, a woman doctor. She was superb—as was her husband—until he fainted when the baby's anterior shoulder wedged and required coaxing. The husband's skull struck the doctor's. The midwife delivered the rest of the baby as the two males struggled to get upright in an exercise of confusion and concussion.

At dawn the police 'phoned to say an attempt had apparently been made on the life of one of my patients. Would I visit?

Miss Hoffman was in a state of great distress. Her paranoia exhibited itself in her claim that the houses around her own were occupied by Russian spies—one of whom had tried to kill her by sending her an explosive cake!

As I sent for psychiatric help and returned to breakfast I learned that a small boy in the practice had been sexually assaulted the previous evening. I confirmed the attack for the police as I was called, apologetically, by a schoolteacher at Bruntsfield.

"It's mother again doctor. She insists she's ill and is screaming."

I visited to hear my patient repeatedly chuntering,

"I want to be cut! Do it! There's a wireless in my stomach."

I left her with a firm guarantee that my new psychotropic medicine would not stop the noise but would change the radio station as she wished.

It was the silly season alright and I was not pleased to be called out at 2 a.m. on Sunday to see a patient with insomnia. Her hysterical attack was due, I finally elicited, to her winning a prize in "the pools"—27/6d.

By Monday I was really trauchled but was restored by two "acute abdomens" and by picking up an early diabetic.

The balancing mechanism is always there.

Thirty years had passed since Professor Davidson described General Practice as "Medicine of Trivialities". How wrong he was! Trivial to whom? To the patient or to the doctor? That which is minor to the doctor may be of horrific proportion to the patient until it is explained—and understood. Align the personal upset of a nose bleed with the apparent insignificance of a small dis-regarded black mole which may, contrariwise, be the harbinger of a rapid malignant death. General practice is NOT therefore the medicine of trivialities, it is the medicine of first encounter, of explanation, of discernment and of orientation giving a real opportunity, perhaps the only one, of cure.

It is the medicine practised by those who have a clinical conscience—without a laboratory mentality. And it is about people's wellness as much as sickness.

"We don't use the other public rooms—only the kitchen" said the young married woman. Her husband nervously chewed his finger nails—safeguarded by the child who was wailing with earache—as he mumbled to the G.P. in what was a residence rather than a home.

"Can't use the lounge or the dining room. Shoes are prohibited and the carpets are protected by newspapers."

After the examination I washed my hands and had stealthy glimpses of the public rooms cocooned in layers of newsprint. The husband saw me to my car as the doctor's tongue broke loose.

"When do you use these magnificent public rooms?"

"We don't. We live in the kitchen. That's how my wife grew up!"

I drove home feeling that I was less unusual than I believed.

At midnight I was trying to keep a woman from throwing herself into the well of her Marchmont flat. She had cut her throat (and her wrists) with a razor blade and was bleeding all over my best suit as I struggled with her. It took an hour to subdue her, arrest haemorrhage and get her away by ambulance to a place of security.

At 6 a.m. I had a delivery and morning surgery began, on time, with a cup of black coffee from the secretariat and the appearance of McHarg of the sore feet. No—NOT Gout, he just had dreadful feet—and he wasn't very bright. Dispersible Aspirin had proved beyond him when the chemist labelled the prescription "Two in water 4 hourly after food."

He had returned to the chemist to elucidate the instructions. "How much water?"

"Oh, about a half tumbler or teacupful."

After this clarification he returned to the doctor.

"Yon chemist's mad. How in God's name can you get your two feet into a tumbler of water? Mind you, doctor, to be fair, my feets much better since I started dissolving they tablets in a large bowl of water."

"Good thinking, Mr McHarg—but if you should relapse let me know."

CHAPTER TWENTY-SEVEN

Mrs Bright's nursing home was immaculately run. The establishment was as graceful and handsome as its owner. Her husband was a local doctor who spared the practice many a night visit by proferring a quick opinion on their patients. The fees were modest—unlike the carbuncle on the neck of one of my diabetics—which was of indecent size and virulence.

Matron Bright and I agreed on penicillin injections and kaolin poultices. An assistant nurse was instructed to prepare the poultice and warm the container. Half an hour later when the Matron asked about the poultice she learned it was still heating in its canister in the gas oven.

"If you prepare a kaolin poultice nurse, you heat the container in water and not in a gas oven." As she opened the oven door the canister of bubbling poultice exploded in her face.

It was three months before I saw Matron bright again. One eye was artificial, the other was partitioned in a patchwork of scar tissue and grafted skin.

I wanted to say "I wish I had half your courage," but felt I might seem patronising.

I wished I had spoken up when, two weeks later, Dr Bright had a terminal heart attack.

Miss Andrew, a new patient, was being asked when she last felt perfectly well.

"When I was six months old, doctor."

"Now, Miss Andrew, although you're only forty, you can't remember much about your babyhood. When did you REALLY first feel ill.

"I've told you, doctor! About three months before I was born."

As I hesitated, lost for a reply, she continued, "You don't believe me—so you won't believe that when I look in the mirror I can't see myself."

This I did believe as I realised that my new patient was seriously ill mentally and had become depersonalised. A wall of delusions, hallucinations and obsessions was then breached over the next hours. She failed to keep her specialist appointment and sent in a series of threatening letters. I would see her in the shadowy distance occasionally. She didn't use the gun she claimed to have in her handbag. After a year of haunting me and that one significant consultation, she disappeared. The mystery remains. It was all rather intimidating and we were quite unable to trace her.

One of my few distinctions was that I cared for the oldest pacemaker patient in Britain. But at 93 years, she developed sudden cardiac failure and died. Her daughter was helpless with grief in the lounge and sobbed.

"It's at a time like this that you need a man. Would you please arrange the cremation? There's the 'phone!"

I called up my favourite undertaker who had a concerned, genuinely caring, graveside manner. I recounted the circumstances of the death to Mr Purves as the daughter lay sobbing on the couch—listening intently however.

So I finished the conversation with a few words from which Miss Whytock could perhaps draw comfort.

"She even had a pacemaker inserted and was remarkably well until her sudden and graceful end."

Mr Purves' telephone voice became quieter but more insistent.

"What type of pacemaker was it? Some of the new ones are explosive!"

A shocked doctor chose his words with care.

"Please continue the arrangements—but await my telephone call in five minutes—from my consulting rooms."

"What on earth do you mean, Mr Purves, about exploding pacemakers?" I said from the seclusion of my own office.

Mr Purves chuckled down the 'phone.

"Sounds ridiculous—but it's true. In a London Crematorium, last month, the explosion was so loud they thought the I.R.A. had attacked. You must 'phone the cardiologist and ascertain that an inert device was implanted.

The heart consultant didn't mince his words.

"You're crazy, Dr Illingworth "It just doesn't happen."

I informed the undertaker—but on the morning of the crematorium service the cardiologist telephoned to apologise.

"I'm sorry, doctor, but one of the registrars here says that some of the new pacemakers ARE potentially explosive. Indeed such a model was fitted to your patient."

Mrs Whytock already lay in the undertaker's chapel. But Mr Purves was firm.

"No cremation is possible with that pacemaker in position, doctor. You must take it out."

I demurred and appealed to the cardiologist who finally, with his team, removed the device just before the service.

The concept of the dear old lady blowing up the crematorium and taking revenge on her many self- seeking relatives appealed perversely to my sense of justice.

"Why not let her go out with a bang?" queried my student.

Each year contained a week or two adorned with a concentrated period of bizarre events. A series of unrelated professional absurdities would occur which always stirred Morton to warn his partners. "The silly season has started." While Lamont would reiterate yet again his belief that life came in lumps. Half of me revelled in these medical farragoes; the other half worried about their unreality and my unpreparedness—especially with psychiatric problems.

Mrs McRae's telephone voice had the clipped tension of controlled fear.

"Dr Illingworth, my husband hasn't gone to work this morning. Something strange has happened. He came down to breakfast and said he's had 'an experience of grace'. He was wrapped in a sheet—like those Greek things, 'togas' I think they're called. And he said he was Jesus—a second coming or something. He asked me to kneel down. I did! Now he's back in bed talking to God."

Mr McRae was well known to me as a sober, stable, Scottish lawyer and I did not delay in driving to the house. On arrival I found an incoherent wife sitting on a settee. She was tearfully confirming the story when her husband appeared at the head of the staircase. He was wrapped in a sheet and came slowly down the staircase. Silenced by the manifestation and struggling to find a form of address, I said,

"Good morning, Mr McRae, and how are you?"

"Ah, you're the doctor and you're using my other name—but of course you know who I really am."

"Indeed I do," I replied. My neurones rebelled. "But naturally I'm curious, as a thinking man, to find out what has happened."

"Doctor, it's quite simple. I am the reincarnation!"

My brain suffered instant stasis before coming up with a telling phrase. "Obviously the general public would want some sort of proof. Perhaps faith is not enough." I was scraping the bottom of the barrel to find a legal argument.

The tearful wife sat beside her toga-ed husband. The lawyer pondered this point. "I know what I am, but I accept that there may be scepticism."

"Let's have a second opinion," I replied.

As in all urgent problems the Health Service was magnificent. Within the hour a consultant psychiatrist was looking at the reincarnate deity. He was advised to rest up quietly at home for two weeks—on phenothiazine drugs. To my astonishment the lawyer gradually lost his delusion and came even to smile about it; the case of the man who thought he was God had a little black humour about it but there was nothing funny about the spate of hoax calls which came in shortly after this incident.

At a time when each partner slept with the telephone for two nights each week—and might have up to four house calls after 11 p.m. it was upsetting, to say the least, to be called to a non-existent patient or a counterfeit address.

Slithering through the midnight snow, I knew I had the details correct. I paused momentarily at the door of the tenement block to reassure myself and ran madly up the stairs. The voice on the telephone had given the name and address and had then continued.

"I've got this awful pain in my chest!" An audible groan was followed by silence.

I reached the front door of the house and hammered vainly for admission. There was no sign of life in the flat but a small gathering of people in night attire appeared outside the door.

"Urgent call! Suddenly cut me off with a groan. Sounds really bad. Where's the key?"

The neighbours said they didn't have a key and one thought the owner was away—but became less certain when I showed her the message slip. The doctor made the decision and, using a technique learned from the police, kicked down the door. The would-be helpers poured in. Everything was spick and span. The telephone was on its rest. There was nobody lying beside it. All the rooms were empty and tidy.

"Must be a mistake. Someone's playing tricks", said I, moving swiftly away.

"We'll get the door fixed."

As I stopped my car at my home I walked into the arms of two policemen.

"My God, doctor, you've wakened up half of Morningside. You've alarmed the lieges and smashed down the door of an empty house whose owner is in Shetland for two weeks. She telephoned us before she left."

I sighed and produced the message slip indicating the nature of the "emergency" call. The officers groaned and shook their heads.

"Next time you want to bash down a door tell us first. You've created a right old collieshangie!"

Apologies made, I crawled, ice-cold, back into bed. The sound of silence was about to enfold me when the telephone by my ear came alive again. The voice gave precisely the same message as before; the groan followed and then came a loud snigger. I went berserk.

Lesley, lying awake beside me, was horrified by what I said to the hoaxer. Two hours later I traversed a snow-bound city to a genuine patient—with a stone in the kidney.

That at least was rewarding and restored proper values—as does almost all nocturnal and week-end family medicine.

CHAPTER TWENTY-EIGHT

The years were still contracting together as it became more difficult to find reference points in time. Twenty-five years had passed. Lamont had retired after an acrimonious dispute about research in general practice. New partners were being brought to maturity in a race against time which was not going well for Morton and me. Both men had peaked physically and mentally and yet the workload of each seemed only to increase. Neither would surrender to deputies for the nights and weekends on call. Both believed that these were the times when they did their best medicine—with the acute clinical contingency—when knowledge of the patient was a vital factor.

But the golf games were becoming fewer and each of the senior partners was now committed to a hospital appointment and a snowballing succession of meetings and boards. Not that it was tedious! It was exciting and productive, but there was never peace—only pressure. Our home lives were suffering as we neglected our wives and our animals. My permanent companion on my rounds was an elderly Alsatian, 'Fagin', a beautiful gentle creature who doted on human beings—none of whom was really worthy of his attention. That loyalty was to be repaid when the dog developed "frequency". A middle aged doctor was watched by several startled residents of Merchiston, pursuing his dog down the road, as he successfully snatched a urine sample for analysis to exclude diabetes.

"We share the same problem chum," said I. "We're getting old." A further opportunity to repay the dog's devotion came very soon.

"A bone has got stuck in Fagin," said Lesley. "You know how he loves bones. He just gulped this big knuckle—and it won't come out. The poor dog keeps looking at his rear end."

At midnight I was still making encouraging noises and walking round and round the block. Finally, in desperation, I 'phoned a vet.

Fagin and I drove across Edinburgh to a cheerful veterinarian. "Impaction! I'll just hook it out." But Fagin had a strong sense of dignity and resented the examining finger—which rapidly withdrew.

Unperturbed, the vet injected a tranquilliser and left the two friends together in the waiting room—looking at the linoleum. Ten minutes later the clinician reappeared with a pile of old newspapers.

"You may need these," he said ominously as he disappeared again.

Dog and man eyed each other briefly before the animal's forelegs gave way and he sank bow first to the floor. His stern rapidly followed and Fagin then rolled over on his side and respiration appeared to cease.

"My God, he's dead", I thought, as the dog's mouth opened and his huge tongue fell out on the linoleum.

Just then the vet returned and the bone delivered itself spontaneously—although the newspapers were useful. In went the antidote and up came the dog as the strong young vet lifted him from the floor. The linoleum came up also; the dog's massive dry tongue was stuck to it. The vet laid the dog down again and soaked the tongue off the linoleum with water, before carrying the unconscious animal to the car.

When the pair arrived home the one with four legs was still quite unsteady—intoxicated with the tranquilliser. His two-legged friend sought out a friendly bottle, feeling that he had somehow settled a debt. Dogs give so much and expect so little.

Medical practice remained a precious compound of infinite variety and rapid change. At three in the morning the 'phone rang. The policeman's voice was strained. "Doctor, we've been called by one of your patients in Morningside. She says she's worried about a horse in her kitchen."

I was always suspicious of such strange messages since the series of hoax calls. "Don't you think, officer, that you need a vet or the Cruelty to Animals team? I haven't been a horse-doctor for many years. Why don't you go and see for yourself first?"

"Well, doctor, I don't mind going with you but it WILL proved to be a medical problem. The lady lives in the TOP flat of a tenement."

The policeman and I sat in the kitchen trying to persuade the lady that no horse on earth could ascend sixty feet into her kitchen.

"He's been coming and going for a few days," said the husband. "I can't convince her—and as you know she never touches drink."

"He's back," shouted the patient. "Over there—in the corner."

The others jerked their heads round, seeking some equine manifestation.

"She's had no peace for seventy-two hours and she's terrified," said the distraught husband.

"She's also ill and exhausted, " I said. "We'll take the horse first and then your wife. Have you any sugar lumps—or a carrot?"

The Psychiatric Unit responded at once when telephoned. Together we got the imaginary animal and patient down the long, steep, narrow stone staircase. The patient was securely sedated in hospital within an hour.

It wasn't Morton's 'Silly Season' after all. It transpired that her thyroid gland function had totally ceased. I was mortified—I had failed to identify the only patient with 'myxoedematous madness' I was ever to see.

In spite of its stresses night work was always dramatic and worthwhile. The frivolous house calls of the early years of the Health Service had faded away as people became more responsible. No longer were the doctors invited to cope with toothache, simple stomach upsets or insomnia at 2 a.m. The requests for help out of hours were almost always necessary—or, at least, understandable. The problem would be clear and the therapy dramatically effective. The city in the small hours was an entirely different and much more romantic place. I could look back on many dawns in Edinburgh with sharply luminous skyline images of spires, roof-tops, crags and the everchanging Pentland Hills.

Even my encounters with the denizens of the night were contributory—foxes in Merchiston, hares at Marchmont, drunks in the Grassmarket; while Edinburgh's small, discreet red-light area added a little prurient lustre to the city's perjink patina. I had a few patients among the ladies of the town and was in their vicinity more than once at some unearthly hour.

The bowler hat and torch would provoke instant interest. A window would be raised,

"Hullo darling, are you looking for me?"

The reply, "No thanks, I'm working." produced a loud chuckle.

"That's O.K. Jimmy, I'm working too! You can always change your mind."

But another piece of life's patchwork was nearing completion.

Dr Morton was wakened by chest pain and was at once transferred from his house to the Coronary Care Unit. After twenty-four hours his tests had given no evidence whatsoever of cardiac problems and he was allowed home. The following afternoon I was standing in the practice office when the emergency signal was sounded off from the extension in Morton's house. The message was unequivocally urgent. Mrs Brown and I ran the necessary hundred yards to find an open door.

In the lounge Dr Morton was still slipping down his armchair towards the floor. He was pulseless and breathing had ceased. Four minutes into cardiac arrest was quite a long period but Robert Morton had to get his chance. His wife telephoned the Mobile Coronary Unit as Mrs Brown and I laboured to the last extremity with cardiac massage and artificial respiration. Nine minutes into the arrest a few heart beats were noticed. Exhaustion was near as assistance arrived to take over these fragile human attempts to keep flickering this one special candle of human life.

Returned to the unit which had so recently discharged him as normal, Robert began to make a physical recovery. His acute brain, had, however, been damaged by blood deprivation during the period of cardiac arrest. Immediately, feelings of guilt enveloped Mrs Brown and me. We had succeeded in preserving only part of Dr Morton for his wife to contend with. The real man—the excellent doctor, partner and friend had died. Dr Morton looked and sounded the same but the recovery, if such it was, was entirely a physical phenomenon.

Intervention (C.P.R.) had left Mrs Morton with the husk of a fine human being. Loss of dignity is infinitely worse than death and I came to curse an ability which restored only a fraction of life to the dead.

Six terrible months ensued before a series of natural assaults on the heart muscle subdued Robert's spark of existence.

For me it was a dreadful personal and professional deprivation. While I was happy that Robert had escaped from his mockery of life I was overwhelmed with guilt, isolation and insecurity. Never more vulnerable, not only was I alone at the top of the heap, I was caught up in a battle to build a medical centre for the people of the area. It was plain that there was a process of attrition in store.

Unhappily I did not have a peaceful mind over the death of my partner. As usual in times of personal clinical odium I appealed to a fictitious panel of physicians. There was no comfort for me. Hippocrates and Galen were strongly against attempts to raise the dead—an action which resembled witchcraft. Dunlop was charmingly non-committal—but understanding. Turner was extremely angry and reacted with words on "salvage medicine" and "the quality of life". The only consolation was that they all agreed that survival shorn of former glory is worthless.

The letter of referral was being written on the beautifully waxed surface of the dining-room table. Harassed to distraction by the histrionic posturings and protestations of the practice's star hypochondriac, I wrote a firm note to the consultant psychiatrist—using a ball-point pen. Perhaps the pressure I was under was transmitted in my penmanship. The effect of years of patient-initiated contacts was revealed in the letter. As I re-read this chilling but accurate indictment of character and personality, I marvelled at the remarkable tolerance which had been shown to the lady. She was still dwelling on the skatolic caprices of her intestine as I rose, folded the letter and licked the gum on the envelope—which I addressed as I steeled myself to endure yet once again the rigours of a voyage in the patient's unnavigable alimentary canal.

"Here's the letter," I interrupted. "I'll telephone you after I've spoken to the nerve specialist. I handed over the document which now bore my monogram on the sealed flap—to discourage any idea of steaming it open. Stooping to retrieve my hat and gloves from the table, my own gut suddenly tied itself in a knot. It had been a VERY firm letter and on the glossy surface of the table was reproduced every piquant word written by the ball-point pen.

Then I noticed a vase of flowers in the centre of the table.

"My God, doctor, what a mess!" shouted the lady as, in stretching for my gloves, I succeeded in knocking over the vase. A puddle of water covered my harmful engraving work on the tabletop.

"Please forgive me. Have you a towel?" I pleaded—as I mopped, and rubbed, at the letter in wax polish. Five minutes later I made a breathless departure.

"The only alternative," Lesley said, "would have been to take the table with you for French polishing."

> "*Dear Dr Illingworth*
> *I have to tell you that you behaved very strangely when you visited me recently. Not only did you upset a vase and damage a MOST valuable table but passed me on to a psychiatrist who asked me some very strange questions and plainly needed medical help himself.*

In spite of our long association things could
never be the same again and I intend to transfer to
another doctor's panel.
Yours faithfully
FIONA FORGAN."

I felt years younger although I knew that another "Fiona"
would inevitably take the place of Miss Forgan.

The Italian prima donna who spoke no English lingers in my
mind as a small portion of eternity. This massive contralto
wheezed from the theatre to my room. She shook her head at
my pantomime of undressing and the chest-piece wandered
through an acreage of rhonchi and mysterious lacing before it
lost its way as I hauled it up. I felt like a frustrated angler as I
searched vainly for the Italian for "The chest-piece of my
stethoscope has fallen off and is lodged near the top of your
body armour"—No, I would not flinch! I insinuated my fingers
down the back of her clothing to be rewarded with a shriek and
a right hook worthy of Rocky Marciano.

I recovered in an empty room awaiting the arrival of the
police force.

At best, Morton's premature death confirmed Dick Turner and
me in our stance on the value of Preventive Cardiology. I found
myself in considerable demand as a speaker. It was obvious that
the responsibility for the introduction of a healthy lifestyle was
with the General Practitioner's team. And I was bold enough
and certainly sincere enough to undertake what had to be done.
Doctors, nurses and interested lay people who wanted to survive
were nagged at. To help with the exercise needs of our generally
inert medical practice I approached the Principal of my school.
We organized a programme of exercises, gentle running and
swimming. In 1968 we started with 50 men of over 50 years. At
first, jogging down Colinton Road, we attracted surprise,
curiosity and comment. As time passed, however, imitation of
our odd behaviour became the norm. Roy Castle, the
entertainer, arranged a television show in which we featured.

And now we no longer need to lead by example because our strange huffings and puffings are commonplace. Prevention has replaced salvage!

10,000 patients and one toilet sums up our practice dilemma regarding size. The walls of the old house were bulging. We HAD to move. With luck, pleading and exhausting attrition, slow progress began and, after two years, negotiations for a medical Centre reached a critical phase. But there was a price to pay and it was not the time to be formally ill. Yet, here was my old chum, the radiologist, looking at me over the desk at the Western General Hospital.

"It's really quite painful at times, Hunter. I've had a little bleeding—but that may be the occasional Aspirin I take. Work pressure has been unbelievable." Hunter Cummack didn't waste words, "Barium meal and a gall bladder X-ray. The radiographer will give you the instructions. Nothing to it!"

Unfortunately there was an emergency next morning and the appointed time was well past before I was led into Hunter's presence—feeling rather coy in a patient's smock and irritated by the threat of a late schedule.

"I hate to say it, Hunter, but please make it fast. It's going to be one of those days."

Hunter remained silent as he peered at my abdomen. After five minutes he uttered. "Lovely gall-bladder, laddie. Now drink from the container and keep still. That's great. It's going through fine. Drink some more. Now I'll tilt you up and down on the table. Any tenderness? The stomach and the first part of the duodenum are normal, David."

I leaped off the table. "Sorry I wasted your time, Hunter. Must get on with it."

Dr Hunter Cummack frowned as the lights went on. "I'd like to follow it on a bit—but I suppose it's alright."

I finished tying my shoes at the traffic lights. I had a reprieve. Cummack, the doyen of alimentary radiologists, had found nothing. I took Lesley to Fred's Restaurant that night.

The next six months proved a nightmare of committees, cajolings and chicanery while I struggled to keep up my clinical work. At the end of this time the battle for the Medical Centre was won and a great load was lifted from my shoulders.

There remained only one real problem and that was myself. I had occasional nagging doubts about having hurried Hunter's examination. There were intermittent problems with my inside. I was tiring of pretending that all was well and my stiff upper lip was beginning to cramp with tension.

Now the senior doctor, I was curiously isolated—mainly by reason of age, from my colleagues. This was my own fault—I could not adapt to the mechanical type of clinical practice which was being imposed on me. The six- minute consultation was an affront to a doctor who had, with age and service, inevitably attracted an impossible load of chronic sick, geriatric problems and medico-social disasters. A tonsillitis, a chest infection and a peptic ulcer, together took less time than sorting out a penniless, sleepless old lady with a leaking roof. The doctor had to reap the inevitable harvest of the maturing process—in his patients and himself—the unrelenting progression of wear and tear.

"God, please send me a young fresh acute problem," I used to request. I now understood why I so valued my nights and weekends on call—when I would see the patients of the pristine days as a doctor—and the smouldering fires of clinical enthusiasm would briefly rekindle.

The proof that all was not well came on a perfect autumn Sunday morning. Tiers of spiders' webs on the apple trees glistened with dew—reminding me of tinselled Christmas trees. I wondered what Lesley would like as a present as the syboes came away in my hand for the lunch-time stovies—cooked with the late potatoes which I had just unearthed.

I stooped to gather a few more of the delicate onion plants when a warm salty fluid welled up into my mouth. Within minutes I vomited the "coffee-grounds" evidence of a bleeding duodenal ulcer. From the cloakroom mirror a pale damp face peered anxiously back at me.

"It's in the family." How often had I heard my mother say this? I shivered as I recalled that my mother's side were plagued with peptic ulcers.

"Mustn't panic", I told the pallid creature I was studying. "Be detached. Get some iron tablets." I was glad that Lesley was out visiting, and two hours later, though a bit "peelie wally", my smile deceived my wife on her return. The iron tablets were wonderful and, after all, I had misled Hunter into giving me a normal barium meal result.

CHAPTER TWENTY-NINE

At the bar of the University Club Sir John Bruce tapped my shoulder.

"Large scotch, David please. It's almost 1970." And, as his victim grudgingly complied, "Any word from the Palace yet?" Mystified, I eyed Sir John warily. Good friends, yet distant, we had once appeared together at a clinical presentation when the professor had described me as an 'arcane human palindrome'—but in a kindly humorous vein. I had learned to monitor any conversation with Sir John—whose bluff manner concealed an intricate being. It seemed wise to trivialise the enquiry until the substance was plain.

"Sorry John, I don't understand you. I only know the Palace Hotel and the Palace Picture House."

Sir John smiled tolerantly.

"Still the daft laddie, David? I'm talking about Buckingham Palace. You may be offered a job and, if you are, I think you must accept it."

I composed myself.

"I wouldn't like a job in London. Anyway I'm N.H.S.!"

Sir John recaptured the urbane benevolence familiar to students whom he was about to fail in the Finals. He shook his massive head.

"No, no, David, in Holyrood; you'd be working for the Queen. But keep it dark."

The words trailed behind Sir John as he departed. There was a letter the following morning stating that I had entered The Royal Household occupying—"The branch surgery at the bottom of the Canongate"—as "The Surgeon Apothecary." My feelings of inadequacy were soon dispelled by the people with whom and for whom, I worked. Nominally always available as "the man in charge", for three weeks each year I moved in a world of kindness, consideration and grace. My first official visit to Holyroodhouse was memorable. As the guards checked my car through, the lower radiator hose ruptured to envelope them in a cloud of steam and boiling water. I stumbled on to meet the Lord Chamberlain who seemed at least eight feet tall.

"How are you doctor?"

"Nervous, sir, my radiator blew out at the front gate as I was looked over. Different environment if you know what I mean."

"Absolutely, old chap," said Lord Cobbold, but believe me, when the palace is in use nobody will be looking at YOU! I doubt if you'd be noticed if you walked around minus your trousers." This put things in perspective anyway, although I didn't test the hypothesis. I at once felt that I had been assimilated into a family and began one of the most enjoyable periods of my life. Medical privilege of all types demands discretion and confidentiality but the new job added a dimension of personal loyalty stimulated by the gentle devotion of those whom I served.

No sycophant, I was surprised to find myself developing a strong protective feeling towards "The Royals". I was astonished by the volume, intensity and timing of their work. Kindness, discipline, dedication, compassion and tolerance are the essential attributes of the family doctor—and now I was working beside people with the same ideals—with whom I could communicate through shared beliefs.

There was invariably banter about my ambition to deliver a baby in Holyrood. No baby had ever been born in the Palace. On formal occasions I was always accused of "studying form" and dreaming of professional immortality. The chaffing increased as the years passed until I was called from my home on one occasion to supervise a female in labour in the Palace. Hastening to great achievement I misinterpreted the significance of the comment.

"There's more than one, doctor!" And found myself looking at a duck which had wandered in and was laying a clutch of eggs.

But, as I was quick to point out when mixing Dry Martinis in the Equerries' room, although I had brought nobody into the world I hadn't allowed anyone to die in the Palace. The Lord Chamberlain, now "Chips" Maclean, murmured, "I wonder if they've found out who would be responsible for them if they come here ill or pregnant. Perhaps that's why there's no medical drama." But even as the observation was being made an unstable man in a turret bedroom was swallowing a hundred phenobarbitone tablets. I examined the apparently unconscious patient who still cradled in his hand the empty bottle. I dashed for the 'phone to alert security and the ambulance service. The security chief arrived at once and pointed out that there were still some members of the public in the building and that the King of Sweden was to dine in the Palace in one hour.

"Maximum discretion, doctor, please. I'll bring the ambulance round by the north gate."

I met the ambulance and raced with the sturdy men of the ambulance service to the turret bedroom as I clarified the problem.

"Overdose! Stretcher essential!" I opened the door. "Sorry he's so large. He's had a packet of phenobarb., too!" The ambulance officers rushed in but immediately reappeared.

"The room's empty!" The bed was a crumpled vacancy. The security chief swore and grabbed the nearest 'phone.

"There's a man in bare feet on the top floor. No, wait! He's on the second floor and is curiously dressed! He's coming down, doctor!"

I walked quickly to the first floor and waited anxiously. "Chips" Maclean, the new Lord Chamberlain joined me. Suddenly the corridor was full of the patient, six feet three inches of red hair and wearing only a string vest. I put my head down as the apparition charge. At the last moment the patient swerved neatly past me and accelerated down the vast corridor pursued by "Chips", the ambulance officers and the doctor. In full public view we made two circuits of the first floor before the quarry vanished through a door. The pursuit followed—into a bathroom. The huge vision of auburn hair in an abbreviated semmit was cornered. Heavily sedated but coherent he swayed near the window.

"If you move I'll jump" he slurred as I insinuated myself between patient and window—only to freeze as I looked down. There, twenty feet below, stood the King of Sweden talking to the Duke of Edinburgh—oblivious to the human projectile poised above. Perhaps, if I could keep the man talking, the barbiturates would take effect before the man in the string vest, attached to a doctor, plummeted from above to join the Royal meeting.

Happily I had in my pocket kit of emergency drugs an injection—which I sank into his buttock. A minute passed.

The bathroom—which was larger than my drawing room—was now uncomfortably congested with onlookers. "Chips" babbled hypnotically on at the man in the string vest—whose eyes were gradually closing with barbiturates, paraldehyde—and perhaps boredom. Suddenly he passed out, the ambulance team moved in, strapped him onto a trolley and whisked him off in their ambulance to the Poisons Unit. In record time and with maximum discretion all the participants disappeared.

Two days later the patient was discharged from hospital and, to the enternal credit of all, the affair was never mentioned thereafter.

Not that I was content. I'd got it wrong! A crestfallen doctor reviewed the differential diagnosis of coma. As a casualty officer I had been similarly wrong and had sought out Ben Murray—who was disturbed when I admitted an hysteric to the wards. Ben's eyebrows had met in the midline as I tremulously muttered.

"It can be difficult in casualty to know whether unconsciousness is I real or feigned. Hysteria can closely mimic coma, can't it?"

"But there's a test, pommie—named the "Aboriginal Criterion of Consciousness"—and it's a 100% accurate. You turn the patient on his back and fill his navel with methylated spirits—which you then light with a match. If he's shamming he recovers at once. If he really is unconscious—well he's got to be admitted anyway, hasn't he?"

Fortunately the unsophisticated casualty officer saw the joke before I was ever given the chance to employ Murray's procedure.

Employment in The Household was no sinecure. It was a tremendously satisfying and entertaining job. I catered for a select group of unusual people who existed to give, to lead and to support. It took me some time to adjust to the fact that I was part of an organisation the members of which were not too good to be true but were truly good people—highly trained and disciplined. In contrast, and only in general, the politicians I encountered compared badly. Their self-interest was a constant reminder of our Nation's good fortune in having a Head of State who is above politics.

Initially perplexed by a new environment I was greatly helped by the High Constables of Holyroodhouse. This Guard of Honour reflected the standards of the Sovereign whom they served. Each member, personable and humorous, became a valued and entertaining friend.

The Royal Company of Archers—The Queen's Bodyguard in Scotland, were more distant and the relationship remained professional rather than personal. Handicapped by their attire, I used to speculate on their uniform which was more rigid than their discipline. I became convinced that an Archer could die inside his supportive sheath of finery and yet remain at attention. The immobility imposed by their garments provoked several faints, and it was difficult to get at the body inside the fustian armour. There was a carapace which made the vital organs as inaccessible as tinned sardines.

"Have you ever tried to undress an Archer?" was my querulous cry. "No zips for easy access! If there's ever a cardiac arrest in an Archer, please get me garden shears and a can-opener." The Moderator of the High Constables smiled patronisingly.

"Of course we of the Guard of Honour DON'T faint. It isn't permitted!"

Strangely enough, in seventeen years I never attended a High Constable—and was once rash enough to make that observation. The Moderator again smiled patronisingly.

"Well what do you expect? We all know you very well!"

My Household appointment was to prove the funniest part of my life. "Chips" used to describe me as "humorously decorative—but not useless!"

It was a V.I.P. Royal Reception and the room glittered with the splendour of full evening dress and decorations. I weaved in and out enjoying the sight and sound of the famous and identifying those who might be at high risk because of the excitement, the heat and the stress of standing.

When the taxi disgorged its occupant at the main entrance, word of mouth reached me before the eminent author had failed to find his invitation card. The giant in highland dress was supported by one High Constable as he was gently searched (for authorisation) by another. Even his sporran was empty and, as tension heightened, the Assistant Comptroller was called in to permit access of the befuddled Scot. Large and persuasive, the Lord Chamberlain's representative got the guest into the reception where I received him and sat him in a chair.

"Tell Her Majesty I'm here and ready to discuss my problems" ordained the literary figure. I acquiesced—but when nothing had happened after five minutes the large man in the kilt pushed me to one side.

"There she is! I must show The Queen my war wounds—for which I have no pension!"

Having ascertained where the wounds were I immediately toppled the Scotsman back into his chair.

"Good Lord, you can't! In public! Before the Queen?" And as the war veteran/author/supplicant persistently struggled to his feet again he was grabbed, stuffed into the lift and penned up in the medical room. At this point he was given a drink which contained a strong sedative. Ten minutes later he was manoeuvred out a side door into my car and locked in until the reception ended. Next day an enquirer was told he was out shooting! His reputation remained untarnished!

Mrs Ford's beauty was startling. The 40 year old wife of a doctor, this was the woman who had everything and her intellect and nature equalled her unaffected glamour. The template was used only once for this unique creature. She arrived with her academic husband—and a history of "spastic colon"—to pay me a courtesy call of introduction. The history didn't seem quite right and that evening, pinioned between my fingers in Mrs Ford's pelvis was a small hard painless mass. Ovarian cancer—an increasing problem—was confirmed next morning by a gynaecologist. Like all cancers this was an emergency. She and her husband insisted on the truth. Six months later hairless and emaciated she was carried into her home by her consultant—who wept unashamedly.

And life came in lumps—at the same time—in Mrs Forbes' breast.

"My husband found it last night", "You told my mother ten years ago that most tumours are discovered by their owners. And Mummy is fine. I shall guide your fingers." And there it was! I could have missed it! It was so gratifying—in contrast to my sense of loss over Mrs Ford.

We have a long way yet to go.

Another cardiac arrest had occurred—at 2 p.m. It happened under my nose as I examined the pale sweating man with chest pain—and a packet of cigarettes on his bedside table. I thought I'd suddenly become deaf when the heart sounds ceased to come through the stethoscope. I had already given the Heroin and Lignocaine. For a fraction of time I recalled the awful results of the "successful" resuscitation of Dr Morton, my friend and partner. On this occasion however the duration of cardiac arrest was measurable in seconds. I began the all too familiar exhausting routine and, before a minute had passed, there was a spontaneous heart beat. Transferred to the Coronary Care Unit, the patient survived.

One year later he called to see me.

"I've got a new symptom, Doctor, it's love. Wait till I get her."

He vanished into the waiting room and extricated his fiancée.

Three years later I passed through the couthie Scottish town to which they had moved and learned, at the local pub, that all was well with the couple. I left a message for them and drove on south to see my grandchildren—feeling strangely at peace and even happier to find, on my return, a letter of thanks and an invitation.

Sheriff Ferguson at our first meeting told me of his frequent problems in getting to sleep after a trying day in court. I saw a handsome, reasonable man, intense but sincere and gave him a prescription for a small number of short-acting hypnotics—for emergency use only. Mrs Ferguson, nervous and uncertain, appeared a few days later to discuss her anxiety about her husband's drinking habits. I pointed out gently that the Scottish legal profession was not renowned for its abstemiousness—perhaps understandably.

"But he comes home late every night, doctor, drunk and irritable, reaches for a bottle, your sleeping tablets and his cigarettes. In a few minutes he leaves our two children and me and goes to bed." The woman looked pleadingly at me. "You won't tell him I've been here, will you? I know he's going to see you again next week."

During the second consultation with Sheriff Ferguson, I vainly tried to force the Sheriff to admit that there was some sort of problem.

"My dear doctor I came back to you as you asked. Your little red pills are grand. And after your enquiry about my alcohol consumption I must remind you that the definition of an alcoholic is somebody who drinks more than his doctor!"

However, the next month's heavy snow brought a brief anonymous letter.

"One of our profession has his carafe of drinking water refilled with vodka!" Any doubts about the direction of this brief communication were dispelled when a gang of men struggling to keep open Edinburgh's snowbound main streets noticed a movement in a roadside pile of snow. They dug out the body of Sheriff Ferguson—before he froze to death and promptly called the police—who equally promptly called in the doctor whose name was muttered by the Sheriff. At my most inventive I straightened up after the physical examination of an extremely intoxicated Sheriff.

"Pneumonia and overwork! I'll take him home now. Can you help me lift him into my car please?" An hour later Ferguson was comfortably tucked up in bed by a worried doctor and a wife—who looked uncertainly at the doctor. As she bade farewell at the front door Mrs Ferguson struggled to control her voice.

"What do we do now, doctor? Any hint of alcoholism and Angus is finished—professionally." I pondered.

"O.K. we'll move him down south to a specialist unit and somehow cover it all up until he's better. I've done it before for others. Mrs Ferguson relaxed for the first time in months and I slithered my car home feeling rather pleased.

It was all in vain. Angus Ferguson refused the escape route and was back on the bench in a few days.

As spring approached I responded to a dawn emergency call from Mrs Ferguson and entered a bedroom reeking of smoke and the smell of the Sunday joint. My eyes, which took in two empty bottles on the floor, cigarettes and matches, had to be forced to look at the charred bedding which enclosed the grilled remains of Sheriff Ferguson. Alcohol, cigarettes and hypnotics make bad bedmates.

I reached home in time to refuse breakfast and drive my daughter to school.

The end of each teaching term was signified by a night out with the medical students attached to the practice. The occasion had a dual purpose. We sat in a private room in a public house and, before we reached the lowest common denominator, there would be a useful interchange of opinion and experience. The second achievement was entirely social and intensified until we were all good friends together—with high levels of ethanol in the blood.

Before this happened, however, I always produced my visiting book and went through the visiting list mainly to indicate to the students our continuing failures to meet and teach the essentials of family doctoring. It was also a wonderful chance for the students to stretch me on the rack of my homespun philosophies; to impersonate me and my colleagues as they mercilessly tormented their teachers and poured beer into them.

"Genes and habits—that's life," says Dr Illingworth. "Listen to the patient he's telling you the diagnosis." "Hospital doctors perceive pathology not people." "Age is biological—not chronological" and so on.

"Future doctors are reflections of their teachers."

"My God, sir! Are we all going to get like you?"

"Well you could do a lot worse—you moronic apprentices. Here's my weekend list. And I'm late because I'm tired. There were five night calls on Saturday and Sunday. How would you cope with these, you cloistered academics? Listen as I read":-

"Man of twenty catches himself in his trousers' zip fastener—and can't move it."

"Cot death at 8 a.m.—but baby's face is flattened—was it smothered?"

"Woman dying at home of cancer, wants analgesia, but wishes to changer her will—and it's Sunday."

"A man of 50 has a cardiac arrest. It's quite dark and pouring rain and I get some response from heart massage. But he's got all his clothes on and I want to pump some drugs into him."

"Shall I continue?"

CHAPTER THIRTY

"My father keeps coming into my bedroom at night."
Alarmed, I studied the girl who was looking fixedly at me—for understanding and help. Fourteen years old, like my own daughter—and equally attractive—I recoiled at the possible inference.

"What happens Margaret?" The girl was determined to see it through.

"He has sex with me. It's been like this for years—since I was quite small."

"But what about your mother?" "Does she know?"

The girl hesitated.

"No, I don't think so—but Mummy works hard and is always tired. In any case it's been happening so long I thought it was normal." She hesitated. "No, I mean I thought it was not abnormal. But you mustn't tell Mummy. You'll upset her terribly—now that I understand."

The child woman didn't hesitate. "Doctor this will separate my parents. I'm the only person who can tell Mummy." She did so.

Next day I was looking at three anguished people.

The mother was a crisp, intense, professional woman who had become the casualty of her ambition and priorities. The father was handsome, artistic and charming—to such a degree as to make his incest even more enigmatic.

"What strange quirk makes him tamper with his own child?" was going repetitively through my head when I realised the man opposite was quietly sobbing.

"Are you going to tell the police? It will ruin us all."

Subsequent patients were displeased by the delay but within half an hour the emotional jigsaw was complete. High earnings make for easy solutions in social medicine. The parents parted. Their child went to an expensive boarding school in England. Within two years the father, his art now a household word, had remarried.

The mother reached the pinnacle of her profession.

We met once more. It was as if nothing had ever happened—but I couldn't tolerate the bland evasion. I segregated my quarry in a corner and compulsively asked about the child.

"I'm so proud of her. She's the head girl of the school. And of course all that unpleasantness has been forgotten."

I held my peace. Forgotten?

The Lord Chamberlain was sorry that Dr Illingworth, a fraction under six feet, wasn't taller and therefore more easily identifiable when needed on official occasions.

"What about a flashing orange light strapped to my skull?" Lord Maclean laughed at the mental image.

"A typically helpful idea, doctor," he mocked. "Just like an undertaker at a wedding! No, no, my dear chap, we'll have you as you are—invisible but vigilant. But I know you worry about these helicopters. We agree that you should be there at landing and take off. But you mustn't be obvious—otherwise you'll create a sensation of impending doom. Let's go and look at the site." Near the "ha-ha" at Holyrood the L.C. selected a small rather undistinguished shrub—henceforward designated as "The Doctor's Bush."

"This one's fine and you'll have a good view of the aircraft. But for heaven's sake if you are needed don't jump over the ha-ha. It's a long way down." It was all rather futile because the occupants of the aircraft had the doctor in full view as they ascended and descended and there were one or two interesting theories about the possible activities of the man with the bag behind the leafy screen. So I soon emerged from the undergrowth and began to respond to the hands waving cheerfully from the aircraft's cabin.

The doctor's bush must have taken its rejection to heart. It died.

Such flimsy drolleries eased any pressure. I was now the senior doctor in the group—wearied by battling to complete the medical centre for the community.

The tensions and pressures were unceasing and increasing as I struggled on in my solitude. There was so little responsibility which could be delegated. This was due to the generation and seniority gap.

The evasive emaciated girl with anorexia nervosa swore she ate ravenously—until she was challenged about the marks on the backs of her fingers—those of provoked vomiting—on the same day as Mrs Edwards stumbled and dropped her baby into a bath of very hot water. That same week Miss Hoffman's acute paranoia again erupted in the shape of other spies who were trying to assassinate her—while the prettiest schoolgirl in the practice visited me at my home—and wept and wept.

"Would you mind explaining to me how this happened?" I was irritated by my own clumsiness.

"My parents were watching the television and we were behind the settee—on the floor."

This notion penetrated even my protective shell. Dammit I'd delivered this baby—now looking at me with woman's eyes.

"I got a bit carried away and he gave me a tablet to take which was to make everything O.K. I trusted him you see. He teaches in the Sunday School."

Wondering what sort of confectionery this girl had been handed, I was still speculating on it at next morning's surgery as I looked at Miss Hunt –"Hunt the Hat" was her practice nickname. It described her well. Fifty years old, she made her own hats—which always matched her gloves—and therefore embodied Morningside fashion.

"My mother is trying to poison me," was uttered with cold precision. I recoiled.

"Surely not, Miss Hunt. I know Mrs Hunt well. She's 85 and a nice lady."

The daughter smiled tolerantly with her ghastly, glossy N.H.S. dentures and I was recalling that as a student I had met several patients who had a complete dental clearance as a 21st birthday present!

"That's the point doctor. Her cunning takes people in. I'm a teacher—out all day—and she cooks for me each evening. But of course I don't eat the food. I put it down the toilet because its full of cyanide. You must get her certified before she kills me—in some other way, I suppose.

It was ludicrous but it was all very real to "Hunt the Hat" and she was advised to be vigilant—but to take tablets to control her emotional upset and distress. Her pathetic old mother when visited, confirmed all the elements of a severe paranoid obsessional state in her daughter. The medication helped to produce a more relaxed attitude in the patient, but the strain told on her mother who rapidly deteriorated and died "from natural causes".

As I handed over the death certificate I scrambled rapidly through my repertoire of condolences—but needn't have bothered.

"God works in a mysterious way and he obviously has saved me for a higher purpose. Mother has been punished. I shall now sell up and go down South to look after her sister." I asked to be informed of Miss Hunt's new address and doctor—"as a matter of professional courtesy"—but heard nothing more. I hate these unfinished stories.

Meantime Alec Muir, a depressed dedicated civil servant awoke at 2 a.m.—the worst time for depression—swallowed all the tablets he could find and climbed back into bed beside his wife. It was Sunday morning anyway, so she gave him a long lie. In the afternoon the doctor told the children that their father had died of a heart attack. I've often wondered about the validity of death certificates.

As I aged, psychiatric problems took up more and more time. Not that it was dull. To be involved with human beings and their problems was an addictive sort of privilege. I loved my environment—if only because my work made a nonsense of such futile trivialities as paying the butcher's bill.

Fred had just written down our order when there was a stunning sound of rending metal and shattering glass as two vehicles collided outside the restaurant. Characteristically, there was about two seconds of intense silence before the screaming started.

"Expect we'd better go. Why is it always us?" said Lesley as she grabbed some cloth napkins from a service table. A crowded motor car had concertinaed under the tail-board of a lorry.

The episode was something of a turning point. It was difficult to go back to Fred's Restaurant. We tried once but the vivid recall of the intrusion of horror into a personal area of pleasant seclusion proved too uncomfortable. Perhaps in time........

Was there time anyway? Where had the years gone? Our three children had married and departed. Lesley and I were back where we started—together with a dog—another mongrel—full of hybrid vigour.

The next few months were clinically satisfying. New ideas matched new equipment and it seemed the entire energies of the practice were able to be directed towards the welfare of the patients. The doctors began to carry "bleeps" to increase their accessibility. Other disciplines in the Health Service began to work closely with us. For a decade we had had the constant physical presence of a Health Visitor but now our patients were to enjoy the full range of community care. It was an extraordinary achievement for our patients and a great encouragement for the doctors to work with these wonderful people. Now I enjoyed the fulfilment of a dream. The course of events had produced small, manageable enduring groups of people working together in the community. Groups which, unlike the rest of society, remained constant and easily identifiable as sources of help in the troubles affecting an unstable and faceless world.

These thoughts encouraged me when I was asked to present the mature (sic) doctor's attitudes to the Problems of Cancer,

Heart Disease and Stroke. The Illingworths began on the national circuit but soon graduated to an international level—we travelled not only to the Continent but to the familiar places in North America of years earlier. Even radio and television lost their terrors. It was stimulating but demanding because the practice came first and medical trips abroad, although part of the work ethic, had to be performed in holiday time.

By chance Dr Denis Burkitt sat beside me on a flight to New York. We were to attend the same symposium on "Cancers, Coronaries and Strokes". This undervalued hero of Medicine had given us the first description of "Burkitt's Lymphoma" and had advanced oncology immeasurably. My opportunities were not wasted as I absorbed and recorded the wisdom of an apostolic medical icon who, effortlessly and unknowingly, taught me so much in these few intense hours. Burkitt smiled quizzically at my attitude of discipleship—"Unlike myself you have a place in history." He replied deprecatingly. "History is only mass memory and is therefore an unreliable commodity. I do have a doctrine if you care to hear it." And I listened—and recorded:-

"Attitudes are more important than abilities. Motives are more important than methods. Character is more important than cleverness and the heart takes precedence over the head."

Burkitt's creed remains engraved on my mind.

The North American visits which we made in the years following the Nuffield Fellowship only served to reinforce the opinions formed in 1966.

Every time we went the Americans were more obese—to the point of revulsion—when one contemplated television pictures of the effects of famine in the Third World.

We retain the poignant memory of dining in the World Trade Centre in New York and the gruesome story told to us by a "Mountie" in Banff who warned us about being familiar with Canadian bears. Two days earlier an American visitor had, after sharing his lunch with a bear, lured the animal into his car and photographed it—driving—with his wife beside the bear. The bear assumed the lady was the main course.

In Kansas City, George Cowan was exactly as he'd been years earlier. He presented me with a copy of Steinbeck's "Travels with Charley". He inscribed it "To one who believes his profound humility sets him above other great men." I'm still working on the inference.

Perhaps it was not surprising that I received an occasional reminder that I had a digestive trace. A message would arrive in some arcane way for food (or antacid tablets) to be taken. Occasionally there would be pain and rarely bleeding. There wasn't time or the inclination to work it out but ultimately I remembered that I did, after all, have a doctor.

Dr Deuchars peered at me in mock surprise.

"I thought smooth operators like you went straight to specialists," he said. "Or have you tried that already?" The patient squirmed.

"To be honest, I have—but it wasn't very successful. My report was virtually negative. Here I am many months later and I still have spells of symptoms. I don't know whether I need a stomach specialist, a colon specialist, a hepatologist or a psychiatrist. I do know I need a doctor and that's why I'm here. Now look here, doctor, that's my six minutes up so I'll make another appointment later.

"You will NOT,"said Deuchars crisply. "You will tell me what the hell's been going on." It was amazingly easy being a patient after all. Deuchars had the gift of listening and, interposing his questions whenever I drew breath, extracted a lucid history—and got his colleague on the examination couch. Two minutes later I was trying to escape the discomfort caused by Deuchars' probing fingers.

"Hurts, doesn't it?" said the G.P. in quiet satisfaction. I think you've got yourself an ulcer in spite of your great age. I'm going to get Jim Thomson to see you and we'll have it confirmed.

A week of the ritual indignities of the gastrointestinal investigation followed. All the invasions of privacy to which I had submitted my patients for decades were perpetrated on me.

It was a learning experience and I wished I could start my medical life afresh with this new insight.

"Crumbs" said Tom Philp as he performed the full barium meal. "It's a beauty. Absolutely circular and in the SECOND part of the duodenum—I must get some films of this rarity. Send them to your friends as Christmas Cards." Sure enough, in the second part of the duodenum there was a neat round crater about the size of a ten-pence piece. The patient wasn't very pleased about this new art form within him.

"Never mind" murmured Dr Deuchars, his judgement vindicated. "We'll heal you with the wonder drug. You haven't even got an excuse to take time off."

The effect was magical. The ulcer healed completely and the University sent me off on tour for a month's "working vacation". This "reprise" of the Nuffield trip finished in Vancouver with Lesley's brother, Professor George Beagrie and his wife. I spoiled this happy interlude by have a small "bleed" on the last evening. Reaching Edinburgh meant more Barium from Tommy Philp and I knew by the radiologist's groans that all was not well. A homily followed the lamentations.

"Second part ulcers are very rare. I've only seen one before—but I know they proceed to duodenal obstruction. You need a gastroenterologist and a surgeon.

Dr Niall Finlayson—later to be President of our Royal College of Physicians—took on the former responsibility, while Jimmy Thomson accepted the latter role. To treat a doctor who has a rare condition is to court disaster. There was much black humour prior to the social event which was the surgical operation. I invited several friends and heard later that there had been complaints about overcrowding in the operating theatre. Possibly people came to see the second part ulcer rather than its owner. Anyway it was all a great success.

On Sunday, September 30th 1978 I read my medical journal which contained some good articles and left it at the top of the staircase to read in my car during my medical round—which was to begin on Monday 1st October at 8.30 a.m. at the Western General Hospital—my first day back at work.

Shaved, bathed and dressed in a fresh suit I crossed the upper landing to the top of the staircase. I remember standing on something slippery before I took off into space. The staircase was made of stone and it was twenty feet to ground level. I opened my eyes again in the lower hall. "Fagin" the dog, ears erect, was looking down on me in astonishment—or admiration. The other face, my wife's, was horror-struck.

I was manipulated into her car disregarding various arguments. After some minutes the numbness wore off and I began to have trouble breathing. Nevertheless I walked up the stairs to my room in the hospital to find Sister Spence looking askance.

"Welcome back" I was going to say. But what's happened?" Six weeks off and you return as your own first patient. Next Stop—X-ray."

The radiologist appeared with the film.

"Shoulder girdle and six ribs!"

I immediately felt much worse.

Dr Ian Allison (Dr Deuchars' partner) was waiting for me at home and cheered me up with his sardonic humour.

"We cure you of one disease and, to show your appreciation, you get drunk at breakfast and fall down stairs. Why not employ a resident physician?"

Two easy chairs were pushed together—with broken ribs you can't lie down in a bed. If you do lie down you can't get up again.

During the first night the chairs separated and I woke up, fixed in a jack-knife position, with my bottom on the floor and my feet up in the air. I was helpless until my wife straightened me out and tied the chair legs together to prevent a recurrence.

Dr Allison was much more solicitous after he saw the X-ray—but I returned to work before the projected date and henceforward treated staircases with more respect. The Editor of the British Medical Journal admitted to its smooth presentation and gave my fall from grace a paragraph headed:

"THE FIRST MANNED FLIGHT OF THE BRITISH MEDICAL JOURNAL"

A Scottish winter will bring a medical practice increased work but, as there are no partners absent on holiday, it may be the best season of the year. Every few years the dreaded influenza strikes. Totally unpredictable in its behaviour the infection may be rampant in one area of the city but comparatively rare in a juxtaposed district. When sixty house-calls pour in daily the men and women working in the practice are separated from the children. The ordeal by fire usually lasts four weeks.

Whenever it happened one simply moved up a gear. Almost all influenza patients who were old were liable to develop chest infections. The pressure was so great that, during one epidemic, the nurses and students volunteered to pay return visits. The work and pleasure balance was restored however by a young woman—with a permanent colostomy—who gave birth to a lovely baby, and, in a different vein, by the attendance of one of my phobic patients at a consulting session.

You know those beasts which I have, doctor?" said the lady with the imaginary infestation. "I've never convinced you—but here's the proof." She produced a small matchbox and gave it to me. I opened it gingerly. Small tiny grey particles lay inside the container and it was hastily snapped shut.

"We'll get these analysed, I promise, " I said, my imagination running riot. "I'll telephone you after the results come through." The patient departed, well satisfied, but as I showed her out I was confronted by the vicar of the local Episcopalian church who had been lurking behind a tree in the garden.

"Doctor, thank heaven I've found you. The lady who came out just now is a parishioner of mine and she came to the meeting in our church hall last night. My wife was sitting beside her at the far end of the hall as I addressed the members." He seized my lapels.

"Your patient ruined my meeting. She informed everyone within earshot—"I'm covered with nasty little beasts!"

"It was awful doctor. Within minutes she was sitting alone at one end of the hall and the rest of the congregation was huddled at the other end."

I flourished the matchbox at the padre.

"She gave me some. They're in here."

The vicar hastily withdrew as I promised that the "parasites" would be identified.

The report of the specimen was unequivocal—"Normal human skin". And with a reassuring word here and there and some medication the patient was allowed to return to the fold. But psychodynamics is the enemy of one's precious time.

The voice from the bleep in my breast pocket said,

"There's a further urgent request from that patient in Morningside. Please expedite."

My dog Fagin and I had halted the car at traffic lights—which seemed interminably red as we waited to turn right. Ye Gods, I couldn't wait any longer and, in my anxiety, accelerated sharply right. I couldn't see anything approaching and knew the intersection had no filter system. It was the element of surprise rather than the violence of the impact with the other car which offended me—and my dog.

Quite properly I accepted the blame, exchanged names and limped on to the urgent house-call only to find that the originator of the urgent call opened the front door himself—and wasn't even one of our patients.

The following night I dug myself out of deep snow at 2 a.m.—about the same time as one of the young fathers in the practice was being blinded as he hurtled through the windscreen of his car after a head-on collision. Everything seemed to be going wrong. My chest hurt, my shoulders were painful and the recent surgery allowed my stomach to empty at a rate of knots—which produced its own clinical and social problems.

But the dream had been fulfilled. The Health Centre was complete and about to be formally opened. I was happy that I could now relax and hand things over to my wonderful partners and nursing and administrative colleagues.

One retains snapshots from a photo album of personal experience. These include a lady smiling with amused concern as her Apothecary lay amongst a confusion of corgis—on his way to a Holyrood emergency. Etiquette makes no provision for such contingencies.

At the other end of the social scale is one of Killin's stokers. After almost every shore leave he would report that he was "squeezing up". "Doc" Goggins had worked hard to persuade him to employ contraception—but failed and passed the responsibility on to me. I called down hellfire, damnation, impotence and retention but made no impression—until he explained.

"Would YOU take a bath with your socks on, sir?"

Mrs Borthwick's hair had been to me a source of wonder and, latterly, of outspoken admiration for over twenty years. Aristocratic in her close resemblance to Queen Mary she would commiserate with me as I aged and my skull became ever more apparent—and her arthritis worsened. When bronchitis complicated her influenza I examined the back of her chest and my elbow struck her head.

"Deus ex machina!"—the secret was revealed—as I appeared to decapitate her and her crowning glory fell onto the counterpane. Time froze as etiquette and protocol remained as mute as the patient and the doctor. So I lifted the "transformation" and hastily replaced it on the bald lady. New to such disasters I got it wrong and she faced back to front. She laughed "I'm in reverse!"

Two days later she died of pneumonia. I kept her secret but I was really upset at the funeral service.

CHAPTER THIRTY-ONE

Belonging to the Royal Household brought certain privileges. I met and often looked after "anybody who was anybody"—known as the "glitterati". Buckingham Palace overawed me but holidays at Balmoral were memorable—particularly the weeks at Alltaguibhsaich when fourteen of us would descend on this magnificent property overlooking Loch Muick and leading by the Scarnoch road to the castle itself—where we attended the renowned "Ghillies' Ball". I could understand Queen Victoria's affection for her Northern home.

I also yearned to return to the Western Isles Hotel, in Tobermory, which I hadn't seen since Navy days. We drove up the winding road. The harbour, once the haunt of many brave ships—including Killin—was empty. No White Ensign fluttered from the hotel's flagpole and the matelots with fixed bayonets must now have become elderly men. There was still the crack, which Chiefie used continually to deplore, in the marble slab over the open fire in the lounge. There were still 109 steps in the shortcut down to the pier! I had some irrational belief that in returning to Tobermory after 36 years I would uncover the vivid ghosts of 15 months of close human contact in a small warship. This period remained sharply illuminated due to its emotional impact on an immature but receptive personality. The medical significance of these early days was small but the lustre, the cachet, of this formative phase was vividly engraved on my soul—and my diaries reflected this. Compared with this wartime era of instant maturation the remainder of my life had become strangely condensed and less vivid.

A great wave of nostalgia gripped me, which intensified when I discovered that Aros House no longer existed. I took

Lesley through the gap in the rhododendrons where so often I had walked the ship's dog.

"That's it. There's the house." I said. Lesley looked and smiled at her puzzled husband.

"Wrong, laddie, there's nothing there." The house had been demolished years before.

I lay back on the hotel bed watching the Sound of Mull. I had put in six months hard labour in the practice and, just before I fell asleep, I looked across at my wife and at old Fagin who had craftily sneaked up on the window seat. I was consoling myself with a Latin tab—"*Tempora mutantur....*", yet hearing again the soporific pinging of Killin's Asdic, when I dozed off. The awakening was sudden and harsh. There was a brief period of displaced bewildered time.

The Bos'n's pipe was shrilling in my imagination. The duty watch was being called to clear the messdecks of hammocks. How did it go?

"Wakey, wakey, wakey! The sun's burning yer eyes out. Heav'o! Heav'o! Lash up and stow. You heard the pipe, Jack."

Though familiar, the feeling was worse than it had ever been. My heart was thumping in my chest; I was soaked in perspiration and intensely afraid. Nothing had occurred to cause this fear. I simply had the abdominal sensations of impending unreasonable doom and an urgent craving for sugar. Lying stickily in the dark, I went rapidly through the differential diagnosis with an enforced state of scientific aloofness. Whatever else, my blood sugar must be low. I crept into the bathroom with a bottle of fruit juice from our portable bar, gulped down a pint, peeled off saturated pyjamas and returned to bed. Within a few minutes the turmoil ceased. I awoke at dawn, a whole man once more.

But this was the forerunner of a series of severe episodes of the "Dumping syndrome".

It was to be a bad week in wonderful surroundings.

One Tuesday afternoon in Edinburgh in the early summer of 1980 my ability to keep the edifice together failed. There was nothing left to give.

It was difficult to express myself—even to Lesley.

"Can't eat; losing weight; if I do eat I feel weird; if I don't eat I get like this—sweaty and scared; sugar is the cure.

Thanks to my wife's intervention I was, by evening, lying in a hospital bed, had given three approximately identical histories, donated a large volume of body fluid for analysis and been twice scrutinised from scalp to sole. I was horrified by how many symptoms I had and pitied my solicitous listeners. Obviously I had forgotten what good health felt like and, after two weeks, my wellbeing contrasted sharply with the miseries of previous months.

But Tom Philp, the radiologist, was not happy. The diagnosis was too vague, he said, as he poured more Barium into me.

"It's just as I prophesied" declared the gleeful radiologist. Your duodenum is now stenosed by the second part ulcer and virtually nothing can get through."

I groaned at the implications.

"More surgery?"

And so it came to pass. When I emerged from repeat surgery I was anatomically functional but biologically older than my chronological age of sixty years.

When the curtain fell it did so gently and humanely. A perplexity of doctors appeared. Each encouraged my personal doubts about my ability to resume the life I had led for over thirty years."If you return you'll have to lower your standards—you might be a bit of a passenger."

I was horrified. I, the senior partner—a real part of the community—a passenger! Why, I had just negotiated the building of the Medical Centre after years of struggle and argument with authority!

But the pressure to leave the N.H.S. was relentless—if kind.

"You've had three serious episodes in six months. Are you prepared to offer your patients a second best?"

This was the most telling argument of all. I hadn't realised how strong was my pride in my chosen vocation as a family doctor. Unashamedly I wept. I couldn't tolerate the idea that I could no longer measure up physically. What would happen to my patients—to whom I was indispensable? Or was I fooling myself?

Deuchars was the last to appear. He, as he always did, struck the right note.

"You can be gracefully invalided out or you can become a part-time nonentity—always assuming that you survive. That's the choice. Incidentally your wife and dog are waiting for you in the car park."

So David Illingworth returned home.

The following morning I went to the study and sat down amid the piles of notes which represented my life. It wasn't going to stop here, I told myself. The first thing I should do was to retrieve and display the buried pearls which must be within reach. I felt compelled to condense almost forty years of medical experience into a discourse which would be added to the corpus of medical knowledge before I finally relinquished professional life. I began to scribble on yet another piece of stationery to add to the towers of paper around me in the study.

The nights were difficult because, although the telephone didn't ring, I imagined that it did. Several times a week I would answer a silent telephone which sounded only in my dreams.

But the vacuum was filled as private work came to me. Government, charities, insurance companies and business people in general began to make use of my instant availability and removed the fear of slow decline on an invalidity pension.

Private medicine with its nuance of a double standard of care had always troubled my rigid medical soul. Yet, I could now reconcile myself. The N.H.S. had, not unreasonably, rejected me. And I had friends—who were determined to make me feel useful. They succeeded in restoring my self-confidence and I continued to work in an advisory capacity, as I made my gentle departure from the sharp end of Medicine.

Additionally, I had the Royal Household to bring me days of responsibility, interest and a certain enchantment.

The Royal Household appointment had begun with a bang when the radiator blew out on my first day. On my last official duty at Holyrood I departed—with a crash.

The forecourt of the Palace was awash with rain as I drove through the mews tunnel to park the car. As I emerged into the mews I realised that I was in a direct course for the Prince of Wales's vehicle. And it was not going to stop. I hastily backed off straining my rain-obscured vision and muttering.

"Oh my God there may be something behind me." There was—the Lord Chamberlain's limousine.

Lord Airlie's car had pulled in behind the hesitant doctor—and his car had been struck fair and square. It was rather like Killin's meeting with the trawler.

There was a large hole in the L.C.'s limousine and nothing in the for'ard part of it seemed quite to fit any longer. And steam was coming out.

The Earl of Airlie was very nice about it.

"Well, I suppose if you had a choice between hitting the Prince of Wales's car or mine you chose the lesser alternative!"

Such is democracy! And I retained my 'no claims bonus'.

At Buckingham Palace the Comptroller said,

"When your name is called, walk forward until you are level with Her Majesty, turn sharp left, bow, and walk four paces. Bow again, then stick out your neck."

I obeyed the rules and didn't stumble on the way to my spellbound summit. A series of memorable parties followed which made me feel that I had come a long way along a strange road—littered with regrets and failures but as the Chinese hope in their proverb, I had had "Interesting times."

Yet something still troubled me and I recorded it.

"There must be something else for me. There must be another hurdle—another contribution. It can't stop here. There is surely something more to pay back." I preserved this vague idea about the balance of nature but couldn't quite verbalise it. Why hadn't I outgrown my relentless self-criticism?

"What have you learned?" I used to ask the students at the end of a teaching session. Now I must ask myself the same question—but in regard to the entire duration of my professional life. My response was aided by my whimsical panel of experts—Hippocrates, Galen, Dunlop, Turner and French who had been joined in the latter years of this personal figment of imagination, by Charles Darwin. My preoccupation with preventive medicine and with the diseases of behaviour, of the environment, of civilisation, had made Darwin—with his views on the preservation of the individual in the struggle to survive—an obvious choice. Now I knew that human life was best conducted within a defined framework of personal behaviour. Problems were less likely if one imposed on oneself a certain style of living. Nature chose to preserve those who adapted best to the changing environment and if these adjustments were not achieved one's continued survival was in doubt. I continued to write.

Our method of living changed hardly at all between the birth of Christ and the coming of the Industrial Revolution. But in the last two hundred years we have been subjected, and have submitted ourselves, to the relentless battering effect of rapid change. We neglect the effect of this speedy alteration at our peril.

For our today is NOT yesterday's tomorrow. In terms of evolution and adaptation, today's environment and that of two hundred years ago are ten thousand years apart. The passage of these two centuries is, in the entire history of the human race, but the flicker of God's eyelid. How then can our bodies adjust in the course of a few generations, to the mental and physical changes of these condensed millennia?

We have produced, been given and perhaps deserve our habitat of devastating transformation. Constitutionally we are not prepared for it because, today, human evolution lags a thousand years or more behind human environment. Until we begin to question and alter the existing order of upbringing and behaviour the greater part of the human race will continue to struggle against increasing hazards to existence—many of which are not yet identified.

Is it too late to return to the essential verities and great simplicities of life? Perhaps it is not—if our patients can be educated to co-operate. At least we know where the obligation lies. Like all else in the animal kingdom the individual human being has a responsibility to preserve and protect his health and his life. He may also have a duty to guide and support other creatures. What proportion of the human race is worthy of this fiduciary relationship? How can one entertain sanguine expectations of a species which, by its unpredictable selfishness and cruelty, promotes only distrust? Coarse and feckless they may be—often less disciplined and caring than the animals over which they presume their advantage and jurisdiction—yet you love these curious creatures in spite of, or because of, their fathomless failings.

Notwithstanding, to accept damaging behaviour, to tolerate harmful sophistication in the name of freedom, is to nullify the process of adjustment. Not only may such an attitude influence generations yet unborn, it is a rejection of one's responsibility to posterity and is contrary to the laws of survival which Nature first promulgated three thousand million years ago.

I had reached the conclusion that the preservation of total health was mainly in the stewardship of the individual.

But what about those who receive a bad inheritance?

In an ideal society they will come into the care of professional advisers. If Life is a game of cards we cannot yet control the hand which is dealt—but one can be helped to play a bad hand as well as possible. I could hear Turner's description of life. "Genes and habits. Nothing else matters!"

It was already plain that there were preventable factors in certain types of cancer, in heart disease and stroke and many lung problems. Forty years from my medical beginnings I could now see that there was a solid future for preventive medicine and teaching the preservation of health. Indeed it was the only moral way ahead. Yet I appreciated that preventive medicine suffered from a surfeit of botanists and shortage of gardeners.

It was getting dark in the study as Lesley, my goddess still, came in, nimbling her way between the looming piles of written notes.

"Aye, aye!! Written your sermon yet, David? Fegs, I needn't have asked—I know that beastly smug look. Nobody will understand your haverings—but you'll feel better; I also was trained to value a good brisk purge, mental or otherwise. Take out the dog like a good chap and tomorrow I can start throwing out these mounds of mouldering papers. I can't even get the vacuum cleaner into this room. What do you mean I'd be chucking out your life if I emptied this pigsty? You're not going to do any more writing—are you?"

I laughed. "That's a long long speech for a Scots lassie of few words. I've even had time to write it down." Lesley peered over my shoulder.

"You've also written that for the first time in your life you can't see the horizon—but that you'll keep looking! Better watch out for the trapdoors in Joe Addison's bridge."